INTEGRATED MATHEMATICS SCHEME

 N2

Peter Kaner

Formerly Inspector for Mathematics
Inner London Education Authority

Bell & Hyman

First published 1985 by BELL & HYMAN
an imprint of Unwin Hyman Limited
Denmark House
37–39 Queen Elizabeth Street
London SE1 2QB

Kaner, Peter
  Integrated mathematics scheme, N2
  1. Mathematics—1961–
  I. Title
  510   QA39.2

Acknowledgements

The publishers would like to thank the following for permission to reproduce the photographs on the
pages indicated:

London Features International, p. 6; James Davis, p. 17; Keystone Press Agency, pp. 39, 180, 209
(*left*), 234; Photographer Freddie Mansfield, Camera Press Ltd., p. 40; The British Tourist Authority,
p. 110; Press Association Photos, p. 124; Foxphotos Ltd., p. 131; Shell International Petroleum Co.
Ltd., p. 161; Texas Instruments, p. 201; David D. Richardson, p. 209 (*top right*), p. 212; Ace Photo
Agency, p. 209 (*bottom right*); DB (Diving and Creative Services) Ltd., p. 226; Bruce Coleman Ltd.,
photograph by David Goulston, p. 238; Central Press Photos, p. 241 (*top right*); Meteorological Office
(with permission of the Controller of Her Majesty's Stationery Office), p. 241 (*left*); Oxfam, p. 248;
Casio Electronics Ltd., p. 289; West Air Photography, Weston-super-Mare, p. 291; Eric and David
Hosking, p. 300.

Illustrations and design by Paul Allingham.

ISBN 0 7135 1371 3

Phototypeset by Tradespools Ltd., Frome, Somerset

Printed and bound in Great Britain by
Blantyre Printing & Bindery Ltd., London & Glasgow

Contents

Unit 1 Fractions

1·1 What is a fraction?

When an object is broken into parts, the size of the part in relation to the whole object is shown by a fraction.

Examples:

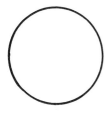

Whole circle

$\frac{1}{2}$

One part of two.
(The circle was divided into two equal parts)

$\frac{1}{4}$

One part of four.
(The circle was divided into four equal parts)

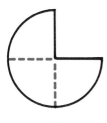

$\frac{3}{4}$

Three parts of four.
(The circle was divided into four equal parts)

$\frac{2}{3}$

Two parts of three.
(The circle was divided into three equal parts)

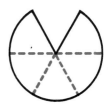

$\frac{5}{6}$

Five parts of six.
(The circle was divided into six equal parts)

A pair of numbers, one divided by the other, forms a fraction.

Example:
$\frac{4}{7}$ is another form of (4 ÷ 7)
$\frac{11}{15}$ is another form of (11 ÷ 15)
Note: The order of dividing is important: $\frac{4}{7}$ is not the same as $\frac{7}{4}$

1

Exercise 1·1

A Make diagrams which show these fractions accurately.

1 $\frac{3}{4}$ of a square   **2** $\frac{7}{8}$ of a square   **3** $\frac{4}{6}$ of a circle   **4** $\frac{7}{10}$ of a circle

5 $\frac{7}{16}$ of a square   **6** $\frac{1}{7}$ of a line   **7** $\frac{3}{5}$ of a rectangle   **8** $\frac{5}{6}$ of a regular hexagon

B Divide a circle to show that these fractions are equal.

1 $\frac{2}{6} = \frac{1}{3}$ **2** $\frac{3}{6} = \frac{1}{2}$ **3** $\frac{4}{6} = \frac{2}{3}$

4 $\frac{2}{4} = \frac{1}{2}$ **5** $\frac{6}{8} = \frac{3}{4}$ **6** $\frac{2}{8} = \frac{1}{4}$

C Work on graph paper. Draw diagrams to show these fractions are equal. (Start with a rectangle)

1 $\frac{4}{8} = \frac{1}{2}$ **2** $\frac{6}{10} = \frac{3}{5}$ **3** $\frac{8}{12} = \frac{2}{3}$

4 $\frac{9}{15} = \frac{3}{5}$ **5** $\frac{12}{20} = \frac{3}{5}$ **6** $\frac{20}{36} = \frac{5}{9}$

1·2 The value of a fraction

When we carry out the division (top ÷ bottom) for a fraction we obtain its value in decimal form. This value can be used in calculating with fractions.

Two fractions with the same value are called equivalent. For example, $\frac{3}{4}$ and $\frac{6}{8}$ both have the decimal value, 0·75.

$6 \boxed{÷} 8 \boxed{=} 0{\cdot}75$ and $3 \boxed{÷} 4 \boxed{=} 0{\cdot}75$

Each fraction has many equivalent forms, made by multiplying top and bottom by the same number: $\frac{3}{4} = \frac{6}{8} = \frac{9}{12} = \frac{12}{16}$ etc.

Example:

Find three equivalent forms of $\frac{5}{8}$. (Value: $5 ÷ 8 = 0{\cdot}625$)

$\dfrac{5 \times 3}{8 \times 3} = \dfrac{15}{24}$ (Value: $15 ÷ 24 = 0{\cdot}625$)

$\dfrac{5 \times 10}{8 \times 10} = \dfrac{50}{80}$ (Value: $50 ÷ 80 = 0{\cdot}625$)

$\dfrac{5 \times 7}{8 \times 7} = \dfrac{35}{56}$ (Value: $35 ÷ 56 = 0{\cdot}625$)

Two fractions can be checked for equivalence by cross-multiplying:

$\dfrac{a}{b} = \dfrac{c}{d} \Leftrightarrow a \times d = b \times c$

Cross-multiplying will also tell you which of two fractions is bigger:

$\dfrac{a}{b} > \dfrac{c}{d} \Leftrightarrow a \times d > b \times c$

Examples:

1 Check $\frac{243}{739}$ and $\frac{1701}{5173}$ for equivalence.

$243 \times 5173 = 1\,257\,039$ (calculator)

$739 \times 1701 = 1\,257\,039$ (calculator)

So the fractions are equivalent. In fact, they both have the value $0.328\,822\,7$:

$243 \boxed{\div} 739 \boxed{=} 0.328\,822\,7$

$1701 \boxed{\div} 5173 \boxed{=} 0.328\,822\,7$

2 Which of $\frac{23}{39}$, $\frac{42}{75}$ is the larger?

Cross-multiply: $23 \times 75 = 1725$ $39 \times 42 = 1638$

Thus $\frac{23}{39}$ is the larger

Alternatively, calculate values: $\frac{23}{39} = 0.589\,743\,5$ $\frac{42}{75} = 0.56$

Thus $\frac{23}{39}$ is the larger

Cancelling

A collection of equivalent fractions can all be reduced to the simplest form by cancelling, i.e. dividing top and bottom by the same number. It is not always easy to find the correct number to cancel, so we usually try prime numbers in turn.

Example:

Find the simplest fraction equivalent to $\frac{75}{100}$

Both 75 and 100 will divide by 5: $\frac{75}{100} \rightarrow \frac{15}{20}$

Both 15 and 20 will divide by 5: $\frac{15}{20} \rightarrow \frac{3}{4}$

No further numbers will divide both 3 and 4, so we cannot simplify any further: $\frac{3}{4}$ is said to be the fraction in its lowest terms.

Exercise 1·2

A Find the values of the following fractions and arrange them into equivalent pairs.

1 $\frac{2}{3}$ $\frac{5}{8}$ $\frac{7}{9}$ $\frac{12}{15}$ $\frac{8}{12}$ $\frac{35}{45}$ $\frac{4}{5}$ $\frac{15}{24}$

2 $\frac{3}{10}$ $\frac{1}{2}$ $\frac{8}{15}$ $\frac{15}{50}$ $\frac{40}{75}$ $\frac{124}{248}$

3 $\frac{4}{5}$ $\frac{70}{100}$ $\frac{8}{20}$ $\frac{3}{9}$ $\frac{16}{20}$ $\frac{35}{50}$ $\frac{1}{3}$ $\frac{2}{5}$

4 $\frac{5}{6}$ $\frac{28}{50}$ $\frac{15}{25}$ $\frac{8}{18}$ $\frac{14}{25}$ $\frac{75}{90}$ $\frac{4}{9}$ $\frac{9}{15}$

B Use cross-multiplication to check these statements. Then check by values. Do your results agree?

1 $\frac{3}{5} = \frac{6}{10}$ **2** $\frac{8}{12} = \frac{2}{3}$ **3** $\frac{15}{40} = \frac{5}{8}$

4 $\frac{7}{9} > \frac{6}{8}$ **5** $\frac{3}{7} > \frac{4}{9}$ **6** $\frac{7}{10} > \frac{4}{7}$

7 $\frac{2}{3} > \frac{5}{8}$ **8** $\frac{3}{4} > \frac{11}{15}$ **9** $\frac{16}{25} > \frac{45}{80}$

C Use cancelling to find the simplest form of these fractions.

1 $\frac{48}{64}$ **2** $\frac{35}{75}$ **3** $\frac{81}{99}$

4 $\frac{37}{111}$ **5** $\frac{108}{396}$ **6** $\frac{225}{500}$

7 $\frac{729}{810}$ **8** $\frac{162}{388}$ **9** $\frac{414}{529}$

1·3 Addition and subtraction of fractions

There are many ways to add fractions. If the calculator is handy you can just add the values. This gives the result in decimal form.

Example:

$$\frac{2}{3} \quad + \quad \frac{3}{5}$$

$$\downarrow \qquad\quad \downarrow$$

Values . . . $0{\cdot}6666 \quad 0{\cdot}6 \rightarrow 1{\cdot}266\,66$

Fractions to be added can be changed to equivalent forms with the same denominator (bottom number).

Examples:

1 $\dfrac{2}{3} \; + \; \dfrac{3}{5}$
$\qquad \dfrac{2}{3} \times \dfrac{5}{5} + \dfrac{3}{5} \times \dfrac{3}{3}$

$\qquad\qquad \downarrow \qquad\qquad \downarrow$

$\qquad \dfrac{10}{15} \quad + \quad \dfrac{9}{15} = \dfrac{19}{15}$

The simplest number to use for the denominators is $3 \times 5 = 15$

2 $\dfrac{3}{4} \; + \; \dfrac{5}{8}$
$\qquad \dfrac{3}{4} \times \dfrac{2}{2} + \dfrac{5}{8}$

$\qquad\qquad \downarrow$

$\qquad \dfrac{6}{8} \quad + \quad \dfrac{5}{8} = \dfrac{11}{8}$

The simplest number to use for the denominators is 8

3 $\dfrac{4}{5} \; - \; \dfrac{1}{2}$

$\qquad \downarrow \qquad\quad \downarrow$

$\qquad \dfrac{8}{10} \quad - \quad \dfrac{5}{10} = \dfrac{3}{10}$

The simplest number to use for the denominators is 10

If fractions are in the form $\dfrac{1}{a}$ and $\dfrac{1}{b}$ their sum is $\dfrac{a+b}{ab}$:

$$\frac{1}{a} + \frac{1}{b} = \frac{a+b}{ab} \quad \begin{array}{l} \leftarrow \text{sum of } a \text{ and } b \\ \leftarrow \text{product of } a \text{ and } b \end{array}$$

Examples:

1 $\dfrac{1}{3} + \dfrac{1}{4} = \dfrac{3+4}{3 \times 4} = \dfrac{7}{12}$

2 $\dfrac{2}{3} + \dfrac{2}{5} = \left(\dfrac{1}{3} + \dfrac{1}{3}\right) + \left(\dfrac{1}{5} + \dfrac{1}{5}\right)$

$\qquad = \left(\dfrac{1}{3} + \dfrac{1}{5}\right) + \left(\dfrac{1}{3} + \dfrac{1}{5}\right) = 2 \times \left(\dfrac{1}{3} + \dfrac{1}{5}\right)$

$\qquad = 2 \times \left(\dfrac{5+3}{5 \times 3}\right) = \dfrac{2 \times 8}{15} = \dfrac{16}{15}$

Exercise 1·3

A Write down the totals of these pairs of fractions:

1 $\frac{1}{2} + \frac{1}{3}$ **2** $\frac{1}{2} + \frac{1}{4}$ **3** $\frac{1}{5} + \frac{1}{6}$

4 $\frac{1}{3} + \frac{1}{7}$ **5** $\frac{1}{10} + \frac{1}{100}$ **6** $\frac{1}{10} + \frac{1}{2}$

7 $\frac{1}{5} + \frac{1}{8}$ **8** $\frac{1}{9} + \frac{1}{3}$ **9** $\frac{1}{6} + \frac{1}{8}$

B Write down the totals of these pairs of fractions:

1 $\frac{2}{3} + \frac{2}{5}$ **2** $\frac{3}{4} + \frac{3}{8}$ **3** $\frac{3}{5} + \frac{3}{8}$

4 $\frac{4}{5} + \frac{4}{9}$ **5** $\frac{2}{5} + \frac{2}{7}$ **6** $\frac{2}{3} + \frac{2}{10}$

C Use two different methods to calculate each of these sums of fractions:

1 $\frac{2}{3} + \frac{1}{2}$ **2** $\frac{3}{5} + \frac{1}{4}$ **3** $\frac{2}{3} + \frac{3}{5}$

4 $\frac{1}{2} + \frac{3}{10}$ **5** $\frac{3}{8} + \frac{4}{5}$ **6** $\frac{1}{5} + \frac{3}{4}$

7 $\frac{5}{8} + \frac{3}{16}$ **8** $\frac{4}{5} + \frac{3}{4}$ **9** $\frac{2}{5} + \frac{4}{10}$

D Find methods to subtract these fractions. Give the result in fraction form and check your results with a calculator using decimal values.

1 $\frac{1}{2} - \frac{1}{4}$ **2** $\frac{2}{5} - \frac{1}{10}$ **3** $\frac{4}{5} - \frac{3}{10}$

4 $\frac{1}{2} - \frac{1}{8}$ **5** $\frac{2}{3} - \frac{1}{6}$ **6** $\frac{3}{4} - \frac{1}{2}$

7 $\frac{7}{10} - \frac{3}{5}$ **8** $\frac{5}{9} - \frac{3}{10}$ **9** $\frac{3}{4} - \frac{2}{5}$

1·4   Whole numbers mixed with fractions

Measurements often contain whole and part units. Usually it is best to keep to decimal measurements; the parts can then be written either as a decimal or as a separate unit.

$3\frac{3}{10}$ metres should be written $3 \cdot 3$ m

$4\frac{5}{100}$ litres should be written as $4 \cdot 05$ litres.

Some units (such as hours and minutes) are not decimal, so you may meet measurements of time involving fractions.

Examples:

A journey takes $2\frac{1}{2}$ hours in one direction and $1\frac{3}{4}$ hours return. How long is the journey altogether?

1 $2\frac{1}{2} + 1\frac{3}{4} = (2 + \frac{1}{2}) + (1 + \frac{3}{4})$

$\qquad\qquad = (2 + 1) + (\frac{1}{2} + \frac{3}{4})$

$\qquad\qquad = \quad 3 \quad + (\frac{2}{4} + \frac{3}{4})$

$\qquad\qquad = \quad 3 \quad + \quad \frac{5}{4}$

$\qquad\qquad = \quad 3 \quad + \quad 1\frac{1}{4} \quad = \quad 4\frac{1}{4}$ hours

2 What is the value of $2\frac{3}{5} - 1\frac{7}{10}$?

Make the second number up to a whole number by adding $\frac{3}{10}$ (you must also add $\frac{3}{10}$ to the first number so that the difference remains the same)

$2\frac{3}{5} - 1\frac{7}{10} = (2\frac{3}{5} + \frac{3}{10}) \quad - (1\frac{7}{10} + \frac{3}{10})$

$\qquad\qquad\quad = (2 + \frac{6}{10} + \frac{3}{10}) - \quad\quad 2$

$\qquad\qquad\quad = 2 + \frac{9}{10} \quad\quad - \quad\quad 2$

$\qquad\qquad\quad = \frac{9}{10}$

The problem may be done by direct subtraction as follows:

$2\frac{3}{5} - 1\frac{7}{10} = 1\frac{3}{5} - \frac{7}{10}$ (subtracting 1 from each number)

$\qquad\qquad = \frac{8}{5} - \frac{7}{10}$

$\qquad\qquad = \frac{16}{10} - \frac{7}{10} = \frac{9}{10}$ (Check with a calculator)

Exercise 1·4

A Add the following pairs of numbers:

1 $2\frac{1}{3} + 1\frac{1}{6}$ 2 $4\frac{1}{2} + 1\frac{3}{4}$ 3 $2\frac{3}{10} + 3\frac{1}{2}$

4 $2\frac{3}{4} + 7\frac{1}{5}$ 5 $4\frac{1}{3} + 6\frac{2}{3}$ 6 $2\frac{1}{2} + 2\frac{2}{3}$

7 $5\frac{1}{4} + 2\frac{3}{8}$ 8 $2\frac{2}{3} + 1\frac{3}{5}$ 9 $2\frac{4}{5} + 3\frac{1}{2}$

B Work out the following subtractions:

1 $2 - \frac{3}{4}$ 2 $1\frac{1}{2} - \frac{5}{8}$ 3 $2\frac{1}{4} - 1\frac{1}{2}$

4 $2\frac{2}{3} - \frac{5}{6}$ 5 $3\frac{1}{2} - 1\frac{3}{4}$ 6 $4\frac{1}{10} - 1\frac{2}{5}$

7 $3\frac{1}{5} - 1\frac{3}{4}$ 8 $4\frac{7}{12} - 1\frac{2}{3}$ 9 $4\frac{1}{3} - 1\frac{3}{5}$

C 1 A board $\frac{3}{4}$-inch thick is to be fastened to the wall by $1\frac{1}{2}$-inch screws. How far into the wall will the screws go?

   2 A container for carrying dangerous chemicals is made of special material. There is an asbestos lining $3\frac{1}{4}$ inches thick, then $2\frac{1}{2}$ inches of steel. The outside is coated with $\frac{5}{8}$ of an inch of plastic. How thick are the sides of the container altogether?

Note: Questions 1 and 2 both use inches as units of length. If the metric system is used, all measurements are in decimal form.

   3 At a music festival a band plays three pieces: the first lasts $7\frac{1}{2}$ minutes, the second $12\frac{1}{4}$ minutes and the third $10\frac{3}{4}$ minutes. How long does the band play altogether?

   4 A concert two hours long altogether has three intervals, lasting $8\frac{1}{2}$ minutes, $7\frac{3}{4}$ minutes and $9\frac{1}{2}$ minutes. How long is the show, apart from the intervals?

   5 Lamb, when roasting, should be cooked for $\frac{3}{4}$ hour per kilogram of meat, plus an extra $\frac{3}{4}$ hour. For how long should these pieces of meat be cooked?

    (a) a 2 kg joint   (b) a 2·5 kg joint   (c) a 3 kg joint   (d) a 1·5 kg joint

1·5   Multiplying and dividing fractions

It is easy to show that $\frac{1}{2} \times \frac{1}{4} = \frac{1}{8}$ by checking the decimal values.

$\left.\begin{array}{l} \frac{1}{2} = 0 \cdot 5 \\ \frac{1}{4} = 0 \cdot 25 \\ \frac{1}{8} = 0 \cdot 125 \end{array}\right\}$ and $0 \cdot 5 \times 0 \cdot 25 = 0 \cdot 125$ (calculator)

Similarly $\frac{1}{2} \times \frac{2}{3} = \frac{2}{6}$, $\frac{1}{3} \times \frac{4}{5} = \frac{4}{15}$ and so on.

This leads to a general rule for fractions:

$$\frac{a}{b} \times \frac{c}{d} = \frac{a \times c}{b \times d}$$

In words, this is: The product of two fractions is a new fraction whose numerator is the product of the numerators and whose denominator is the product of the denominators.

Examples:

1 $\frac{3}{8} \times \frac{5}{7} = \frac{15}{56}$ Calculator check:

$$3 \div 8 \quad = 0 \cdot 375 \qquad \left.\right\} \text{multiply together}$$
$$5 \div 7 \quad = 0 \cdot 714\,285\,7 \left.\right\} \to 0 \cdot 267\,857\,1$$

$$15 \div 56 = 0 \cdot 267\,857\,1$$

This calculation can be checked in one sequence:

3 ⊡ 8 ☒ 5 ⊡ 7 ⊟ ☒ 56 ⊟

If the product is correct the display should show 15.

2 $\frac{2}{3} \times \frac{3}{8} = \frac{6}{24} = \frac{6 \div 6}{24 \div 6} = \frac{1}{4}$

Check: 2 ⊡ 3 ☒ 3 ⊡ 8 ⊟ ☒ 4 ⊟ 1

Note: If a decimal form is required, the product may be found by feeding the calculation into the calculator:

2 ⊡ 3 ☒ 3 ⊡ 8 ⊟ 0·25

Dividing by a fraction

Whenever it is necessary to divide by a fraction we multiply by its inverse instead. (This method can also be used for dividing by whole numbers.)

Examples:

1 $42 \div 8$ is the same as $42 \times \frac{1}{8}$

$42 \div 8 = 5 \cdot 25$ 42 ⊡ 8 ⊟

$42 \times \frac{1}{8} = 42 \times 0 \cdot 125 = 5 \cdot 25$ 42 ☒ 8 ⅟ₓ ⊟   or   8 ⅟ₓ ☒ 42 ⊟

2 $\frac{2}{3} \div \frac{1}{2}$ is the same as $\frac{2}{3} \times \frac{2}{1} = \frac{4}{3}$ (since $\frac{2}{1}$ is the inverse of $\frac{1}{2}$)

Exercise 1·5

A Multiply the following fractions:

1 $\frac{1}{2} \times \frac{3}{4}$ **2** $\frac{1}{4} \times \frac{1}{3}$ **3** $\frac{2}{3} \times \frac{3}{4}$

4 $\frac{1}{5} \times \frac{4}{5}$ **5** $\frac{3}{10} \times \frac{2}{3}$ **6** $\frac{4}{5} \times \frac{2}{3}$

7 $\frac{1}{10} \times \frac{1}{2}$ **8** $\frac{4}{5} \times \frac{3}{8}$ **9** $\frac{3}{5} \times \frac{4}{9}$

B Use a calculator to find these products in decimal form. Check that the results agree with the answers in fraction form.

1 $\frac{1}{4} \times \frac{1}{3}$ **2** $\frac{2}{3} \times \frac{3}{5}$ **3** $\frac{3}{10} \times \frac{2}{3}$

4 $\frac{3}{8} \times \frac{1}{4}$ **5** $\frac{3}{10} \times \frac{2}{5}$ **6** $\frac{3}{8} \times \frac{5}{8}$

7 $\frac{1}{2} \times \frac{5}{8}$ **8** $\frac{2}{3} \times \frac{7}{10}$ **9** $\frac{7}{8} \times \frac{3}{4}$

10 $\frac{7}{12} \times \frac{8}{10}$ **11** $\frac{3}{5} \times \frac{5}{8}$ **12** $\frac{3}{5} \times \frac{7}{12}$

C The diagram shows $\frac{2}{3} \times \frac{1}{3} = \frac{2}{9}$

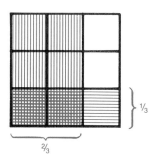

$\left.\right\}$ ⅓

The double-shaded area
shows that $\frac{1}{3} \times \frac{2}{3} = \frac{2}{9}$

⅔

Draw similar diagrams to show the following products:

1 $\frac{1}{2} \times \frac{1}{2} = \frac{1}{4}$ **2** $\frac{1}{4} \times \frac{3}{4} = \frac{3}{16}$ **3** $\frac{2}{3} \times \frac{3}{4} = \frac{6}{12}$

4 $\frac{2}{5} \times \frac{3}{10} = \frac{6}{50}$ **5** $\frac{3}{5} \times \frac{7}{8} = \frac{21}{40}$ **6** $\frac{3}{4} \times \frac{4}{5} = \frac{12}{20} = \frac{3}{5}$

D Use inverses to find the results of the following divisions:

1 $2 \div \frac{1}{2}$ **2** $3 \div \frac{3}{4}$ **3** $5 \div \frac{2}{3}$

4 $\frac{1}{2} \div \frac{1}{4}$ **5** $\frac{3}{4} \div \frac{1}{4}$ **6** $\frac{2}{5} \div \frac{3}{5}$

7 $\frac{5}{9} \div \frac{3}{4}$ **8** $\frac{2}{5} \div \frac{3}{5}$ **9** $\frac{3}{10} \div \frac{2}{5}$

1·6 Multiplication and division of mixed numbers

Before multiplying or dividing by mixed numbers, either:

    1. Change the fractional part to decimal form

or   2. Change the whole-number parts to fractional form with the same denominators as the fractions.

then 3. Multiply or divide by the ordinary rules.

Examples:

1 Find the value of $3\frac{1}{4} \times 2\frac{1}{2}$

    (*Note:* Do **not** multiply 3×2 and $\frac{1}{4} \times \frac{1}{2}$ to get $6\frac{1}{8}$. This is WRONG.)

Method 1 $\quad 3\frac{1}{4} \times 2\frac{1}{2}$
$\qquad\qquad\downarrow\qquad\downarrow$
$\qquad 3{\cdot}25 \times 2{\cdot}50 = 8{\cdot}125$

Method 2 $\quad 3\frac{1}{4} = 3 + \frac{1}{4} = \frac{12}{4} + \frac{1}{4} = \frac{13}{4}$
$\qquad$ Likewise $2\frac{1}{2} = 2 + \frac{1}{2} = \frac{4}{2} + \frac{1}{2} = \frac{5}{2}$
$\qquad$ So $3\frac{1}{4} \times 2\frac{1}{2} = \frac{13}{4} \times \frac{5}{2} = \frac{13 \times 5}{4 \times 2} = \frac{65}{8} = 8\frac{1}{8}$

2 Find the value of $14 \div 3\frac{1}{2}$
$\quad$ Method 1 $\quad 14 \div 3\frac{1}{2}$
$\qquad\qquad\qquad\downarrow\qquad\downarrow$
$\qquad\qquad 14 \div 3{\cdot}5 = 4$

$\quad$ Method 2 $\quad 14 \div 3\frac{1}{2}$
$\qquad\qquad\qquad\downarrow\qquad\downarrow$
$\qquad\qquad \frac{14}{1} \div \frac{7}{2}$
Multiply by inverse to divide $\quad \frac{14}{1} \times \frac{2}{7} = \frac{28}{7} = 4$

Exercise 1·6

A Find the value of these products as fractions.

1 $2\frac{1}{2} \times 2\frac{1}{2}$	**2** $1\frac{3}{4} \times 2\frac{1}{2}$	**3** $1\frac{1}{8} \times 2\frac{1}{4}$
4 $2\frac{3}{4} \times 2\frac{1}{4}$	**5** $3\frac{1}{2} \times 1\frac{1}{3}$	**6** $2\frac{1}{3} \times 3\frac{1}{2}$
7 $3\frac{1}{3} \times 3\frac{1}{3}$	**8** $2\frac{3}{8} \times 1\frac{1}{2}$	**9** $1\frac{3}{4} \times 1\frac{3}{10}$
10 $2\frac{3}{4} \times 2\frac{1}{10}$	**11** $4\frac{1}{2} \times 1\frac{7}{10}$	**12** $5\frac{1}{4} \times 3\frac{1}{5}$

Check each calculation using your calculator.

B The division $5 \div \frac{1}{2} = 10$ can be explained by considering how many $\frac{1}{2}$-inch lines there are in 5 inches.

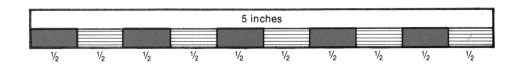

1 Draw diagrams to show
$\quad$ (a) $2 \div \frac{1}{2} = 4$ $\qquad\qquad$ (b) $2 \div \frac{1}{3} = 6$ $\qquad\qquad$ (c) $3 \div \frac{1}{5} = 15$
$\quad$ (d) $2\frac{1}{2} \div \frac{1}{2} = 5$ $\qquad\quad$ (e) $3\frac{3}{4} \div 1\frac{1}{4} = 3$ $\qquad$ (f) $3\frac{1}{2} \div \frac{7}{10} = 5$

2 Write down the inverses of the following mixed numbers
$\quad$ (a) $3\frac{1}{2}$ $\qquad\qquad$ (b) $2\frac{1}{4}$ $\qquad\qquad$ (c) $1\frac{3}{10}$ $\qquad\qquad$ (d) $\frac{4}{5}$
$\quad$ (e) $2\frac{1}{5}$ $\qquad\qquad$ (f) $1\frac{1}{3}$ $\qquad\qquad$ (g) $3\frac{7}{10}$ $\qquad\qquad$ (h) $3\frac{3}{8}$
$\quad$ Check by multiplying each inverse by the number you started with.

3 Use inverses to divide these:
$\quad$ (a) $4\frac{1}{2} \div 1\frac{1}{2}$ $\qquad\qquad$ (b) $3\frac{4}{5} \div \frac{2}{5}$ $\qquad\qquad$ (c) $5\frac{1}{4} \div \frac{7}{10}$
$\quad$ (d) $5\frac{1}{4} \div 1\frac{2}{5}$ $\qquad\qquad$ (e) $3\frac{2}{3} \div 1\frac{1}{2}$ $\qquad\qquad$ (f) $\frac{4}{5} \div 1\frac{1}{2}$

1·7   Application of fractions

Common weights and measures

Many weights and measures make use of halves and quarters, eighths and sixteenths. These units are being replaced by metric units but many of them are still in use in trade, engineering and the home.

Example:

Boards $\frac{3}{8}$ of an inch thick are stacked in a pile 8 ft high. How many boards are there in the stack?

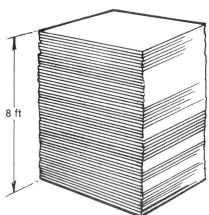

$1\,\text{ft} = 12$ inches
$\Rightarrow 8\,\text{ft} = 96$ inches
$\Rightarrow$ number of boards is $96 \div \frac{3}{8}$
$= \frac{96}{1} \times \frac{8}{3} = \frac{768}{3} = 256$ boards

8 ft

Conversions

A useful relationship to remember is $1\,\text{km} = \frac{5}{8}\,\text{mile}$
Put another way, $8\,\text{km} = 5\,\text{miles}$

Example:

Given that $1\,\text{km} = \frac{5}{8}$ miles, find:
(a) 20 km in miles   (b) $\frac{1}{2}$ km in miles   (c) 20 miles in km   (d) $\frac{1}{2}$ mile in km

(a) $20\,\text{km} = 20 \times \frac{5}{8}$ miles $= \frac{100}{8}$ miles $= 12\frac{1}{4}$ miles

(b) $\frac{1}{2}\,\text{km} = \frac{1}{2} \times \frac{5}{8}$ miles $= \frac{5}{16}$ miles

(c) $20\,\text{miles} = (20 \div \frac{5}{8})\,\text{km} = 20 \times \frac{8}{5} = 32\,\text{km}$
    (Every $\frac{5}{8}$ miles will be one km so the problem is 'how many $\frac{5}{8}$ miles in 20 miles?')

(d) $\frac{1}{2}\,\text{mile} = (\frac{1}{2} \div \frac{5}{8})\,\text{km} = \frac{1}{2} \times \frac{8}{5} = \frac{8}{10}\,\text{km}$

Exercise 1·7

1 Mrs Green has a radio ($\frac{1}{20}$ kW), reading lamp ($\frac{1}{10}$ kW), electric fire ($2\frac{1}{2}$ kW) and hair drier ($1\frac{1}{4}$ kW) all plugged into the same power point. What is the total amount of electricity she is using?

2 A recipe says 'use $\frac{1}{2}$ lb of rice for every two persons'. How much rice would be needed for (a) 7 persons (b) $8\frac{1}{2}$ persons (including one child!).

3 Formica, $\frac{3}{16}$ of an inch thick, is glued to $\frac{3}{4}$-inch block-board to make a kitchen worktop. What is the thickness of the worktop?

4 19 strands of cord, each $\frac{1}{4}$ inch in diameter, are woven into a rope. What is the diameter of the rope?

5 A boy collects 12 programmes from the radio on to his tape recorder. Each programme lasts 40 minutes ($\frac{2}{3}$ of an hour). How many $\frac{1}{2}$-hour cassettes will he need altogether?

6 A shop selling clothes has a '$\frac{1}{3}$ off' sale. How much do these items cost in the sale?
  (a) Jeans, usually £12
  (b) Anorak, usually £15.50
  (c) Boots, usually £14
  (d) Coat, usually £28.40

7 Two large aircraft with 240 seats are going to Singapore. One is $\frac{1}{3}$ empty, the other is $\frac{1}{4}$ empty. Would one aircraft be sufficient for all the passengers?

8 Taking 1 km $= \frac{5}{8}$ miles find (a) how many kilometres equal $8\frac{1}{2}$ miles (b) how many miles equal 24 km.

9 At a time when £1 was equal to $4\frac{1}{2}$ Deutschmarks what was (a) £5.50 worth in Deutschmarks (b) 85 Deutschmarks worth in pounds.

10 If you start with two fractions, say $\frac{2}{3}$ and $\frac{3}{4}$, then add the tops together and the bottoms together to form a new fraction (in this case, $\frac{5}{7}$), then the new fraction will lie between the two you started with!

$$\frac{2}{3} < \frac{5}{7} < \frac{3}{4}$$

  (a) Show that this is true whatever two fractions you start with
  (b) Investigate the fraction you get if you multiply the tops and the bottoms.

1·8 Algebraic fractions

The values of fractions such as $\dfrac{ax}{x^2 + 2x}$ cannot be found by calculator until the values of a and x are known. However, the rules of fractions can still be applied to simplify, cancel, add, subtract, multiply and divide such algebraic fractions.

Examples:

Simplify   **1** $\dfrac{2ax}{x^2 + ax}$ **2** $\dfrac{a}{b} + \dfrac{a^2}{b^2}$ **3** $\dfrac{x^2 - a^2}{2x(x + a)}$

1 $\dfrac{2ax}{x^2 + ax} = \dfrac{2ax}{x(x + a)}$ (x is a factor of both numerator and denominator, so we cancel it)

$= \dfrac{2a}{x + a}$

2 $\dfrac{a}{b} + \dfrac{a^2}{b^2}$

$= \dfrac{ab}{b^2} + \dfrac{a^2}{b^2} = \dfrac{a^2 + ab}{b^2}$ (The two fractions have been combined over one denominator)

3 $\dfrac{x^2 - a^2}{2x(x + a)} = \dfrac{(x - a)(x + a)}{2x(x + a)}$ ($x + a$ is a factor of both top and bottom, so we cancel it)

$= \dfrac{x - a}{2x}$

Exercise 1·8

A   Simplify the following algebraic fractions:

1 $\dfrac{x - y}{2(y - x)}$ **2** $\dfrac{3x - 6y}{2(x^2 - 4y^2)}$ **3** $\dfrac{4a^2 bc}{2ab^2}$

4 $\dfrac{1}{a} + \dfrac{1}{b}$ **5** $\dfrac{a - b}{a} + \dfrac{a + b}{b}$ **6** $\dfrac{x^2}{2y} - \dfrac{y}{2}$

7 $\dfrac{x(x + y)}{xy} - \dfrac{(x - y)}{y}$ **8** $\dfrac{(p + q)^2}{p} - \dfrac{2q}{1}$ **9** $\dfrac{2xy}{3} \times \dfrac{3x^2}{y^2}$

10 $\dfrac{a(b + c)}{3} \div \dfrac{b^2 - c^2}{3}$

B   Solve the following equations:

1 $\dfrac{2t - 7}{5} - \dfrac{t - 2}{2} = 1$ **2** $\dfrac{2}{3m} - 4 = 3 - \dfrac{9}{m}$

3 $\dfrac{7}{3z} - 5 = \dfrac{1}{2} - \dfrac{5}{z}$ **4** $\dfrac{p + 1}{3} - \dfrac{p - 1}{2} = 1 + \dfrac{2p}{3}$

5 $\dfrac{2x - 1}{5} - \dfrac{3x + 1}{2} = \dfrac{2}{5}$ **6** $\dfrac{2z + 7}{4} - \dfrac{z + 1}{3} = \dfrac{3}{4}$

7 $\dfrac{3x + 2}{5} - \dfrac{2x + 5}{3} = x + 3$ **8** $\dfrac{1 - y}{2} = \dfrac{3 + y}{3} - \dfrac{9 + y}{4}$

Exercise 1·9: Investigations

A *Fibonacci sequences*

Starting with any fraction $\frac{a}{b}$ we can form a new fraction $\frac{a+b}{a}$. This process can be repeated,

giving $\frac{(a+b)+a}{a+b}$ for the third fraction, $\frac{(a+b)+a+(a+b)}{(a+b)+a}$ for the fourth, and so on. Such a

sequence of fractions is called a Fibonacci fraction sequence

If $a = 1$, $b = 1$ we obtain the simplest sequence:

$$\frac{1}{1} \quad \frac{2}{1} \quad \frac{3}{2} \quad \frac{5}{3} \quad \cdots$$

1 Write down the first ten fractions of the sequence for $a = 1$, $b = 1$.

2 Work out the values of the fractions. Does the value appear to approach some special value?

3 Continue working out values until you feel confident that the first four decimal places are unchanging.

4 Show that the value in question 3 satisfies the equation

$$x - \frac{1}{x} = 1$$

5 Investigate other Fibonacci fraction sequences in which a, b take different values; e.g. $a = 1$, $b = 2$; $a = 3$, $b = 4$.

B *Equivalent fractions*

1 Give numerical examples for the following proofs.

(a) $\frac{a}{b} = \frac{c}{d} \Leftrightarrow ad = bc$

Proof

1∅ $\dfrac{a}{b} = \dfrac{ad}{bd}$ $\qquad$ (multiplying top and bottom by d)

2∅ $\dfrac{c}{d} = \dfrac{bc}{bd}$ $\qquad$ (multiplying top and bottom by b)

3∅ $\dfrac{a}{b} = \dfrac{c}{d} \Rightarrow \dfrac{ad}{bd} = \dfrac{bc}{bd}$ $\qquad$ (equal fractions with same denominator)

4∅ $\qquad\qquad \Rightarrow ad = bc$

(b) $ad = bc \Rightarrow \dfrac{a}{b} = \dfrac{c}{d}$

Proof

1∅ $ad = bc \Rightarrow \dfrac{ad}{bd} = \dfrac{bc}{bd}$

2∅ $\qquad\qquad \Rightarrow \dfrac{a}{b} = \dfrac{c}{d}$

The two statements can be combined using a double arrow $\Leftrightarrow$.

Thus we have $\dfrac{a}{b} = \dfrac{c}{d} \Leftrightarrow ad = bc$

2 If we start with a pair of equivalent fractions (e.g. $\frac{2}{3} = \frac{4}{6}$) more equivalent pairs can be formed as follows:

$$\frac{2+3}{3} = \frac{4+6}{6} \qquad \frac{3-2}{3} = \frac{6-4}{6}$$

$$\frac{2+3}{3-2} = \frac{4+6}{6-4} \qquad \frac{(2 \times 2) + 3}{3} = \frac{(2 \times 4) + 6}{6}$$

(a) Check that the given new pairs are equivalent.

(b) Start with another pair of equivalent fractions and produce four equivalent pairs.

(c) Prove that the changes will produce equivalent pairs:

start with $\frac{a}{b} = \frac{c}{d}$ (*Hint:* Use $\frac{a}{b} = \frac{c}{d} \Leftrightarrow ad = bc$)

3 (a) Show, by replacing a, b, c and d with numbers, that

$$\frac{a}{b} < \frac{c}{d} \Leftrightarrow ad < bc$$

Prove this result.

(b) Show, by replacing a, b, c and d with numbers, that

$$\frac{a}{b} < \frac{c}{d} \Rightarrow \frac{a}{b} < \frac{a+c}{b+d} < \frac{c}{d}$$

Prove this result.

C *Binary fractions*

When, in decimals, we write 0·75, we are using a shorthand for $\frac{7}{10} + \frac{5}{100}$. It is natural therefore to write $0·1_2$ for $\frac{1}{2}$ and $0·01_2$ for $\frac{1}{4}$ and to call these forms bicimals

1 You know that any number can be made up from powers of 2, e.g.:

$41 = 32 + 8 + 1 = 2^5 + 2^3 + 2^0 = 10\,101_2$

Investigate how fractions can be made up from negative powers of 2.

2 Study the following demonstrations of the fractional form of the recurring bicimal
0·010 101 01 . . .

(a) 1∅   Let $x = 0·010101010101 \ldots$
  2∅ $4x = 1·010101010101 \ldots$
  3∅ $3x = 1$ (subtract line 1∅ from line 2∅)
  4∅ $x = \frac{1}{3}$

(b) 1∅   Let $x = 0·010101010101 \ldots$
  2∅ $2x = 0·101010101010 \ldots$
  3∅ $3x = 0·111111111111 \ldots$ (add lines 1∅, 2∅)
  4∅ $3x = 1$
  5∅ $x = \frac{1}{3}$

3 Use similar methods to demonstrate the fractional form of the following
     (a) $0·101\,010\,1010 \ldots_2$ (b) $0·110\,11_2$ (c) $0·001\,001\,001\,00 \ldots_2$
     (d) $0·001\,100\,110\,011 \ldots_2$ (e) $0·010\,100\,100\,1_2$ (f) $0·111\,011\,101\,110 \ldots$
Do you think that every fraction has a bicimal form?

4 Follow the flow charts, choosing values for *a* and *b*. Do both flow charts give the same result?

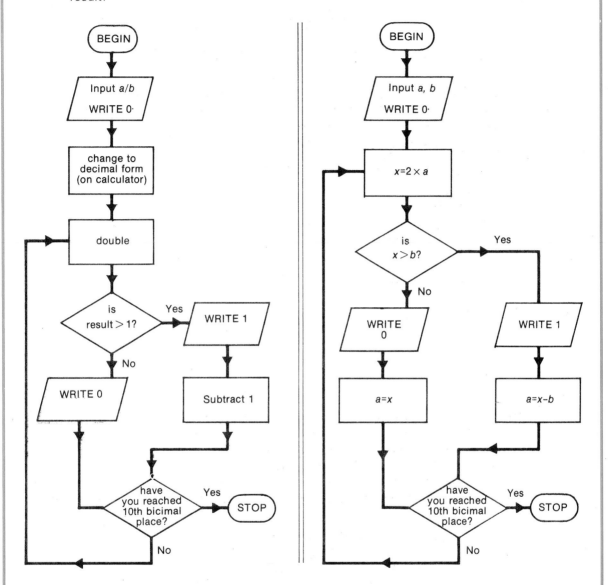

Explain how these programs convert fractions to bicimals.

Unit 2 Standard form, errors and significant figures

2·1 Multiplying and dividing by 10s (Revision)

Multiplying by 10 has the effect of changing the position of the decimal point, moving it one place to the right.

23·54
$\times 10$
235·4

The 20 becomes 200
The 3 units become 30
The 0·5 becomes 5
The 0·04 becomes 0·4

Similarly, dividing by 10 appears to move the decimal point one place to the left.

23·54
$\div 10$
2·354

The 20 becomes 2
The 3 units become 0·3
The 0·5 becomes 0·05
The 0·04 becomes 0·004

Multiplying by 100 moves the decimal point two places to the right.
Dividing by 100 moves the decimal point two places to the left.

Exercise 2·1

A Write down the results of the following multiplications:

1 2·0 × 10	**2** 23·0 × 10	**3** 3·6 × 10	**4** 4·8 × 10
5 51·2 × 10	**6** 36·9 × 10	**7** 85·4 × 10	**8** 77·3 × 10
9 4·5 × 100	**10** 7·0 × 100	**11** 15·2 × 100	**12** 48·5 × 100
13 2·72 × 100	**14** 4·45 × 100	**15** 32·07 × 100	**16** 0·452 × 1000

Check your results with a calculator.

B Write down the results of the following divisions:

1 30 ÷ 10	**2** 42·0 ÷ 10	**3** 523 ÷ 100	**4** 48·7 ÷ 10
5 3·5 ÷ 10	**6** 4·82 ÷ 10	**7** 88·65 ÷ 10	**8** 1803 ÷ 10
9 23 ÷ 100	**10** 14·4 ÷ 100	**11** 360 ÷ 100	**12** 4520 ÷ 100
13 7800 ÷ 100	**14** 4·26 ÷ 100	**15** 0·31 ÷ 100	**16** 15·24 ÷ 100

Check your results with a calculator.

C Which of the following are true statements?

1 30 ÷ 100 = 0·3 × 10   **2** 1·4 × 10 = 140 ÷ 10   **3** 15·2 ÷ 100 = 0·152 × 10
4 36·2 ÷ 10 = 0·362 × 10   **5** 4·83 ÷ 100 = 0·0483 × 10   **6** 25·6 × 10 = 2560 ÷ 10
7 52·84 ÷ 100 = 0·5284 × 100 **8** 1·73 ÷ 100 = 17·3 ÷ 10
Write correct statements to replace the false ones.

2·2   Standard form

In Unit 29 (M1) you learned how to use numbers in Standard Form.
Numbers in standard form can be multiplied and divided, but care must
be taken not to mix up the number part and the power part.

Examples:

1   Multiply 4×10^4 by 1.5×10^{-2}

$$4 \times 10^4 \times 1.5 \times 10^{-2}$$
$$= 4 \times 1.5 \times 10^4 \times 10^{-2}$$
$$= 6 \times 10^2$$

2   Divide 2.6×10^4 by 3.8×10^5

$$(2.6 \times 10^4) \div (3.8 \times 10^5) = (2.6 \div 3.8) \times (10^4 \div 10^5)$$
$$2.6 \div 3.8 = 0.68$$
$$10^4 \div 10^5 = 10^{-1}$$
so $(2.6 \div 3.8) \times (10^4 \div 10^5) = 0.68 \times 10^{-1} = 6.8 \times 10^{-2}$ (standard form)
$$= 0.068 \text{ (decimal form)}$$

Note: The division can be written as a fraction
$$\frac{2.6 \times 10^4}{3.8 \times 10^5} = \frac{2.6}{3.8 \times 10} = \frac{0.68}{10} = 0.68 \times 10^{-1} = 0.068 \text{ as before}$$

Rounding and accuracy

Data cannot be more accurate than the measuring instruments used. It
would be ridiculous to say that the weight of a lorry was 5286·457 kg,
because a weighing machine that could weigh a heavy lorry could not be
sensitive enough to measure parts of a kilogram. Some things even
change while they are being measured, such as the number of people in
a city or the depth of the sea at a particular point.

Remember too that the calculator will often give an answer that is *too* accurate for the problem, i.e. it will give too many significant figures. When the standard form is used, the degree of accuracy is shown by the number of decimal places.

Examples:

1 The population of a city is given as $2 \cdot 8 \times 10^6$. What does this tell you about the exact population?

The exact population is between 2 750 000 and 2 850 000: the measurement of population has been given to the nearest 100 000.

2 In 1975 the USSR produced $66 \cdot 224 \times 10^6$ metric tonnes of wheat.

This information is given to the nearest 1000 metric tonnes: the exact production was between 66·2235 and 66·2244 million metric tonnes.

In the population example the data is given to two significant figures, while in the second example the figure is given to five significant figures.

Exercise 2·2

A Multiply these standard form numbers, giving the result in standard form to three significant figures.

1 $(4 \cdot 2 \times 10^2) \times (3 \cdot 6 \times 10^5)$ **2** $(0 \cdot 36 \times 10^4) \times (2 \cdot 8 \times 10^{-2})$ **3** $(4 \cdot 45 \times 10^3) \times (1 \cdot 3 \times 10^{-3})$

4 $(3 \cdot 6 \times 10^8) \times (1 \cdot 65 \times 10^{-7})$ **5** $(2 \cdot 85 \times 10^{-4}) \times (3 \cdot 5 \times 10^7)$ **6** $(1 \cdot 75 \times 10^{-4})^2$

Note: If you have a scientific calculator you will be able to enter numbers in standard form using the exp button.

$4 \cdot 2 \times 10^2$ is entered as 4·2 exp 2
$3 \cdot 75 \times 10^{-3}$ is entered as 3·75 exp 3 +/−

and the product is found as follows:

4·2 exp 2 × 3·75 exp 3 +/− = 1·575

B Divide the following standard form numbers, giving the result in standard form to two significant figures.

1 $(5 \cdot 6 \times 10^4) \div (3 \cdot 2 \times 10^3)$ **2** $(6 \cdot 1 \times 10^3) \div (7 \cdot 8 \times 10^4)$ **3** $(4 \cdot 2 \times 10^{-2}) \div (2 \cdot 2 \times 10^{-2})$

4 $(8 \cdot 4 \times 10^5) \div (6 \cdot 3 \times 10^{-2})$ **5** $(4 \cdot 1 \times 10^{-3}) \div (2 \times 10^3)$ **6** $(5 \cdot 2 \times 10^{-2}) \div (2 \cdot 6 \times 10^{-3})$

Check using the calculator. Use the exp button if your calculator has one, otherwise change to decimal numbers before dividing.

C **1** The population of the USA in 1978 was 218·06 million. They consumed 9·954 million tonnes of sugar. How much was this per person?

2 Italy, with a population of 56·7 million people, consumed 1·507 million tonnes of sugar. How much was this per person? Would you agree that people in Italy eat more sugar than people in the USA?

3 The average consumption of water per person per day is 48 litres. How much is this in a year? How much water would a population of 55 million use in a year?

4 A certain bacterium weighs about 4×10^{-5} g per 100 cells. How many cells would there be in 20 g of the bacterium?

5 The mass of a proton is $1 \cdot 672\,61 \times 10^{-24}$ g. Hydrogen gas is made up almost entirely of protons. One litre of hydrogen gas weighs $8 \cdot 9 \times 10^{-2}$ g: how many protons are there in this one litre?

D *Examination questions*

1 Change 0·0123 into standard form. *(NREB 1979)*

2 Write $1 \cdot 76 \times 10^3$ as a whole number. *(NI 1978)*

3 Given that $A = 6 \cdot 4 \times 10^6$ and $B = 4 \times 10^2$ find, in standard form, the value of $A \div B$. *(NREB 1979)*

4 The standard form of 256 is
(a) $2 \cdot 56 \times 10^1$ (b) $2 \cdot 56 \times 10^3$ (c) $2 \cdot 56 \times 10^2$ (d) $2 \cdot 56 \times 10^4$.

5 Evaluate $3 \cdot 1 \times 10^3 + 2 \cdot 01 \times 10^2$ giving your answer in standard form (i.e. $A \times 10^n$). *(NREB 1978)*

6 Express the number 93 000 000 in standard form. *(NREB 1978)*

7 Write the numbers 350 and 0·035 in standard form. *(NREB 1979)*

8 In a normal life-span, the human heart will beat approximately 2 649 000 000 times. Express this number in standard form, i.e. $a \times 10^n$ where $1 \leqslant a < 10$ and n is an integer.

2·3 Errors

If you round off numbers you introduce errors. An error is the difference between the rounded-off estimate and the exact number. This is not to be confused with a simple mistake, when you get an answer wrong.

Example:

$2 \cdot 4 \times 3 \cdot 4 \ldots$ (exact) $= 8 \cdot 16$
$2 \ \times 3 \ \ldots$ (rounded off) $= 6$
                           ERROR $\to \overline{2 \cdot 16}$

The error is quite large!

We often compare errors by taking the errors as a percentage of the exact result. In the above example the error per cent is
$(2 \cdot 16 \div 8 \cdot 16) \times 100 = 26 \cdot 5\%$
The error may or may not be important. If you were cutting glass to fit a window, an error would mean that the glass would not fit. Nor are rough estimates good enough when giving change in a shop. However, if someone asked you the time they would probably not need to know it to the nearest second even if you had a digital watch that displayed it.

Exercise 2·3

In each of the following questions work out the absolute error and the error per cent. Discuss whether the error is important or not.

1 A window is 48 cm × 36 cm. Glass is cut 491 mm × 352 mm for the window. Find the errors in the lengths and in the area.

2 148 × 63 is calculated to be about 9000.

3 An aircraft is supposed to be flying at 10 000 m. In fact it is flying at 10 120 m.

4 The world population of whales is estimated at 10 000. The actual number is 7390.

5 The petrol consumption of a car was said to be 42 mpg. A driver tested his car and found that he travelled 160 miles on 4·5 gallons.

6 A sports stadium is in the shape shown. The area of the stadium is estimated as though it were a rectangle 150 m × 50 m. What is the error of this estimate?

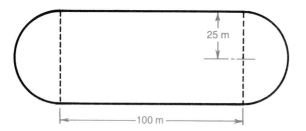

25 m

100 m

(Remember that the area of a circle is πr^2.)

7 4000 is divided by 65. The result is estimated as 60.

8 The international paper sizes are (in mm):

A0   841 × 1189
A1   594 × 841
A2   420 × 594
A3   297 × 420
A4   210 × 297

Find the errors per cent if the areas are calculated as:

A0   800 × 1200 = 960 000 mm²
A1   600 × 800 = 480 000 mm²
A2   400 × 600 = 240 000 mm²
A3   300 × 400 = 120 000 mm²
A4   200 × 300 = 60 000 mm²

9 A 3000-year-old formula gives the area of a circle as $A = (D - \frac{1}{9}D)^2$ (where D = length of diameter). Use the formula to calculate the area of a circle, radius 5 cm.

10 Compare your result for question 9 with the accurate result obtained from $A = \pi r^2$
(a) What is the error of the ancient result?
(b) What is the percentage error?
(c) Investigate whether the percentage error is the same for all circles, whatever radius.

2·4 Avoiding mistakes

Using a calculator can cause mistakes. The machine cannot make a mistake if properly used (unless the battery is flat), but the person using the machine can easily make slips. Thus every calculation should be checked, by either:

(i)   repeating the calculation using a different sequence
or (ii)   estimating the result in advance
or (iii) working back from the result to the original numbers

Common mistakes are:

- Leaving off a zero
- Putting the decimal point in wrongly
- Pressing wrong number buttons
- Pressing wrong function buttons
- Working out problems in the wrong order
- Leaving out numbers in a list
- Forgetting to clear before starting

You should always have a rough idea of the final answers and organise
the work to avoid mistakes.

Exercise 2·4

A Carry out the following calculations. If you do them all correctly, the answers should add up to 1991·3 correct to 1 decimal place.

1 Add: 21·34
          141·77
          54·82
          66·67
          102·38

2 $43·27 \times 0·0653$

3 $43\,715 \div 27·8$

4 $\sqrt{4·3656}$

5 $\dfrac{3·7}{14·9} + \dfrac{2·62}{18·3}$

6 $\dfrac{17·54 \times 6·11}{4·045}$

B Explain how you would check the calculations that follow.

1 $2·3 \times 0·67 \times 11·45$

2 $(3·4 + 1·75) \times (14·05 + 26·8)$

3 $(44·2 \times 0·035)^2$

4 $(5·25 \div 0·75) \times (6·32 \div 1·14)$

5 $\dfrac{(8·32)^2 \times \pi}{(2·16)^3}$

6 $(371·2)^2 - (4·41)^2$

7 $(2·83)^3 - 3 \times (2·83)^2 \times 1·76$

8 $(2·48 \div 42)^2 + (37 \div 1·9)^2$

9 $(45·37 - 2·81)^3 \times 82$

10 $(12·8)^2 + (11·7)^2 + (3·65)^2$

Carry out the calculations. The answers are given below (in the wrong order).

210·3775	137 770	379·2278	2·393	− 19·6218
38·807	314·0525	17·644 45	21·579	6 321 479

C If your calculator has a memory, $\boxed{M+}$ should be used for adding long strings of numbers. Investigate and discuss the advantages of using $\boxed{M+}$ rather than $\boxed{+}$.

2·5 Accuracy

The number 3·8 has an exact value, but a length, such as 3·8 cm, is only
as accurate as the instrument used to measure it.

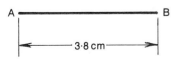

The line AB, marked 3·8 cm, could
be 3·804 cm long, but this could not be
established without a very accurate
measuring instrument.

Thus 'length = 3·8 cm' really means that the measured length is between
3·75 cm and 3·84 cm. (If it were 3·85 or over it would be read as 3·9.)

Example:

A piece of metal is measured to be
5·7 cm long and 3·8 cm wide. What
are the maximum and minimum
possible lengths and areas for the
metal?

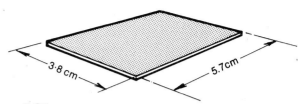

The length ... maximum 5·74 cm   minimum 5·65 cm
The width ... maximum 3·84 cm   minimum 3·75 cm
Area   ... maximum 5·74 × 3·84 = 22·0416 cm²
           ... minimum 5·65 × 3·75 = 21·1875 cm²

The accuracy of a measurement is shown by the number of decimal places that are used to express the result.

4·5 kg ⇒ 'measured to the nearest 100 g: lies between 4·45 kg and 4·54 kg'
4·50 kg ⇒ 'measured to the nearest 10 g: lies between 4·495 kg and 4·504 kg'
4·500 kg ⇒ 'measured to the nearest 1 g: lies between 4·4995 kg and 4·5004 kg'

The accuracy of a measurement can alternatively be indicated by stating the range of possible error.

Example:

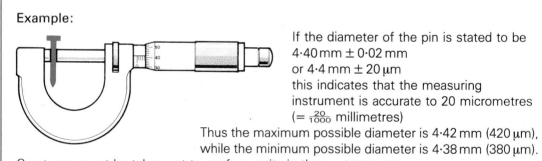

If the diameter of the pin is stated to be
4·40 mm ± 0·02 mm
or 4·4 mm ± 20 μm
this indicates that the measuring
instrument is accurate to 20 micrometres
(= $\frac{20}{1000}$ millimetres)
Thus the maximum possible diameter is 4·42 mm (420 μm),
while the minimum possible diameter is 4·38 mm (380 μm).
Great care must be taken not to confuse units in these statements.

Exercise 2·5

A   Write down maximum and minimum values for:
   1   A length of 100 m measured to the nearest 10 cm
   2   A length of 5·1 cm measured to the nearest 1 mm.
   3   A length of 2·65 cm measured to the nearest 100 μm
   4   A length of 586·8 km measured to the nearest 50 metres
   5   A mass of 25 kg measured to the nearest 10 g
   6   A mass of 4·5 tonnes
   7   A mass of 7·25 tonnes
   8   An interval of time measured (to the nearest 10 secs) to be 4 hours 25 minutes 30 secs

9 An interval of time measured to be 4·1 minutes

10 A national budget of $485 million to the nearest $1 000 000

B Find the maximum and minimum possible areas for figures measured as follows:

  1 A square, side 4·5 cm

  2 A rectangle 4 cm × 3·5 cm

  3 A circle of radius 2·85 metres

  4 A parallelogram whose base is 4·2 cm and height 1·3 cm

Find the maximum and minimum possible volumes for shapes measured as follows:

  5 A cube 12 cm × 12 cm × 12 cm

  6 A cuboid 150 mm × 32 mm × 45 mm

  7 A cuboid 8·2 cm × 12·9 cm × 36·5 cm

  8 A cylinder whose radius is 4·5 cm and whose length is 25 metres

  9 A cylinder whose radius is 14 cm and whose length is 32·5 metres

  10 A triangular prism whose section is a half-square, side 13·6 cm, and whose length is 4·35 metres

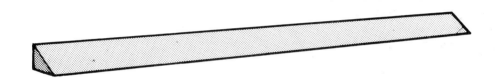

C **1** A motorist travels at a steady 60 miles per hour on a motorway. He estimates his time of travel to be 2 h ± 10 minutes. What distance may he have travelled if:

  (a) His speedometer is correct to the nearest 5 mph.

  (b) His speedometer is correct to the nearest 1 mph.

  2 A manufacturer making steel rods knows he can sell 600 000 ± 100 000 tons in a year. He also knows that the price will be £13 ± 1·50 per ton. What is the difference between the best and the worst results he can expect?

  3 An international cricket-ball must have a circumference of 22·6 ± 0·25 cm. What are the maximum and minimum possible values for the volume of the ball? If the mass of the ball must be 150–165 g, find the maximum possible density of the ball.

  (*Note:* density = mass/volume)

D *An investigation*

Draw a line and ask all the other people in the class to estimate its length to the nearest millimetre, using a plain ruler (or strip of paper) marked only in centimetres.

Measure the line accurately and plot a frequency graph showing the number of people having an error of − 3, − 2, − 1, 0, 1, 2, 3 . . . . mm. Comment on the shape of the graph.

Repeat the experiment using some sort of curved line.

Unit 3 The trapezium

3·1   Introduction

A trapezium is a quadrilateral with **one** pair of sides parallel. The
distance between the parallel sides is usually known as the height.

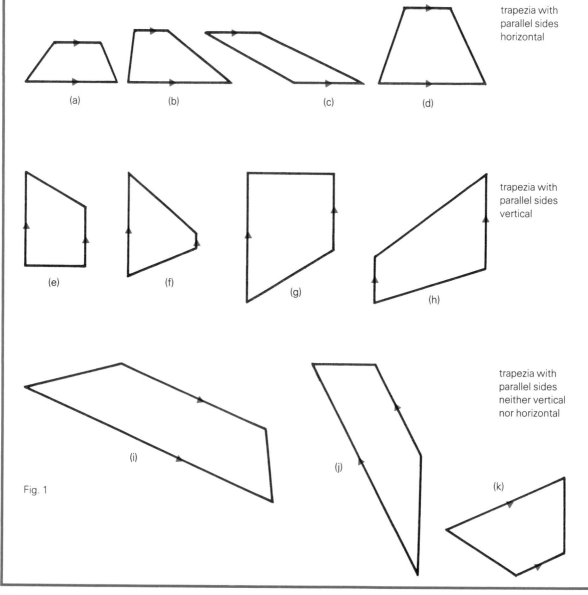

trapezia with
parallel sides
horizontal

(a)   (b)   (c)   (d)

trapezia with
parallel sides
vertical

(e)   (f)   (g)   (h)

trapezia with
parallel sides
neither vertical
nor horizontal

(i)   (j)   (k)

Fig. 1

Note: **1** All trapezia can be turned so that the longest of the parallel sides is horizontal and at the base of the figure.

2 If the shorter parallel side shrinks to nothing, a **triangle** is formed.

The word 'trapezium' comes from a Greek word which means 'table'.

The pair of muscles at the back of the neck are called trapezia, because of their shape.

A trapeze is used in circus acts. It is usually a bar suspended from a pair of ropes.

Exercise 3·1

A **1** Measure the lengths of the parallel sides for each trapezium in Figure 1.

2 In which of the trapezia is the total length of the parallel sides more than the total length of the non-parallel sides?

3 Measure the height of each trapezium (distance between the parallel sides). Which trapezium has the greatest height?

4 Measure the diagonals in each trapezium. Which trapezium has equal diagonals?

B From the measurements you made in section A, make exact copies of the trapezia labelled (b), (d), (g) and (i). (*Hint:* Start with a triangle. Draw the base and then the coloured triangle – you can work out the lengths of XC and DX.)

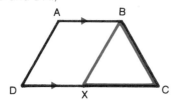

C Copy the figures given below, then measure all the **different** trapezia you can find in each design.

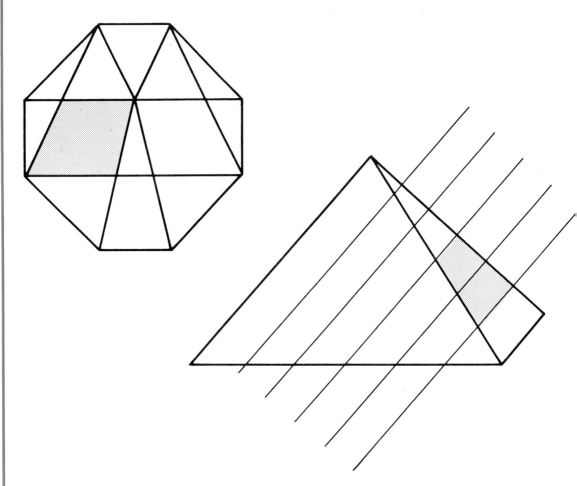

3·2 Area of a trapezium

Any trapezium can be cut and reshaped as a rectangle (see below). h is the perpendicular distance between the two parallel sides. This shows that the area of a trapezium $= \frac{1}{2}h(a + b)$

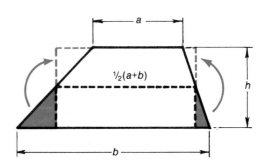

Example:

A trapezium ABDC, with AB parallel to CD, has a height of 5 cm. AB is 4 cm and CD is 7 cm. Calculate the area of the trapezium.

$$\text{Area} = \tfrac{1}{2} \times (a + b) \times h$$
$$= \tfrac{1}{2} \times 11 \times 5$$
$$= 27 \cdot 5 \text{ cm}^2$$

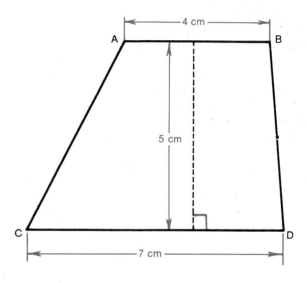

Note: **1** If the shorter side were to shrink to a point, the trapezium would become a triangle, area $\tfrac{1}{2} \times b \times h$ ($= \tfrac{1}{2} \times 7 \times 5$ for ABDC above)

2 If the shorter side were to stretch to the same size as the longer side, the trapezium would become a parallelogram. The area would then be $\tfrac{1}{2} \times (b + b) \times h = b \times h$ ($= 7 \times 5$ for ABDC above)

Area formulae:

	Shape	Area
	trapezium	$\tfrac{1}{2} \times (a + b) \times h$
	parallelogram	$b \times h$
	triangle	$\tfrac{1}{2} \times b \times h$

Exercise 3·2

A Calculate the areas of the trapezia given below.

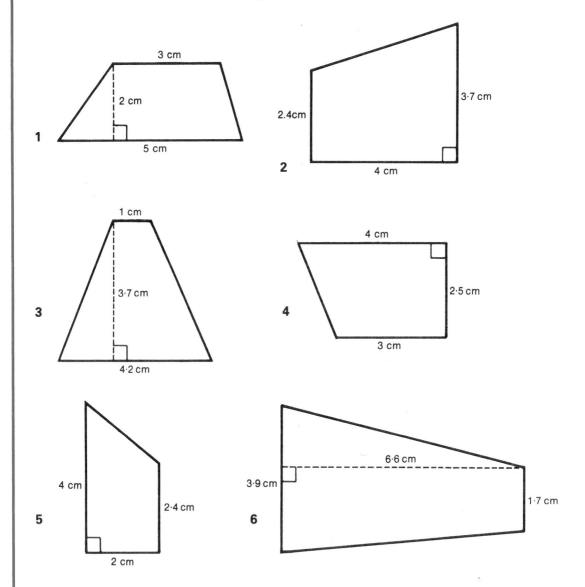

B 1 A trapezium ABCD has AB parallel to CD. What is the area of the trapezium if
   (a) AB = 2·4 cm, CD = 3·9 cm, and the distance between the two parallel sides is 5·5 cm.
   (b) AB = 6 cm, CD = 4·8 cm, and the distance between the two parallel sides is 3·9 cm.
   (c) AB = 4·4 cm, CD = 6·5 cm, and the distance between the two parallel sides is 0·34 cm.
  2 A trapezium is drawn with sides AB and CD parallel. AB = 3 cm and CD = 7·5 cm. The other two sides are 5·7 cm and 6·2 cm long. Draw the trapezium and find its area. Compare your result with that obtained by other people.
  3 Draw all the trapezia of questions 1 and 2 on 1 mm² paper. Draw rectangles round the trapezia and use them to find the area. Compare your results with the calculated results you have already found.

C The following questions refer to Fig. 2

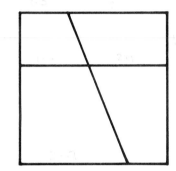

Fig. 2

1 Find the area of the trapezium if $a = 12$ cm, $b = 18$ cm and $h = 5$ cm.

2 Find a if $b = 12$ cm, $h = 8$ cm and the area of the trapezium is 192 cm².

3 Find b if $a = 10$ cm, $h = 20$ cm and the area of the trapezium is 220 cm².

4 Find h if $a = 12$ cm, $b = 16$ cm and the area of the trapezium is 70 cm².

5 Find the area of each of the four trapezia that make up the square shown in Fig. 3. Check that the areas add up to the area of the square.

Fig. 3

3·3 Use of the trapezium in finding areas

Areas which cannot be found by direct measurement can be found using trapezia.

Example:

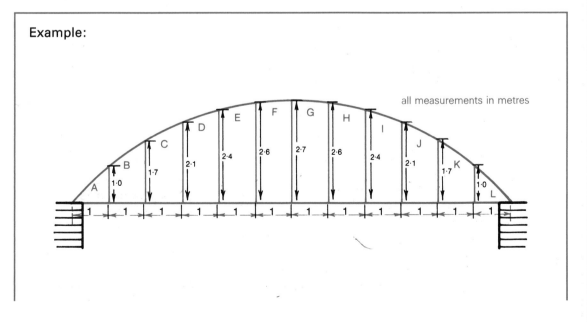

all measurements in metres

The area between the curved arch and the straight base of this bridge can be estimated by treating each of the 12 sections as a trapezium.

Area of section A = $\frac{1}{2} \times (0 + 1 \cdot 0) \times 1 = 0 \cdot 5\,\text{m}^2$

Area of section B = $\frac{1}{2} \times (1 \cdot 0 + 1 \cdot 7) \times 1 = 1 \cdot 35\,\text{m}^2$ etc. . . .

Exercise 3·3

A **1** Find the areas of the remaining 10 sections of the bridge in the example above.

  2 If you add all the heights together, you get $0 + 1 \cdot 0 + 1 \cdot 7 + \ldots + 1 \cdot 7 + 1 \cdot 0 + 0$. Compare this total with the area in question 1. What is the connection?

  3 A similar bridge has 5 m intervals between the verticals. The verticals measure 0 m, 1·2 m, 1·8 m, 2·3 m, 2·5 m, 2·3 m, 1·8 m, 1·2 m and 0 m. What is the area of the space between the arch and the straight base?

B Find the areas of the shapes below (measure first).

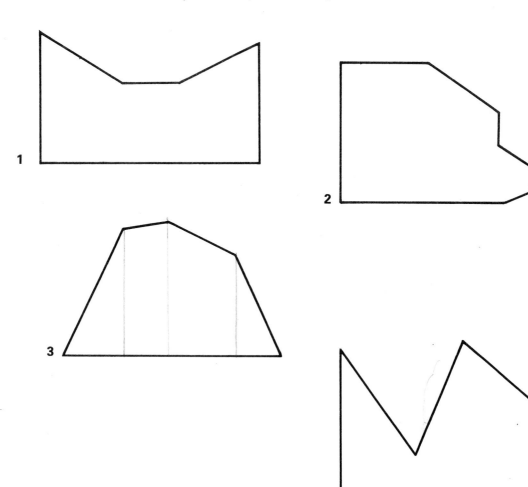

C　**1**　Draw a semicircle, diameter 10 cm, on 1 mm² paper.
　　2　Measure the height of points on the semicircle at 1 cm intervals along the base.
　　3　Use your results to estimate the area of the semicircle (*A*).
　　4　Using ⠀$A = \frac{1}{2}\pi r^2$⠀ gives the area as $12\frac{1}{2}\pi$ cm². Use **your** result for the area in question 3 to obtain an estimate for π.
　　　　($A = 12\frac{1}{2}\pi$, so $\pi = A \div 12\frac{1}{2}$)

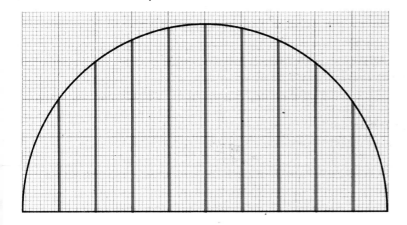

Fig. 4

　　5　Use trapezia to estimate the area of this ellipse.

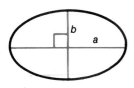

2*a* is the length of the long diameter,
2*b* is the length of the short diameter. Calculate πab. Does it agree with your estimate of the area?

3·4　Offset survey

The trapezium is used as the basis of one method of measuring the area of pieces of land.

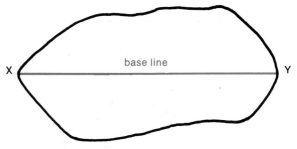

First a base line is chosen.

Then distances are measured from the base line to points on the edge of the land. These distances are called off-sets.

Example:

The sections marked as B, C, F, G, H are regarded as trapezia and their areas calculated. The areas A, D, E, and I are calculated as triangles.
The work is set out as a table.

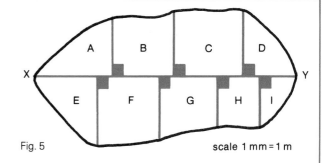

Fig. 5

scale 1 mm = 1 m

Region	Base (measured)	Offset 1 (measured)	Offset 2 (measured)	Area	Working
A	21 m	0	16 m	168 m²	$\leftarrow \frac{1}{2}(0 + 16) \times 21$
B	17 m	16 m	17 m	280·5 m²	$\leftarrow \frac{1}{2}(16 + 17) \times 17$
etc.					

Exercise 3·4

1 Complete the table and work out the total area enclosed in Figure 5.
2 A plot of land is shown in Figure 6. Make a copy of the figure and use an offset-survey method to find the area.

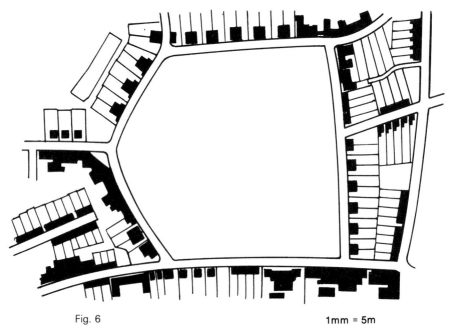

Fig. 6

1mm = 5m

Would the land be sufficiently large to make a new park?

3 A small airport has a central runway and a control tower, as shown on the plan. Estimate the total area of the airport, given that the runway is 1880 metres long.
(You will have to work out the scale first.)

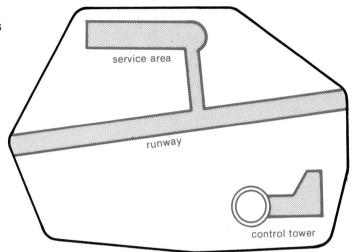

4 Find the area of a sportsfield, playground or park near your school. You will need measuring tape (100 m) and a large set square. Choose a fine day!

3·5 Isosceles trapezia and tessellations

The isosceles trapezium has one pair of parallel sides and one pair of equal sides.
It has an axis of symmetry.

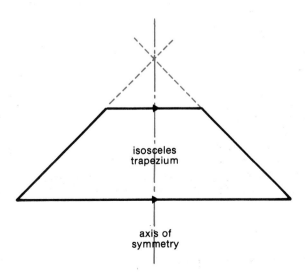

Exercise 3·5

A Which of the following statements are true about all isosceles trapezia?

1 The long parallel side is twice the short parallel side.
2 The base angles are equal.
3 The top angles are equal.
4 The diagonals are equal.
5 The diagonals bisect the base angles.
6 The diagonals bisect the top angles.
7 The diagonals bisect each other.
8 The trapezium can be cut just once and reformed into a rectangle.

B

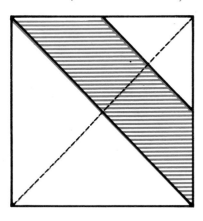

The figure shows an isosceles trapezium that can be cut from a square. Cut a similar trapezium from thin card and use it to make a tessellation.

C Figure 7 shows part of a tessellation made with squares and isosceles trapezia.

1 Make a copy of the tessellation of Fig. 7 and colour squares and trapezia in different colours.

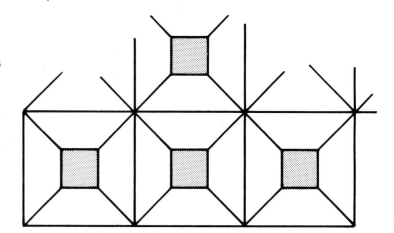

Fig. 7

2 Make a tessellation from isosceles trapezia only.
3 Make a tessellation based on the trapezium which is half of a regular hexagon.

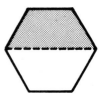

4 Make a tessellation based on the trapezium cut from a regular pentagon.

5 Copy these tessellations on to a large piece of paper and extend them.

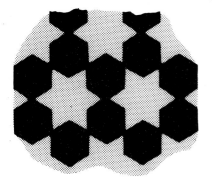

Hexagons and stars

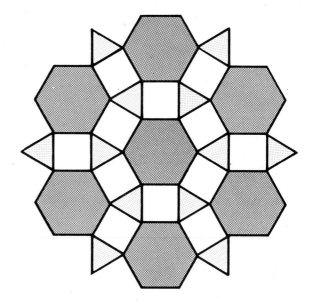

6 Design a tessellation for yourself using two different but related trapezia.

3·6 Areas under straight lines

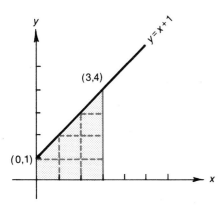

The line $y = x + 1$ passes through $(0, 1)$ and $(3, 4)$ The area in colour is known as the area under the line, although more exactly it would be called 'the area enclosed by the x axis, the y axis, the line $x = 3$ and the line $y = x + 1$'.

The area can be calculated from the coordinates. The parallel sides of the trapezium are 1 unit and 4 units in length. The depth of the trapezium is 3 units.

Area $= \frac{1}{2} \times (1 + 4) \times 3 = 7\frac{1}{2}$ square units (see figure)

We can find similarly the area under the same line from $x = 1$ to $x = 3$.

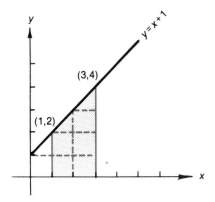

Parallel sides of trapezium: 2 units, 4 units
Depth of trapezium: 2 units
Area $= \frac{1}{2} \times 2 \times (4 + 2) = 6$ square units

If the equation of the line is known (in this case $y = x + 1$) the areas can be found without even drawing a figure.

Example:

Find the area bounded by $y = 2x + 3$ and the lines $x = 2$, $x = 7$ and $y = 0$.
(*Note:* $y = 0$ is the x-axis.)

Step 1∅   The four vertices of the trapezium are (2, 7) (7, 17) (2, 0) and (7, 0)

Step 2∅   The parallel sides of the trapezium are 7 and 17 units in length

Step 3∅   The depth of the trapezium is 5 units

Step 4∅   The area required is $\frac{1}{2} \times 5 \times (7 + 17) = 60$ square units

---

Exercise 3·6

A   Find the areas under the given straight lines between the points indicated.

1   $y = 2x + 1$ from $x = 1$ to $x = 4$. Check by drawing on squared paper
2   $y = 3x$ from $x = 2$ to $x = 5$. Check by drawing
3   $y = 3x - 2$ from $x = 3$ to $x = 6$. Check by drawing
4   $y = 3x + 2$ from $x = 2 \cdot 5$ to $x = 5 \cdot 5$
5   $y = 2x - 3$ from $x = 10$ to $x = 20$
6   $y = 6x + 4$ from $x = 1 \cdot 5$ to $x = 5 \cdot 5$
7   $2x + 3y = 5$ from $x = 0$ to $x = 1$. Check by drawing
8   $3x - 2y = 1$ from $x = 2$ to $x = 8$

B   1   Find the area between the lines $x = 0$, $y = 0$, $y = mx + c$ and $x = x_1$. Your answer should be in terms of x_1, m and c only.

2   Use the general answer found in question 1 to confirm your results in the exercises of Section A.

3   Show that, if A_1 is the area under $y = mx + c$ to the point (x_1, y_1) and A_2 is the area under $y = mx + c$ to the point (x_2, y_2), then the area from $x = x_1$ to $x = x_2$ is $A_2 - A_1$.

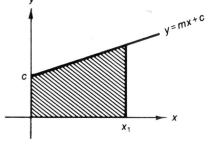

3·7 Applications of trapezia to problems of velocity and acceleration

When an object is moving, the distance travelled is represented as an area on the velocity/time graph.

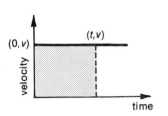

Distance = speed × time
= vt

Steady Speed

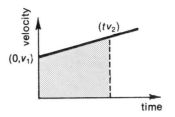

Distance = average velocity × time
$= \frac{1}{2}(v_1 + v_2)t$

Accelerating

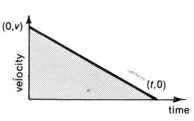

Distance $= \frac{1}{2}vt$

Stopping

Exercise 3·7

Calculate the distance travelled in each of the following cases.

1 A man runs at 10 km/h for 3 hours.

2 A ship sails at 12·5 knots for 36 hours (e.g. a sailing ship running before the wind in a storm).

3 A train travels at an average speed of 116 miles per hour for 2 hours (Paris–Bordeaux).

4 A car is accelerated from 0 mph to 60 mph in 7·7 seconds. How far does it travel in this time? (Draw a graph first.)

5 Before take-off a jet aircraft increases its speed from 50 km/h to 250 km/h in 45 seconds. What is the length of runway needed for this acceleration?

6 A satellite is launched by a rocket which increases its speed steadily from zero to 4000 m/sec in 6 minutes. How far does it travel in this time?

7 An object falls freely under gravity: the velocity is 9·81 t m/sec after t seconds (ignoring air-resistance).
   (a) What is the velocity after 5, 10, 15, 20 seconds?
   (b) What is the distance fallen during the first 5 seconds?
   (c) What is the distance fallen during the next 5 seconds?

8 A parachutist jumps from an aeroplane and waits 10 seconds before pulling his rip-cord. In the following 5 seconds the parachute reduces his falling speed to 10 m/sec. How far does he fall altogether during the 15 seconds?

9 A car travelling at 70 mph is stopped in 4 seconds. How far does it travel in that time?

10 A driver travelling at 120 km/h sees an obstacle 100 metres distant. It takes her 0·4 secs to react and apply the brakes and a further 4 seconds to stop the car. Does she hit the obstacle?

Investigate some similar problems of your own invention.

Unit 4 Inverse variation

4·1 The principle of inverse variation

Sometimes two things are related so that one gets bigger when the other gets smaller. This relation is called inverse variation.

Three ways of describing inverse variation by formula are:

(i) $y \propto \frac{1}{x}$ y varies with $\frac{1}{x}$

(ii) $y = \frac{k}{x}$ y = a fixed number divided by x

(iii) xy = constant   The product of x and y is always the same

---

Examples:

1   Price and the quantity you can buy, for a fixed sum of money.

With £5 you can buy 10 pairs of socks at 50p a pair

                   5 pairs of socks at £1 a pair

                   1 pair of socks at £5 a pair.

(Number of pairs) × (cost of each pair) = £5

       x × y = constant

The dearer the socks the fewer you buy.

2   Time for a journey and speed travelled.

You can travel 200 km by travelling 1 hour at 200 km/h

                           or 2 hours at 100 km/h

speed × hours = 200 km   or 4 hours at 50 km/h

    x × y = constant   or 8 hours at 25 km/h

The greater the speed, the shorter the time.

Exercise 4·1

All the following are examples of inverse variation in some way. Explain each case. If you know of direct variation connected with each situation give that too.

1   The number of cassettes you can buy for £10.

2   The number of stitches to the inch and the thickness of knitting wool.

3   The number of lengths of wood that can be cut from an 8 m plank.

4   The depth of water in a pool and the area of the pool, if it contains 10 000 gallons of water.

5   The number of people sharing a pools win of £500 000 and the amount each receives.

6   Given the world's oil reserves ... the amount of oil burned each year and the number of years the oil will last.

7   The pressure and volume of a given mass of gas.

8 The population of a country and the average number of calories per person, eaten each day. (Consider industrial nations and third world.)

cereal, milk, sugar, 285 calories

steak, potatoes, carrots, 286 calories

apple pie, custard, 498 calories

egg, bacon, 305 calories

banana 46 calories

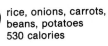
coffee, milk, sugar, 85 calories

toast, butter, marmalade, 254 calories

tea, milk, sugar, 94 calories

rice, onions, carrots, beans, potatoes 530 calories

milk 95 calories

coconut 107 calories

rice, lentils, carrots, beans, potatoes 609 calories

9 Make a list of any relations you think are examples of inverse variation. Discuss your list with a friend and compare lists.

4·2 Calculations with inverse variation

The method is very simple if you take it in two steps:

Step 1∅   Use a known pair of values to find the constant
Step 2∅   Use the constant to find an unknown value.

Examples:

1 A building job will take 40 days if 10 people are working on it. How many days will it take if 25 people are working on the same job?

Step 1∅   The constant is $40 \times 10 = 400$ work days
Step 2∅   If 25 people are working, $25n = 400 \Rightarrow n = 16$ 16 days

39

2 A steel wire can be cut into 100 lengths of 2·4 metres. How many lengths of 8 m could be cut from the wire?

Step 1∅   The constant is $100 \times 2 \cdot 4 = 240$ metres (the total length)

Step 2∅ $8n = 240 \Rightarrow n = 30$ 30 lengths

Exercise 4·2

A
1 A bridge takes 200 people 60 working days to build. How many people would be needed to build it in 40 working days? (Do you think your calculation is realistic?)

2 A roll of carpet can be cut into 20 lengths of 5 metres.
   (a) How many 4 m lengths could be cut from the roll?
   (b) How many 2 m lengths could be cut from the roll?
   (c) How many 2·5 m lengths could be cut from the roll?

3 A prize worth £4000 is shared between 16 people. How much does each person get? How much would each get if 80 people shared the same prize? How is this question related to wins on the football pools?

4 A group of workers in a factory combine to do the pools. In a week in which there was a dividend of £160, everyone received £6.40. How much would they receive from a win of £2800?

5 An advertising company telephones 4800 people each week, offering to sell double glazing. How long would it take to contact the same number of people if they used 6 telephonists instead of 20?

6 A room requires 1750 square tiles to cover the floor. The tiles are 5 cm × 5 cm. How many 8 cm × 8 cm tiles would be needed to cover the same floor?

7 Two boys going on holiday take money to last 30 days, (estimating that they will spend £10 per day). In fact they spend £16 per day. How many days do they have to cut from the end of the holiday?

8 A TV takes 90 minutes to assemble if four workers are assembling it. How long should it take one worker to assemble 100 sets? How long would it take six workers to assemble 100 sets?

B **1** A space capsule is on a journey from Earth to Mars. If it travels at 10 000 km per hour it reaches Mars in 3000 hours. How long would the journey take at:
(a) 100 000 km/h   (b) 5000 km/h   (c) 1000 km/h – the speed of an ordinary jet aircraft
(d) 50 000 km/h?

2 The astronauts in the capsule have sufficient food for 300 days if they eat 1 kg per day. How many days would the food last if they ate
(a) 200 g per day   (b) 400 g per day   (c) 500 g per day   (d) 1·5 kg per day?
Make up a story about their flight.

3 Joanna has been promised enough money to buy 11 metres of curtain material at £2.50 per metre. How much could she buy of material costing
(a) £3.75 per metre?
(b) £1.80 per metre?

4 What is the maximum price Joanna can afford if she must have 16 metres of material to make curtains for her window?

5 Mrs Jones can drive to her mother's house in $4\frac{1}{2}$ hours if she keeps up an average speed of 50 mph. How long would the journey take if her average speed were:
(a) 30 mph   (b) 60 mph   (c) 70 mph?

6 A village water supply is stored in a water tower. The tank can be filled from the pumping station (at 500 litres per minute) in four hours if no water is being run off. How long will the tank take to fill if water is being used at the rate of:
(a) 100 litres/minute   (b) 200 litres/minute   (c) 400 litres/minute?

C **1** The capsule in question B.1 has enough fuel to fire the engines at full power for 30 minutes. For how long could the engines be fired at
(a) 10% power   (b) 20% power   (c) 40% power   (d) 80% power?

2 The harvest of a farm's crop takes 12 days to gather using three combine harvesters. How long would the harvest take if
(a) one harvester were used?
(b) four harvesters were used?
Does the assumption of inverse variation give sensible results for more harvesters? Explain the 'limits' on the number of harvesters that could be used.

3 During a period of drought a city has only 10 million gallons of water in reserve. If each family uses 5 gallons a day, the reserves last 10 days. How long would the reserves last if each family used
(a) $\frac{1}{2}$ gallon   (b) 1 gallon   (c) 3 gallons, each day?

4 An army has enough fuel to supply 240 tanks in full battle for 8 days. How long would the fuel last if the commander deployed
(a) 300 tanks   (b) 50 tanks   (c) 24 tanks   (d) 64 tanks?

5 The maximum load allowed for a liquid transporter is 4200 kg, which is the load when the transporter is filled with petrol (density 0·85 g/cm³).
What volume can be carried of
(a) pure water (1 g/cm³)?
(b) salt water (1·025 g/cm³)?
(c) fuel oil (0·9 g/cm³)?
(d) sulphuric acid (1·41 g/cm³)?

4·3 Graphs

The graph of an inverse variation always has the same shape – a hyperbola

---

Example:

Draw a graph which shows the speed of a car when it is driven 100 miles in   (i) 2 hours   (ii) 3 hours   (iii) 4 hours   (iv) 5 hours   (v) 6 hours.
Use the graph to find the speed if the journey takes   (a) 5 hours   (b) $3\frac{1}{2}$ hours.

First a table of values is constructed, then the graph is drawn.

Time (hours)	Speed (mph)
2	50
3	33·3
4	25
5	20
6	16·6

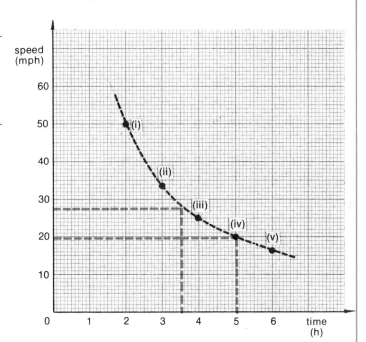

Note: The points of the graph are joined by a 'smooth' curve.

From the graph: If the journey takes 5 hours, the speed is 20 mph
             If the journey takes $3\frac{1}{2}$ hours, the speed is 28 mph

---

Exercise 4·3

Draw graphs of the following situations, then use the graph to find the extra values.

1   A rectangle has an area of 48 cm². Draw a graph showing the breadth of the rectangle if the length is 2 cm, 4 cm, 6 cm, 8 cm, 12 cm. Use the graph to find the breadth if the length is (a) 7·5 cm   (b) 9 cm.

2   A prize of £12 000 is shared between a number of people. Draw a graph showing the size of each person's share (y-axis) against the number of people (x-axis).

3   The basic cost of hiring a coach and driver is £96 per day. Draw a graph showing the cost to each person (y-axis) against the number of people hiring the coach. At what number of people does the cost fall below £3 each?

4 When electric current passes along a wire:
Voltage = Current × Resistance
volts = amps × ohms
(a) Calculate the current when the mains is connected across a resistance of (i) 10 ohms
   (ii) 20 ohms (iii) 48 ohms. UK mains voltage is 240 volts.
(b) Draw a graph showing resistance in ohms (x-axis) against current in amps (y-axis).
(c) Plot points on the graph to show the current flowing in:
   (i) An electric kettle (resistance 20 ohms) (ii) A TV set (resistance 160 ohms)
   (iii) A hair drier (resistance 80 ohms) (iv) An electric drill (resistance 120 ohms)
During a short circuit the resistance can fall to 0·01 ohms. What happens to the electric current (amps)?
The power released (in watts) is equal to volts × amps (divide by 1000 for kilowatts)
How much power is released during a short circuit? Why could this be dangerous?

5 The volume occupied by a given mass of substance depends on the density.

Mass = Volume × Density

Draw a graph which shows the volume of 1 tonne of each of the following substances.

Substance	Density (kg/litre)	Volume of 1 tonne
Gold	19·64	1000 ÷ 19·64 = 50·9 litres
Silver	11·09	
Iron	7·64	
Granite	3·00	
Brick	2·00	
Coal	1·25	
Water	1·00	
Pine	0·55	
Cork	0·24	
Air	0·0012	

4·4 The function $y = \frac{1}{x}$

Investigation A

Find out all you can about the function $y = \frac{1}{x}$ (in mapping notation f: $x \rightarrow \frac{1}{x}$).

1 Investigate + and − values of x.
2 Draw the graph from $x = -10$ to $x = 10$.
3 Investigate $(\frac{1}{x})$ on your calculator (e.g. most calculators display E (error) for the value when $x = 0$. How small will your calculator allow x to be before displaying E ?).
4 Investigate the symmetry of the combined graphs of $y = \frac{1}{x}$ and $y = -\frac{1}{x}$.
5 In some ways the graph of $y = \frac{1}{x}$ resembles a circle. What corresponds to the centre of the circle and the diameters? Are all diameters of equal length? Can you find any special properties of chords, or any angle properties, that remind you of a circle?

Investigation B

Find out all you can about the family of curves $xy = k$.

Investigation C

The Decca navigation system uses families of hyperbolae to map ocean and air space. You can find out how this works from your public library or on application to Decca Navigation Limited.

Unit 5   The circle (I)

5·1   Definitions and formulae

Word	Picture	Example/notes
Area The space inside the circle	 Area = πr^2	The area of a circle of radius 5 cm is $\pi \times 5 \times 5$ cm² $\pi = 3\cdot142$ so the area $= 25 \times 3\cdot142$ $= 78\cdot55$ cm²
Chord A line from one point of the circumference to another	 PQ and RS are chords of the circle	Interesting fact Equal chords of the circle are the same distance from the centre
Circumference The distance round the edge of the circle	 Circumference = $2\pi r$	The circumference of a circle of radius 5 cm is $2 \times \pi \times 5$ cm $= 10 \times \pi = 31\cdot42$ cm Any part of the circumference is called an arc
Cyclic quadrilateral A quadrilateral whose four corners lie on a circle		Interesting fact Opposite angles of a cyclic quadrilateral add up to 180°

Word	Picture	Example/notes
Diameter Chord through the centre of a circle	 Some diameters of the circle	**Interesting facts** Every diameter is an axis of symmetry for the circle. All diameters have the same length.
Radius Line from the centre to a point on the circumference	 Some radii of the circle	A diameter is twice as long as a radius of the same circle
Sector Part of a circle between two radii		The sector is bounded by two radii and an arc
Segment Part of a circle cut off by a chord		Major segment: more than half the circle Minor segment: less than half the circle
Tangent A line that touches a circle at one point only		Two tangents from the same point are equal. A tangent is perpendicular to the radius at the point of contact

Exercise 5·1

A **1** Draw a circle and three of its diameters.

2 Draw a circle, radius 5 cm. Draw chords which are 6 cm, 7 cm and 8 cm in length.

3 Calculate the circumference of a circle whose radius is 4 cm.

4 A sewage plant processes the sewage in circular tanks of 20 m circumference. What are the diameters and areas of the tanks?

5 Draw a circle. Choose four points on the circle and draw the cyclic quadrilateral. Measure the diagonals of your cyclic quadrilateral.
(a) Are they equal?
(b) Are they equal to the diameter of the circle?

6 Draw a circle and any two radii. Draw the axis of symmetry of your drawing.

7 Draw a circle. Draw a sector with a 70° angle at the centre. Is this sector more than half the circle?

8 Draw any circle and divide it into two segments. Shade in the major segment.

9 Draw a circle of radius 6 cm. Draw one radius, and a tangent where the radius meets the circumference.

10 Draw a pair of circles, radius 4 cm. Show how it is possible to draw a line which is a tangent of both circles. Such a line is called a common tangent.
What could be said about a pair of circles which have
(a) Exactly two common tangents?
(b) No common tangents?
(c) Just one common tangent?
Draw a pair of circles which have exactly three common tangents.

B **1** Measure the diameter of each of the circles below. Calculate the circumference and area for each circle.

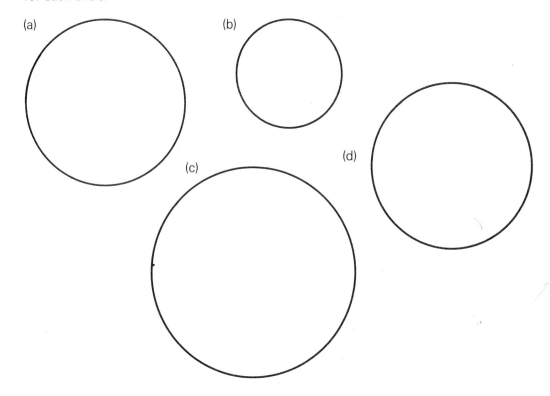

(a)

(b)

(c)

(d)

2 (a) Draw a circle of radius 4 cm, using compasses.
  (b) Draw a cyclic quadrilateral in the circle.
  (c) Draw a rectangle with vertices on the circle.
  (d) What differences can you find between the rectangle and the cyclic quadrilateral? (e.g. The angles of the rectangle are equal, but the angles of the cyclic quad are not.)

3 (a) Draw a circle with radius 5 cm.
  (b) Draw any pair of equal chords of the circle which do not meet (use your compasses). Name them PQ and RS (see diagram).
  (c) Investigate   (i) PR and QS   (ii) PS and RQ.

4 Investigate equal chords which meet inside the circle.

5 Draw a circle of radius 4 cm. Mark a sector AOB, where A and B are on the circumference and O is the centre of the circle. Draw the axis of symmetry for the sector. Is this also an axis of symmetry for the other sector formed by OA and OB?

6 Draw a circle, radius 5 cm. Divide the circle into two segments by a chord 8 cm long. Shade the major segment with vertical lines and the minor segment with horizontal lines.
  Estimate the ratio area of major segment : area of minor segment.

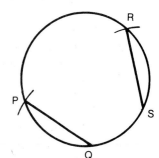

7 Measure the lengths of the tangents in the figures below (AX, XB, etc.).

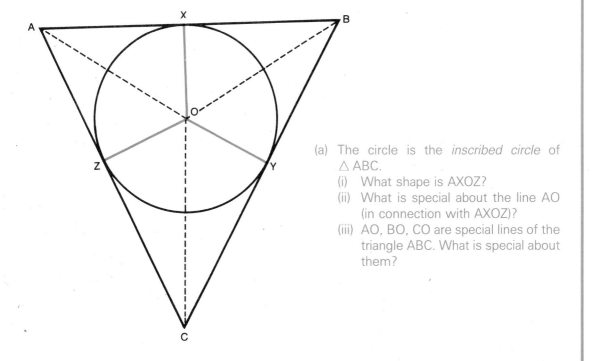

(a) The circle is the *inscribed circle* of △ ABC.
  (i)   What shape is AXOZ?
  (ii) What is special about the line AO (in connection with AXOZ)?
  (iii) AO, BO, CO are special lines of the triangle ABC. What is special about them?

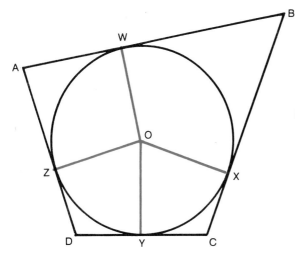

(b) The circle is the *inscribed circle* of quadrilateral ABCD.
  (i) Is it true that OA, OB, OC, OD are bisectors of angles A, B, C and D?
  (ii) Is it true that AW = AZ, BW = BX, CX = CY and DY = DZ?
  (iii) Do you think it is *always* possible to draw an inscribed circle, for any quadrilateral?

8 Follow the program for drawing a tangent to a circle from a point outside.

1∅ Draw OP

2∅ Find X, the centre of OP

3∅ Draw a circle with centre X and radius XO. Mark the points where this circle cuts the original as A, B.

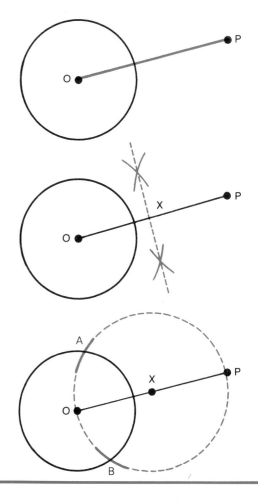

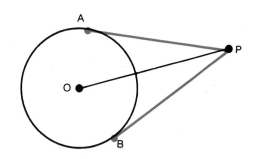

40   Join PA, PB.
     These are the tangents.

Why does this program work?

5·2   Properties of chords

Properties of chords follow from the symmetry of the circle.
Any diameter XY is an axis of symmetry.
If the circle were folded
along XY, A would fall on B,
so $AM = BM$ and $A\hat{M}O = B\hat{M}O = 90°$

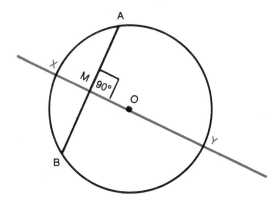

The following results are true for any chord of the circle:

1   The line joining the centre of the circle to the midpoint of the chord
    is perpendicular to the chord (i.e. XY is the perpendicular bisector
    of AB).

2   The line from the centre, perpendicular to the chord, bisects the
    chord.

3   The perpendicular bisector of the chord passes through the centre of
    the circle.

Properties of equal chords follow
from the rotational symmetry of the circle.

Since AB = CD, the circle can be
rotated so that A comes over D
and B comes over C.

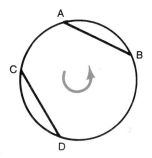

It follows that:

4   Equal chords must be equal distances from
    the centre.

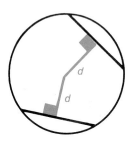

5   Equal chords subtend equal angles
    at the centre.

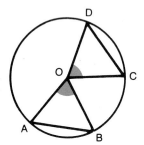

Exercise 5·2

A **1**   In the diagram AB = CD = 21 mm.
            (a) What are the lengths of
                AX, XB, CY and DY?
            (b) What line has the same
                length as OY?

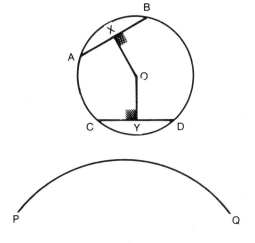

2   It is known that PQ is the arc
        of a circle. Explain how the
        radius of the arc can be found
        by drawing.

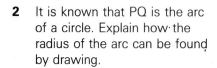

3 Which length must be equal
to BC? Give your reasons.

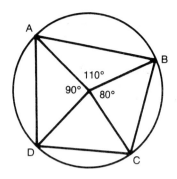

4 Copy the diagram carefully.
Draw in the axis of symmetry.
Explain why both BD and AC
are perpendicular to the axis of
symmetry. What does this tell
you about the lines BD and AC?

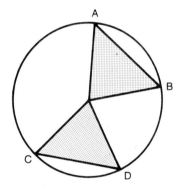

B 1 Draw a circle, radius 4 cm. Draw any chord you like and label it AB. Find the midpoint M of
the chord. Check that the line from O to M is exactly perpendicular to the chord.
Measure OM. Check that $OM^2 + MA^2 = 16$.

2 Draw a circle, radius 5 cm. Draw any chord you like.
   (a) Check that the perpendicular bisector of the chord passes through the centre of the
   circle.
   (b) Draw a second chord anywhere on the circle. Draw the perpendicular bisector of this
   chord. What do you notice?

3 Choose any pair of equal chords on a circle of radius 5 cm.
   (a) Join both ends of each chord to the centre. What do you notice about the angles
   formed at the centre?
   (b) Label the equal chords AB and CD. What do you notice about AC and BD? What do
   you notice about AD and BC?
   (c) Repeat (b) with another pair of equal chords.

4 (a) Draw a triangle ABC with AB = 5 cm, BC = 4 cm and AC = 3 cm.
   (b) Draw the perpendicular bisectors of AC and BC. Where do they meet?

5 (a) Draw any triangle ABC. Draw the perpendicular bisectors of all three sides. What do
   you notice?
   (b) If AB and AC are chords of a circle, where will the centre of the circle be found?

6 A, B, C are any three points. Explain how you would draw a circle which passes through all
three points. This circle is called the circumcircle of triangle ABC.

7 (a) Choose any three points and draw the circumcircle of the triangle they form.
   (b) What could you say about three points if it was not possible to draw their circumcircle?

5·3 Products of lengths of chords

We shall see in Unit 7 that
angles in the same segment of
a circle are equal
i.e. $A\hat{P}B = A\hat{Q}B = A\hat{R}B$ in Fig. 1

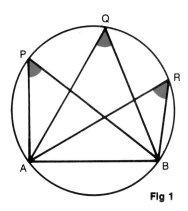

Fig 1

If two chords in a circle meet,
two similar triangles are formed.
In Fig. 2 $A\hat{C}D = A\hat{B}D$ (same segment)
and $C\hat{A}B = C\hat{D}B$ (same segment)

Therefore $\dfrac{AX}{XD} = \dfrac{CX}{XB}$

$\Rightarrow AX.XB = CX.XD$
(The dot between AX and XB means 'multiplied by')

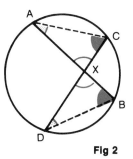

Fig 2

If the two chords meet outside
the circle (see Fig. 3) it is still true that
$AX.XB = CX.XD$
(In Fig. 3 triangles XBD, XCA are similar)

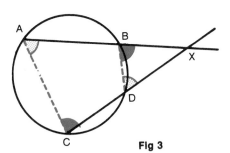

Fig 3

Investigations:

1 Draw a number of chords and check that $AX.XB = CX.XD$ in every case.

2 Explore Figures 2 and 3. Join AD and BC in each case and look for equal angles.

The products of lengths of chords can be used to calculate lengths in a circle.

Example:

A circle is cut by a chord 5 cm long.
What is the height of the minor segment,
if the height of the major segment is
7·5 cm? Deduce the radius of the circle.

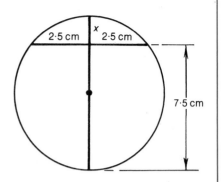

1Ø   Let the height of the minor segment be x cm

2Ø   From the 'product of chords' theorem
$x \times 7\cdot5 = 2\cdot5 \times 2\cdot5$

3Ø $x = (2\cdot5 \times 2\cdot5) \div 7\cdot5 = 0\cdot833$ cm

4Ø   Total diameter $= 7\cdot5 + 0\cdot833 = 8\cdot333$ cm

5Ø   Radius $= \frac{1}{2}$ diameter $= 4\cdot16$ cm

Exercise 5·3

1   Draw a circle of radius 4 cm. Then draw any pair of chords AB, CD which meet at X.
   (a) Measure AX, BX, CX and DX.
   (b) Calculate AX.XB and CX.XD Are they equal?
2   Draw another circle of radius 4 cm.
   (a) Draw chords AB and CD which meet outside the circle at X.
   (b) Measure AX, BX, CX, DX.
   (c) Calculate AX.XB and CX.XD Are they equal?
3   Calculate the unknown lengths in the following figures.

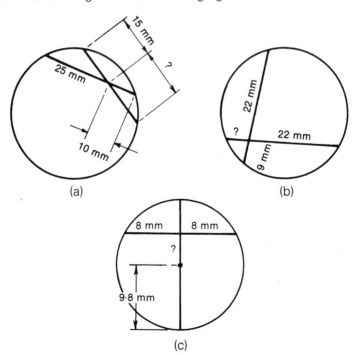

(a)

(b)

(c)

53

4 Calculate the unknown lengths in the following figures.

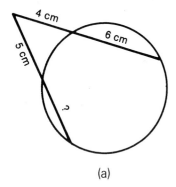

(a)

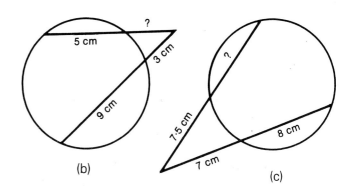

(b)

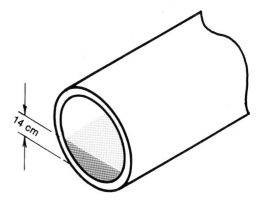

(c)

5 Water in a cylindrical drain has a depth of 14 cm. The diameter of the drain is 48 cm. Calculate the width of the water surface.

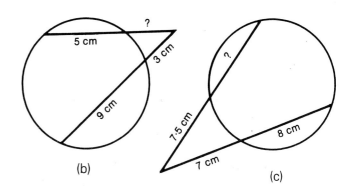

6 The span of the arch of a bridge is 152 m. The height of the middle above the ends is 18 m. Calculate the radius of the circle of which the bridge is an arc.

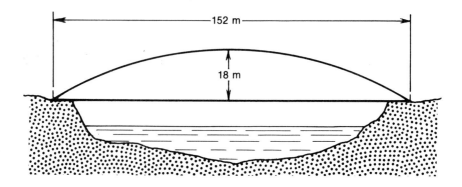

7 (a) Explain why AX.XB = (XT)²
(special case of product theorem)
(b) Show how the above result could lead to the theorem:
Tangents to a circle from a point outside are equal in length.

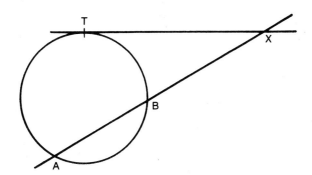

8 Use the result AX.XB = XT² and the fact that the radius of the Earth is 3963 miles to estimate:
(a) The distance of the horizon from a mountain 2 miles high (above sea level).
(b) The distance of the horizon from a balloon 30 miles up.
(c) The distance of the horizon from a satellite 120 miles up.

9 The captain of a ship stands on the bridge 20 metres above the sea. How far could he expect to see on a clear day? (Radius of the Earth 6341 km)
How much further could a sailor see from a
crow's nest 30 metres above the captain?

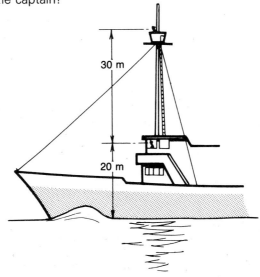

10 A surveyor is measuring a circular tower. Suggest a method which will enable him to find its diameter if:
(a) He cannot walk right round the tower.
(b) He cannot get inside the tower.

Unit 6   Congruent triangles and proofs

6·1   Congruent triangles

If all the sides and angles of one triangle are equal to all the sides and angles of another, the triangles are said to be congruent.

A pair of triangles are bound to be congruent if:

	(i)	All three sides are equal	(SSS)
or	(ii)	Two sides and the included angle are equal	(SAS)
or	(iii)	Two angles and one side are equal	(AAS)
or	(iv)	One angle of each is a right angle, the hypotenuses are equal, and another pair of sides are equal.	(RHS)

The short-hand way of writing 'triangles ABC and DEF are congruent' is $\triangle\,ABC \equiv \triangle\,DEF$. The relative position of the triangles does not affect the congruency, but notice that

$$\triangle\,ABC \equiv \triangle\,DEF \Rightarrow \begin{cases} \hat{A} = \hat{D} \\ \hat{B} = \hat{E} \\ \hat{C} = \hat{F} \end{cases} \text{and} \begin{cases} AB = DE \\ BC = EF \\ AC = DF \end{cases}$$

In other words, the order of the letters is of some importance, as it can be used to specify which angle in the first triangle is equal to which angle in the second triangle, and which sides are equal. You can see how this works in the following examples.

Examples:

1

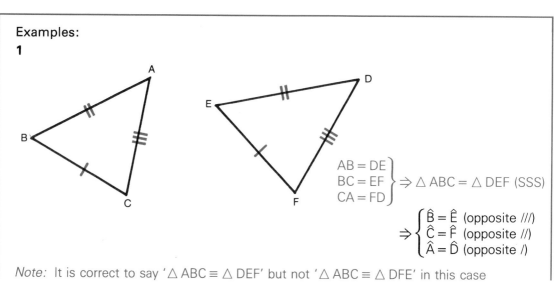

$$\left.\begin{array}{l} AB = DE \\ BC = EF \\ CA = FD \end{array}\right\} \Rightarrow \triangle\,ABC = \triangle\,DEF \text{ (SSS)}$$

$$\Rightarrow \begin{cases} \hat{B} = \hat{E} & \text{(opposite ///)} \\ \hat{C} = \hat{F} & \text{(opposite //)} \\ \hat{A} = \hat{D} & \text{(opposite /)} \end{cases}$$

Note: It is correct to say '$\triangle\,ABC \equiv \triangle\,DEF$' but not '$\triangle\,ABC \equiv \triangle\,DFE$' in this case

---

2

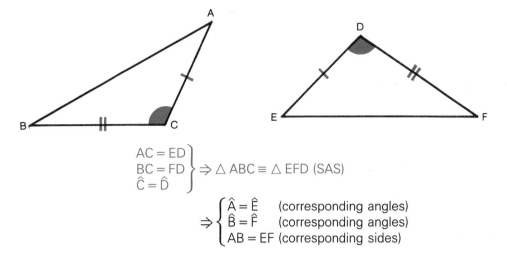

$$\left.\begin{array}{l} AC = ED \\ BC = FD \\ \hat{C} = \hat{D} \end{array}\right\} \Rightarrow \triangle\,ABC \equiv \triangle\,EFD\ (SAS)$$

$$\Rightarrow \begin{cases} \hat{A} = \hat{E} & \text{(corresponding angles)} \\ \hat{B} = \hat{F} & \text{(corresponding angles)} \\ AB = EF & \text{(corresponding sides)} \end{cases}$$

Note: It would be incorrect in this case to say '$\triangle\,ABC \equiv \triangle\,DEF$' because this would imply $\hat{A} = \hat{D}$ etc.

3

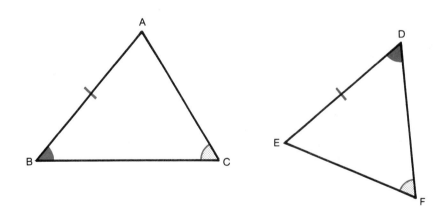

$$\left.\begin{array}{l} \hat{B} = \hat{D} \\ \hat{C} = \hat{F} \\ AB = ED \end{array}\right\} \Rightarrow \triangle\,ABC \equiv \triangle\,EDF\ (AAS)$$

$$\Rightarrow \begin{cases} \hat{A} = \hat{E} \\ AC = EF \\ BC = DF \end{cases}$$

Note: Since two angles are equal, the third angles must also be equal

4

$$\left.\begin{array}{l} \hat{B} = \hat{E} = 90° \\ BC = EF \\ AC = DF \end{array}\right\} \Rightarrow \triangle ABC \equiv \triangle DEF \text{ (RHS)}$$

$$\Rightarrow \begin{cases} \hat{A} = \hat{D} \\ \hat{C} = \hat{F} \\ AB = DE \end{cases}$$

Exercise 6·1

A **1** Two triangles ABC and PQR are congruent (SSS), so AB = PQ, BC = QR and AC = PR.
  (a) Make a sketch of the triangles.
  (b) Which angle of △ PQR is equal to   (i) $\hat{B}$?   (ii) $\hat{A}$?   (iii) $\hat{C}$?

2 Two triangles ABC and XYZ are congruent (RHS):
  $\hat{A} = \hat{X} = 90°$.
  (a) Make a sketch of the triangles.
  (b) Which angle of △ ABC is equal to   (i) $\hat{Y}$?   (ii) $\hat{Z}$?
  (c) Which side of △ XYZ is equal to AC?

3 Two triangles ABC and MNL are congruent (AAS):
  $\hat{A} = \hat{M}$, $\hat{B} = \hat{N}$ and AB = MN.
  (a) Make a sketch of the triangles.
  (b) Which side of △ LMN is equal to   (i) BC?   (ii) AC?
  (c) Explain why $\hat{C} = \hat{L}$.

4 Two triangles PQR and YZX are congruent (SAS):
  PQ = YZ and QR = XZ
  (a) Make a sketch of the triangles.
  (b) Which angles in △ PQR are equal to   (i) $\hat{X}$?   (ii) $\hat{Y}$?   (iii) $\hat{Z}$?

B In each of the figures below pick out a pair of congruent triangles. Explain which of the four conditions for congruence applies and deduce all you can about equal sides and angles.

1

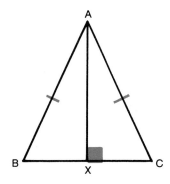

ABC is isosceles
AX is perpendicular to BC

2

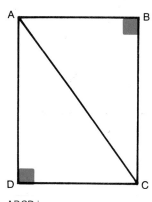

ABCD is a
rectangle

3

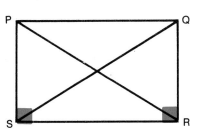

PR = QS
PŜR = QR̂S = 90°

4

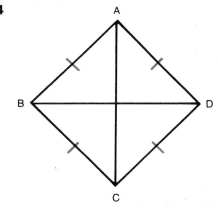

AB = BC = CD = DA

5

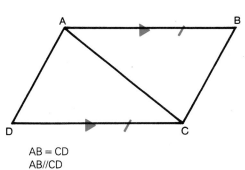

AB = CD
AB//CD

6

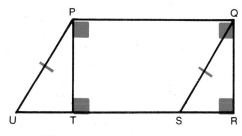

PQRT is a rectangle
PU = QS

C In each figure below there are a number of pairs of congruent triangles. Find them. Deduce as much as you can about the equal lines and equal angles in each figure.

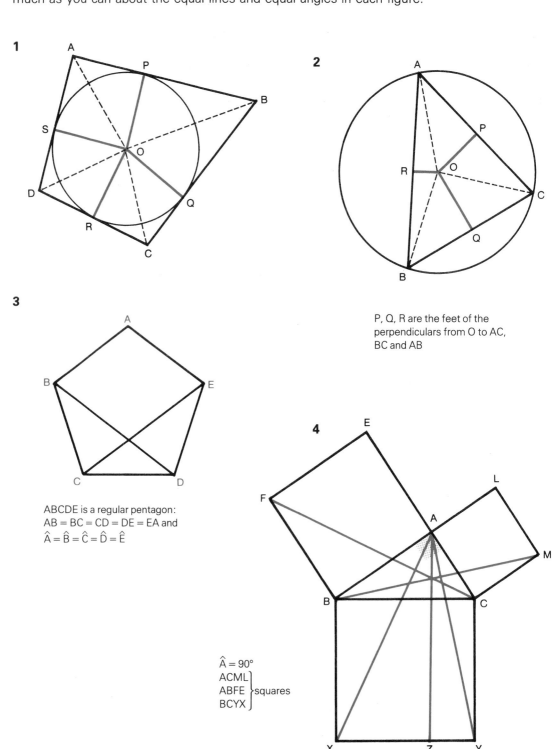

1

2

3

P, Q, R are the feet of the perpendiculars from O to AC, BC and AB

ABCDE is a regular pentagon:
AB = BC = CD = DE = EA and
$\hat{A} = \hat{B} = \hat{C} = \hat{D} = \hat{E}$

4

$\hat{A} = 90°$
ACML ⎫
ABFE ⎬ squares
BCYX ⎭

6·2   Proof by congruent triangles

Many properties of shapes can be proved to be true by considering pairs of congruent triangles.
(This method of proof was developed by the ancient Greeks two thousand years ago and perfected by Euclid. Euclid's books on geometry formed the basis of school mathematics until about 20 years ago.)
First the triangles are proved to be congruent. Then the fact that the triangles are congruent is used to deduce that other sides or angles are equal.

Example:
Prove that the diagonals of a rectangle are equal in length.

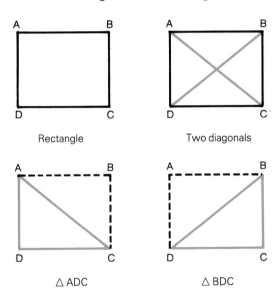

Rectangle   Two diagonals

△ ADC   △ BDC

1∅	Data	ABCD is a rectangle
2∅	Data	opposite sides of a rectangle are equal
3∅	Deduction	AD = BC . . . . from 2∅
4∅	Deduction	AD̂C = BĈD = 90° . . . . from 1∅
5∅	Data	DC is the same length in both △ ADC and △ BDC
6∅	Deduction	△ ADC ≡ △ BCD (SAS) . . . . from 3∅, 4∅, 5∅
7∅	Deduction	AC = BD . . . . from 6∅

Note: A proof shows that the property is true for all rectangles. We begin with any rectangle and label it ABCD: no actual measurements are used.

Example:

Prove that the line from the vertex to the midpoint of the base of an isosceles triangle is perpendicular to the base.

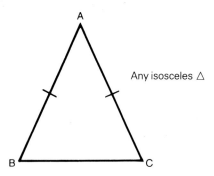

Any isosceles △

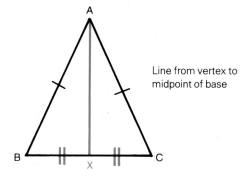

Line from vertex to midpoint of base

1∅	Data	ABC is an isosceles triangle	
2∅	Data	X is the midpoint of BC	
3∅	Deduction	AB = AC.................................	from 1∅
4∅	Deduction	BX = XC...............................	from 2∅
5∅	Data	AX = AX	
6∅	Deduction	△ ABX ≡ △ ACX (SSS)..................	from 3∅, 4∅, 5∅
7∅	Deduction	AX̂B = AX̂C..............................	from 6∅
75	Data	AX̂B + AX̂C = 180°	
8∅	Deduction	AX̂B = AX̂C = 90°	from 7∅, 75
9∅	END		

Exercise 6·2

A Prove the following properties of triangles by using congruent triangles:
1. The line from the vertex of an isosceles triangle, perpendicular to the base, bisects the base.
2. The bisector of the vertical angle of an isosceles triangle is also the bisector of the base.
3. The base angles of an isosceles triangle are equal.
4. Any triangle with a pair of equal angles must have a pair of equal sides.

B Prove the following properties of quadrilaterals:
1. The opposite sides of a parallelogram must be equal.
   (Start with the definition: a parallelogram is a quadrilateral with opposite sides parallel.)
2. A quadrilateral with all sides equal must be a parallelogram.
   (Start with ... Data   ABCD is a quadrilateral, AB = BC = CD = DA.)
3. A parallelogram with equal diagonals must be a rectangle.
4. The diagonals of a parallelogram bisect each other.
5. A parallelogram whose diagonals are perpendicular to each other must be a rhombus*

*A quadrilateral with all sides equal.

C Use congruent triangles to find out something about these figures. Prove any property you find.

   1 The figure formed by joining the midpoints of the sides of a rectangle.
   2 The figure formed by joining the midpoints of the sides of a rhombus.
   3 A quadrilateral with one pair of sides equal and parallel
   4 A quadrilateral whose diagonals are equal and perpendicular
   5 A quadrilateral whose diagonals are equal and bisect each other

6·3 Proof by algebra

Many properties of shapes can be proved by writing letters for angles, ratios, etc. (Letters used in this way are called 'variables'.) Algebra is then used on the letters to obtain a general theorem. The use of letters allows facts to be proved instead of just demonstrated in particular cases.

Example:
Prove that the exterior angle of a triangle equals the sum of the opposite interior angles.

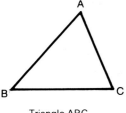

Triangle ABC

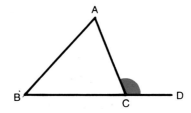

Triangle ABC showing
one exterior angle

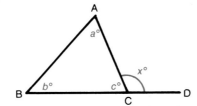

Triangle ABC with angles marked $a°$, $b°$, $c°$

  10   Data   The angles of a triangle add up to 180°

  20   Data   The angles on a straight line add up to 180°

  30   Deduction $a + b + c = 180$..... from 10

  40   Deduction $x + c = 180$ .... from 20

  50   Deduction $x = a + b$......... from 30, 40

  60   END

Example:
A quadrilateral has opposite angles equal. Prove that it must be a parallelogram.

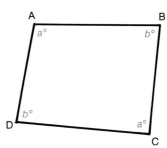

1∅	Data	ABCD is a quadrilateral
2∅	Data	The angles of a quadrilateral add up to 360°
3∅	Deduction	$2a + 2b = 360$ ..... from 2∅
4∅	Deduction	$a + b = 180$ ...... from 3∅

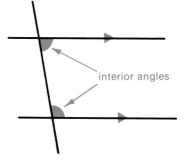

5∅	Data	Interior angles on a pair of straight lines add to 180° only if the lines are parallel

6∅	Deduction	AB//DC .... from 4∅, 5∅
7∅	Deduction	AD//BC .... from 4∅, 5∅
8∅	Deduction	ABCD is a parallelogram..... from 6∅, 7∅
9∅	END	

Exercise 6·3

A The following questions are adapted from examination papers. Prove your answer is true in each case.

1 Calculate all the angles in the figure.

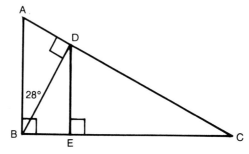

2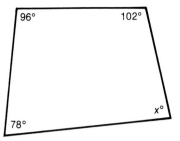

Find *x*.

3 Given $\hat{A} = 50°$, $\hat{C} = 30°$ and $AB = BD$, calculate $A\hat{B}C$.

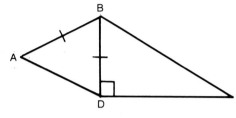

4 Given $E\hat{A}B = A\hat{B}C = B\hat{C}D$, calculate the size of $A\hat{B}C$.

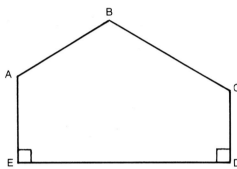

5 Given $AB = AC$, find $B\hat{A}C$.

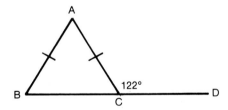

6 BED is a straight line.
Calculate the values of *r*, *s* and *t*.

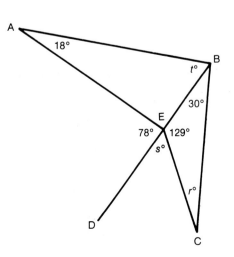

B Prove the following by algebra:

1 A quadrilateral with four equal angles must be a rectangle.

2 A triangle with all its angles equal must be equilateral (the 60° △).

3 The exterior angles of a regular pentagon must be 72° each.

4 The interior angles of a regular pentagon must be 108° each.
(*Hint:* Use the result of question 3.)

5 The interior angles of a regular octagon (8 sides) must be 135° each.

6 In any right-angled triangle the other two angles must total 90°.

7 ABC is a triangle, right-angled at B.
BX is drawn so that BX ⊥ AC
Prove △s ABX, BXC and ABC are
all similar (i.e. have the same three
angles).

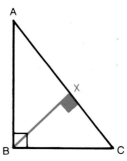

8 The diagonals of a rhombus bisect the angles at
the vertices. Use the fact that
opposite angles are equal to prove
that the diagonals are perpendicular.

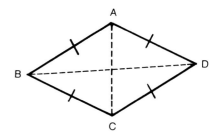

C Prove the following, using any method you like:

1 The opposite angles of a parallelogram must be equal.

2 The regular pentagon ABCDE has
all five diagonals drawn.
Prove that all the angles in the
figure are 36°, 72° or 108°.

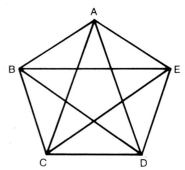

3 In △ ABC, AB = AC and AĈD = 2 AĈB.
Prove that △ ABC is equilateral.

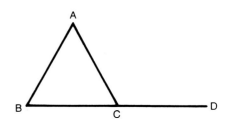

4 △ABC is isosceles with AB = AC. The bisector of angle A is drawn and meets BC at X. Prove AX ⊥ BC.

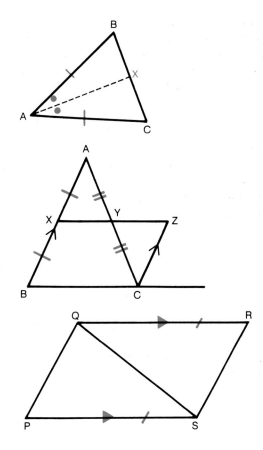

5 In the figure, X is the midpoint of AB and Y is the midpoint of AC. CZ is parallel to BA. Prove △AXY is congruent to △CZY.

6 In the figure, QR = PS and QR is parallel to PS. Prove PQ//SR.

6·4   Use of symmetry in proof

A figure has an axis of symmetry if it can be divided into two halves which are reflections of each other. The dividing line is the axis.

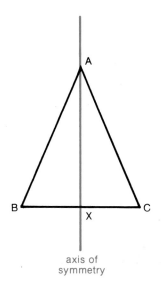

axis of symmetry

The two halves match. They would fit over each other if the figure were folded along the axis.
It follows that:
(i)   AB = AC
(ii) BX = XC
(iii) AB̂C = AĈB
(iv) BÂX = CÂX
(v)   BX̂A = CX̂A = 90°
These facts can all be deduced using congruent triangles.

A figure has rotational symmetry if it can be rotated about some centre so that the new position fits over the old one.

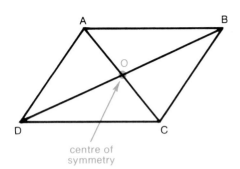

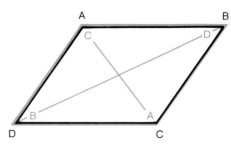

ABCD has been rotated through 180° so that A is over C, C is over A, B is over D, D is over B.

Since any parallelogram ABCD can be rotated through 180° to fit over its old position, we can deduce:
(i)   AB = CD, AD = BC
(ii) Â = Ĉ, B̂ = D̂
(iii) OA = OC, OB = OD

Exercise 6·4

1 The rhombus ABCD has two axes of symmetry. Write down everything you can deduce about the sides, angles, diagonals, etc. of a rhombus. Any properties that you observe should be proved by another method.

2 An isosceles trapezium (a quadrilateral with one pair of sides parallel and the other pair equal) has one axis of symmetry. This suggests that the diagonals are equal. What other properties can you find? Can you prove the properties by any other method?

3 Draw a figure with three axes of symmetry and investigate its properties.

4 What quadrilateral has rotational symmetry but no axes of symmetry?

5 Investigate the geometrical properties of quadrilaterals with two pairs of equal sides. Prove any properties you discover.

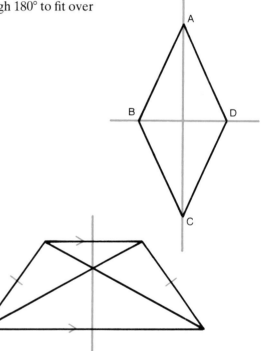

Example:

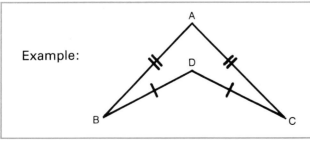

The bisector of Â passes through D. The bisectors of B̂ and Ĉ meet on AD.

68

Unit 7   Circle geometry: angles

7·1   Cyclic quadrilaterals

A quadrilateral with all four vertices on a circle is called a cyclic
quadrilateral. The opposite angles add up to 180°

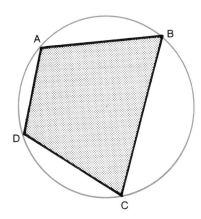

Proof:

1∅	Construction	Join each vertex to the centre of the circle
2∅	Data	The base angles of an isosceles triangle are equal
3∅	Data	The angles of the figure may be marked a, b, c, d as shown in the figure
4∅	Data	The angles of any quadrilateral add up to 360°
5∅	Deduction	$2a + 2b + 2c + 2d = 360°$ ..... from 4∅
6∅	Deduction	$a + b + c + d = 180°$ .... from 5∅
7∅	Deduction	$\hat{BAD} + \hat{BCD} = 180°$ ...... from 6∅
8∅	Deduction	$\hat{ABC} + \hat{ADC} = 180°$ .... from 6∅
9∅	END	

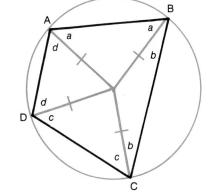

Exercise 7·1

A 1 Study the above proof and make sure you have understood it.

2 Calculate the values of *a* and *b* in the figure.

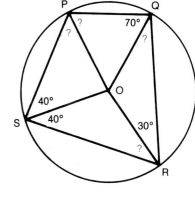

3

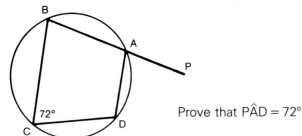

Prove that PÂD = 72°

4 Write down the values of the angles marked ? in the figure. Deduce the values of the four angles at the centre of the circle. What do you notice about the relationship between
   (a) SÔQ and SR̂Q?
   (b) PÔR and PŜR?

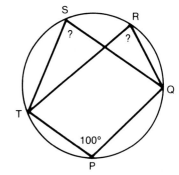

5 Prove that an external angle of a cyclic quadrilateral is equal to the opposite internal angle.

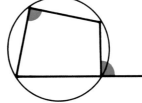

6 (a) PQST is a cyclic quadrilateral. Deduce the size of TŜQ.
   (b) PQRT is a cyclic quadrilateral. Deduce the size of QR̂T.
   (c) What can you say about angles SТ̂R and SQ̂R?

B 1 Calculate the five unmarked angles in the figure. What can you deduce about the triangles XBC and XAD?

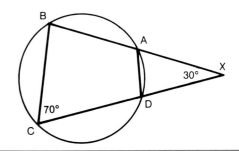

70

2 There are two cyclic quadrilaterals to be found in the figure. Name them. What can you say about
   (a) PÂQ and PX̂Q?
   (b) PQ̂C and PB̂C?
   (c) PÂQ and PX̂B?
   (d) AQ̂P and AB̂C?

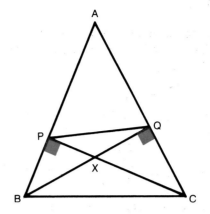

3 Choose any three points and draw the circle which will pass through all three. Explain your method.
   Will it always be possible to draw such a circle? (What happens if the three points are in a straight line?)

4 Choose any four points A, B, C, D. Explain why it will *not* usually be possible to draw one circle through all four. If you *can* draw such a circle, what must be true about the angles of the quadrilateral ABCD? What other special facts must be true about the quadrilateral?

5 Write down all the facts you know about the angles in the diagram.
   (These facts follow from A, B, C and D being on a circle.)

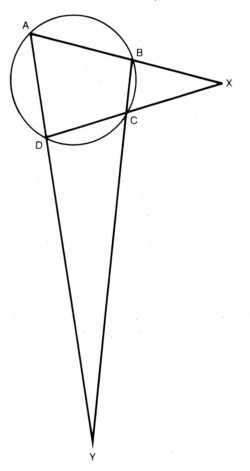

6 Which of the following shapes could not be cyclic quadrilaterals?
Give your reasons.
(a) Square   (b) Rectangle   (c) Rhombus
(d) Parallelogram (not one of above)   (e) Trapezium

7·2 Angles in the same segment

The angle $A\hat{P}B$ will not change if
P is moved around the circumference
between A and B. This is because APBQ
is a cyclic quadrilateral,
so that $\hat{P} + \hat{Q} = 180°$. Q stays the same,
so **P** must stay the same

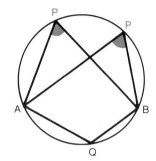

Another way of stating this
result is: Angles in the same segment
are equal

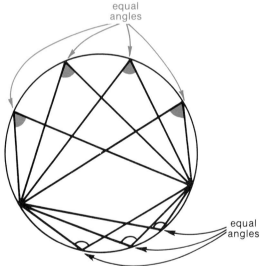

It follows that
the angle subtended by an arc
at the centre of the circle is
twice the angle subtended at the circumference
This result will be proved in Exercise 7·2.

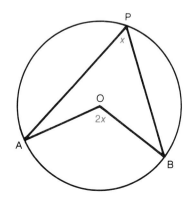

$A\hat{O}B$ is the angle subtended by arc AB at O.
$A\hat{P}B$ is the angle subtended by arc AB at P.

Exercise 7·2

A 1 Draw a circle of radius 5 cm. Divide it into two segments by a chord AB.

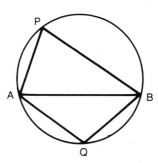

(a) Show that all angles AP̂B in the major segment are the same (by careful measurement or by using tracing paper).

(b) Show that all angles AQ̂B in the minor segment are the same.

2 Write down the size of the angle marked ? in each figure.

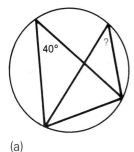 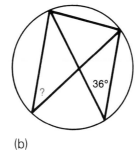 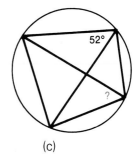

(a)   (b)   (c)

3 A, B, P and Q are any four points on a circle. What can you say about

(a) AQ̂B and AP̂B?

(b) AX̂Q and BX̂P?

(c) QÂX and XB̂P?

What can be deduced about triangles AXQ and BXP?

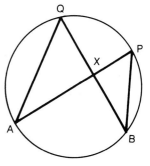

4 Calculate the sizes of these angles in the figure:

(a) BĈD   (b) CB̂E   (c) FD̂C

(d) BF̂D   (e) AF̂B   (f) FB̂A

5 Find two pairs of similar triangles in the figure.

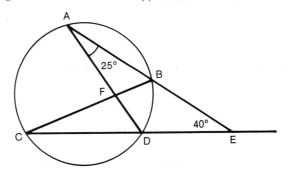

6 Four points A, B, C and D are chosen on a circle. They are then joined up in pairs.
BA and CD meet at Y
AC and BD meet at Z
DA and CB meet at X.
If $\hat{X} = 30°$, $\hat{Y} = 20°$ and $X\hat{C}Y = 65°$,
(a) Calculate angles $X\hat{D}C$ and $Y\hat{B}C$
(b) Deduce angles $A\hat{D}Y$ and $Y\hat{B}X$
(c) Deduce angles $X\hat{A}B$ and $Y\hat{A}D$
What other angles of the figure can you find?

B 1 Using the figure given, prove that $A\hat{O}B = 2A\hat{P}B$ where O is the centre of the circle.

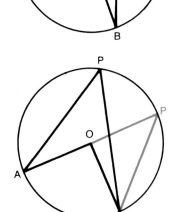

2 What is the size of $A\hat{P}B$ if
(a) $A\hat{O}B = 100°$ (b) $A\hat{O}B = 180°$ (c) $A\hat{O}B = 200°$
(d) $A\hat{O}B = 300°$

Draw diagrams for (b) and (c).

3 P is moved round the circle until AOP is a diameter.
If $\hat{P}$ is 36° what is $\hat{P}$?
What is $O\hat{B}P$?
What is the relationship between $A\hat{O}B$, $O\hat{P}B$ and $O\hat{B}P$?
What is the size of $A\hat{O}B$?

4 Use the method of question 3 to prove that $\hat{A}OB = 2A\hat{P}B$. Write out the proof carefully.

Examination Questions (these include other topics)

5 In the diagram, O is the centre of a circle, radius 6 cm. The size of AÔB is 40°. AÔC is a straight line.

(a) Calculate the sizes of AD̂B and BD̂C

(b) Calculate the area of the shaded sector AOB

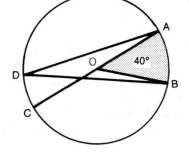

6 O is the centre of the circle and the figure is symmetrical about the diameter COD.
AÔD = 30°, radius AO = 14 cm

(a) Calculate AĈB

(b) Calculate the length of AB

(c) Calculate the area of sector AOBD

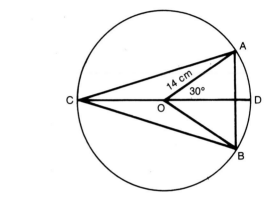

7 (a) What is the size of AB̂D?

(b) Find BÔC

(c) Find BD̂C

(d) Calculate the length of AB

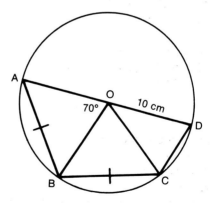

8

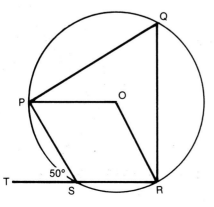

Write down the sizes of

(a) PŜR

(b) PQ̂R

(c) reflex angle PÔR

7·3 Other properties of circles

Some other important properties of circles can be deduced from the
work of this chapter. These are shown in the study exercises which
follow.

Study Exercise 7·3

A *The angle in a semicircle*

1 Draw a circle. Then draw
a rectangle with its
vertices on the circle.

2 Draw DB and AC. What do you
notice? Repeat with a different
circle and rectangle.

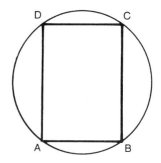

3 (a) Draw a circle of radius 4 cm.
(b) Draw any diameter AB.
(c) Choose points X, Y and Z
on the circumference of the
circle.
(d) What do you notice about the angles
$A\hat{X}B$, $A\hat{Y}B$ and $A\hat{Z}B$?

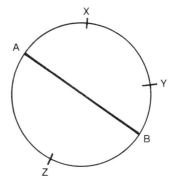

4 Start with the given diagram and
prove that the angle in a semicircle
is 90°.
(*Hint:* Remember that the angles of
a triangle add up to 180°.)

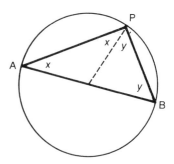

5 O is the centre of the circle.
$P\hat{B}A = 32°$.
Calculate $P\hat{Q}B$.

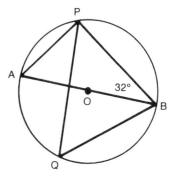

6 ABC is any triangle.
BY and CX are the perpendiculars
from B to AC, and from C to AB.
(a) Where would you find the
centre of a circle which
passes through X, Y, B and C?

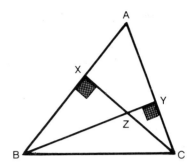

(b) The centre of a circle through A, Y, Z, X would lie on a special line. Which one?
(c) Draw another triangle ABC (any triangle you like) and construct CX and BY as they have
been done here. Then for your triangle check that:
   (i) The midpoint of BC is equidistant from B, C, X and Y.
   (ii) The midpoint of AZ is equidistant from X, Y, Z and A.
(d) Explain why △ ABY is similar to △ AXC.
(e) Show that BY/CX = AB/AC or BY.AC = CX.AB.
(f) Both BY.AC and CX.AB are equal to something special about △ ABC. What is it?

B *Tangents to circles*
1 Prove that the tangents to
a circle from a point
outside are equal.
(*Hint:* The tangent is at
right angles to the radius.)

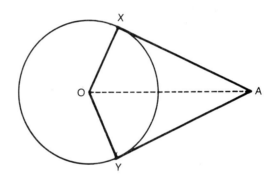

2 (a) A is a point outside a circle. A
line is drawn from A, cutting
the circle at points S and T.
Another line is drawn from A
to cut the circle at points X
and Y. Explain why
A$\hat{S}$X = T$\hat{Y}$X.
(b) If A is fixed and the line AST is
rotated (clockwise) about A,
the points S and T move
closer together. What
happens to S and T if the line
AST becomes a tangent?
(c) What happens to the
quadrilateral TSYX when the
line AST becomes a tangent?
Draw a diagram showing AST
in this position, and prove that
A$\hat{S}$X is still equal to T$\hat{Y}$X.

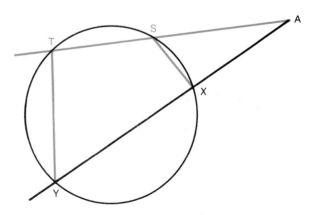

3 Calculate the angle marked ? in these figures.

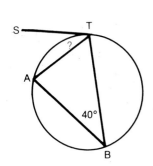

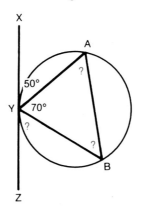

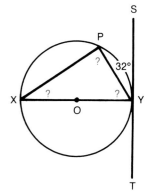

(a) ST is a tangent to the circle

(b) XYZ is a tangent touching the circle at Y

(c) XY is a diameter, ST is a tangent touching the circle at Y.

4 Prove that the angle PÂC between a chord AC and the tangent at one end of it is equal to the angle (AB̂C) in the other segment.
(This is known as the alternate segment theorem.)
Hint: Think about question 3(c).

5 (a) (i) What angle is equal to ST̂U in the figure?
(ii) What angle is equal to TÛS in the figure?
(iii) Name a pair of similar triangles in the figure.
(iv) Deduce a ratio in the figure which is equal to $\dfrac{US}{ST}$.

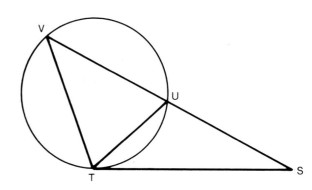

ST is a tangent to the circle.

(b) (i) to (iv) are steps in a proof that
$SU.SV = ST^2$
Complete the proof and write it out in lines numbered 1∅, 2∅, etc.

6 Use the result of question 5 to prove that:
If a pair of chords of a circle
meet at X then AX.XB = CX.XD.
Confirm the theorem by measurement:
draw six circles of radius 5 cm and for
each draw a pair of intersecting
chords. Measure them and calculate
AX.XB and CX.XD for each pair.
Look back to section 5·3 for examples.

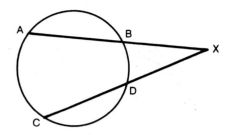

7 Investigate the figure below. ST is a tangent to the semicircle.

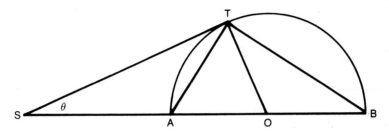

8 Investigate common tangents to a pair of circles.

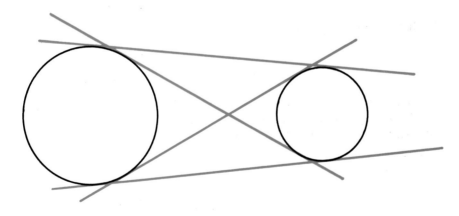

Draw pairs of circles which: (a) Do not have any common tangents
                                     (b) Have only one common tangent
                                     (c) Have three common tangents
                                     (d) Have just two common tangents

Unit 8   Simultaneous solution of equations

8·1   Why 'simultaneous'?

The word **simultaneous** means 'at the same time'. For example, to turn on both taps simultaneously means to turn on the hot and the cold at the same time.

When a pair of equations are solved simultaneously, the solution will fit both equations.

Example:

Solve $\left\{ \begin{array}{l} x+y=6 \\ y=2x \end{array} \right\}$ simultaneously

Solutions of $x+y=6$	Solutions of $y=2x$
$x=0,\ y=6$	$x=0,\ y=0$
$x=1,\ y=5$	$x=1,\ y=2$
$x=2,\ y=4$ ←The only solution→ $x=2,\ y=4$
$x=3,\ y=3$ belonging to	$x=3,\ y=6$
$x=4,\ y=2$ **both sets**	$x=4,\ y=8$
$x=5,\ y=1$	$x=5,\ y=10$
$x=6,\ y=0$	$x=6,\ y=12$
etc.	etc.

Thus if $x+y=6$ and at the same time $y=2x$ then $x=2$ and $y=4$

The above method (listing the solutions), will give solutions to simple pairs of equations. The method is not efficient, however, if the solutions are negative or fractions.

Exercise 8·1

A **1**   What happens simultaneously when . . .
   (a) you clap your hands?
   (b) you skip with a skipping rope?
   (c) you accelerate on a motor bike from a standing position?
   (d) you swim breaststroke?
   (e) a single run is scored in cricket?

   2   Suggest some 'simultaneous' events when you are
   (a) shopping
   (b) dancing
   (c) doing housework
   (d) doing homework
   (e) working in the science lab
   (f) using a video recorder
   (g) cooking
   (h) travelling on your bike

B List the whole-number solutions to each of these equations and find a simultaneous solution to the pair in each question.

1 $x + y = 8$
$x = y$

2 $x + 2y = 12$
$x - y = 0$

3 $2x + 3y = 11$
$2x + y = 9$

4 $y = 3x$
$2x + 5y = 34$

Show that the pairs of equations in questions 5 and 6 do **not** have simultaneous whole-number solutions.

5 $y = 2x$
$x + y = 4$

6 $x + 2y = 5$
$2x + y = 9$

Three methods of solving a pair of simultaneous equations are now given; a graphical method, an algebraic method, and a method using matrices.

8·2 Graphical solution

The graphs of both equations are drawn, using the same set of axes. The solution is the coordinate pair of the point of intersection. (Work on squared or graph paper.)

Example:

$\left.\begin{array}{l} x + y = 6 \\ y = 2x \end{array}\right\}$ Solve the pair of simultaneous equations by graphs.

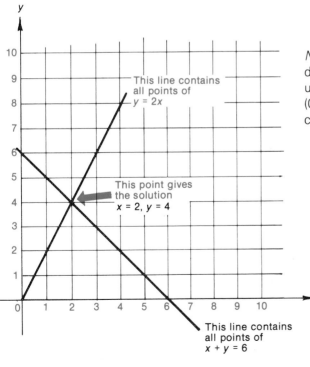

This line contains all points of $y = 2x$

This point gives the solution $x = 2, y = 4$

This line contains all points of $x + y = 6$

Note: Only two points are needed to draw each straight-line graph. I have used (0, 6) and (6, 0) for $x + y = 6$ and (0, 0) and (3, 6) for $y = 2x$. Other points could have been used.

Exercise 8·2

A Draw graphs to find solutions of the following pairs of simultaneous equations.

   1 $x + y = 5$
       $x - y = 1$

   2 $x + y = 4$
       $2x + 3y = 10\frac{1}{2}$

   3 $x + y = 7$
       $2x - y = \frac{1}{2}$

   4 $x + 2y = 1$
       $x - y = 2$

   5 $x + 2y = 5$
       $2x + y = 4$

   6 $x + 2y = 5$
       $3x - 2y = 3$

B Solve the following equations by graphs and by tabulation Compare the two answers.

   1 $2x + y = 7$
       $x - y = 5$

   2 $2x + 3y = 5$
       $x = y$

   3 $2x - y = 5$
       $y = 3x - 8$

   4 $3x - 2y = 1$
       $y = 2x - 1$

   5 $3x - 2y = 5$
       $2x + y = 8$

   6 $2x - 3y = 3$
       $x = y - 1$

C *Enlarging the graph*   If the two lines do not meet at a grid point, it is still possible to produce an accurate answer.

Example:

Find the solution of the simultaneous equations $2x + y = 5$
                                                  $3x - y = 2$

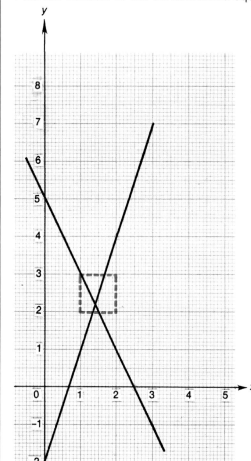

First graphical solution
$2x + y = 5$ contains $(0, 5)$ and $(2\frac{1}{2}, 0)$
$3x - y = 5$ contains $(0, -2)$ and $(2, 4)$
The solution occurs between $x = 1$ and $x = 2$ in the dotted square.
x is between 1·3 and 1·5

Second graphical solution

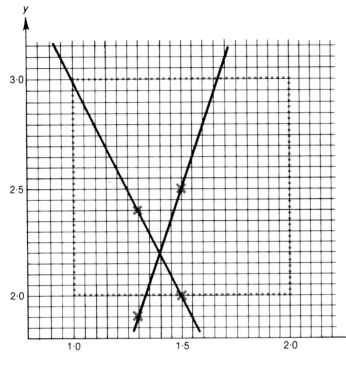

3·0

2·5

2·0

1·0   1·5   2·0

y

x

The lines are now drawn on an enlargement of the dotted square, after calculating y-values for x = 1·3 and x = 1·5 for each line*:

2x + y = 5	
x	y
1·3	2·4
1·5	2·0

3x − y = 2	
x	y
1·3	1·9
1·5	2·5

This gives us the points (1·3, 2·4) and (1·5, 2·0) for 2x + y = 5 and (1·3, 1·9) and (1·5, 2·5) for 3x − y = 2

Clearly the lines meet at x = 1·40, y = 2·20, the exact solution to the equations.

* Use a calculator to find the values for y when x = 1·3
  e.g. on 2x + y = 5
  $2x + y = 5 \Rightarrow y = 5 - 2x$
  so use 2 ⊠ 1·3 +/− + 5 =

Use graphs to find solutions to the following pairs of equations (to two decimal places).

1 2x + 3y = 7
      x − y = 2

2 3x − 4y = 9
      2x + y = 8

3 3x − 4y = 4
      x + 3y = 5

4 y = 3x + 2
      2x + y = 10

8·3 Rules of algebra

Simultaneous equations can be solved without drawing. The method below is called **elimination** (see Unit 15, M1).

Example 1:

Solve 2x + 3y = 7 . . . . . (1)
      x − y = 1 . . . . . . (2)

These equations are solved by **eliminating** x or y. Both methods are shown in this example. In practice, only one method is chosen, usually the method in which the equations are added, as subtraction is liable to introduce mistakes.

Method eliminating x

$$2x + 3y = 7 \quad \ldots \ldots \quad (1)$$
$$2x - 2y = 2 \quad \ldots \text{from (2)}$$

Subtracting, $\quad 5y = 5$
$$\Rightarrow y = 1$$

$$\Rightarrow 2x + 3 = 7 \quad \ldots \text{from (1)}$$
$$\Rightarrow x = 2$$

The law of algebra used here is:
$$\left. \begin{array}{r} a = b \\ c = d \end{array} \right\} \Rightarrow a - b = c - d$$

Method eliminating y

$$2x + 3y = 7 \quad \ldots \ldots \quad (1)$$
$$3x - 3y = 3 \quad \ldots \text{from (2)}$$

Adding, $\quad 5x + 0 = 10$
$$\Rightarrow x = 2$$

$$\Rightarrow 4 + 3y = 7 \quad \ldots \text{from (1)}$$
$$\Rightarrow y = 1$$

The law of algebra used here is:
$$\left. \begin{array}{r} a = b \\ c = d \end{array} \right\} \Rightarrow a + b = c + d$$

Example 2:

Solve $2x + 3y = 10\frac{1}{2} \ldots \ldots (1)$
$\qquad x + y = 4 \quad \ldots \ldots \ldots (2)$

Method eliminating x

$$2x + 3y = 10\tfrac{1}{2} \quad \ldots \ldots \ldots \quad (1)$$
$$2x + 2y = 8 \quad \ldots \ldots \text{from (2)}$$

$$y = 2\tfrac{1}{2}$$

$$\Rightarrow 2x + 7\tfrac{1}{2} = 10\tfrac{1}{2} \quad \ldots \ldots \text{from (1)}$$
$$\Rightarrow 2x = 3$$
$$\Rightarrow x = 1\tfrac{1}{2}$$

Method eliminating y

$$2x + 3y = 10\tfrac{1}{2} \quad \ldots \ldots \ldots \quad (1)$$
$$3x + 3y = 12 \quad \ldots \ldots \text{from (2)}$$

$$-x + 0 = -1\tfrac{1}{2}$$
$$\Rightarrow x = 1\tfrac{1}{2}$$

$$\Rightarrow 3 + 3y = 10\tfrac{1}{2} \quad \ldots \ldots \text{from (1)}$$
$$\Rightarrow 3y = 7\tfrac{1}{2}$$
$$\Rightarrow y = 2\tfrac{1}{2}$$

Exercise 8·3

A Solve the following pairs of simultaneous equations by elimination. Compare your results with the graphical solutions you obtained in Exercise 8·2.

1	$x + y = 5$	**2**	$x + y = 7$	**3**	$x + 2y = 5$	**4**	$2x + y = 7$
	$x - y = 1$		$2x - y = \frac{1}{2}$		$x - y = 2$		$x + y = 2$
5	$2x + 3y = 5$	**6**	$2x - y = 5$	**7**	$2x + y = 7$	**8**	$3x - 2y = 5$
	$x = y$		$y = 3x - 8$		$x - y = 5$		$2x + y = 8$
9	$x + 2y = 5$	**10**	$2x - 3y = 3$	**11**	$4x + 5y = 30$	**12**	$3x + 4y = 5$
	$2x + y = 4$		$x = y - 1$		$3x - 2y = 11$		$x - 2y = 5$

B Equations are often expressed in letters other than x, y. Solve the following equations, using any method. (Sometimes the equations must be rearranged before you start the solution.)

1	$2a - 3b = -6$	**2**	$c - 5d = 4$	**3**	$5c - d = 3$	**4**	$p + 2m = 8$
	$a - 2b = -5$		$c - 2d = 16$		$3d - 8c = 5$		$2p + m = 7$
5	$3s - t = 1$	**6**	$7p - q = 2$	**7**	$2c + d = 10$	**8**	$y - 2z = 5$
	$4s + t = 20$		$6p = q$		$3c - 2d = 1$		$2z + y = 1$

8·4 Problems solved by simultaneous equations

Many problems lead to simultaneous equations. Once the equations are formed, the usual methods are used for solution.

Example:

In △ABC, $\hat{B} = x°$, $\hat{C} = y°$. If $\hat{A} = 2\hat{B}$ and $\hat{C} - \hat{B} = 36°$ find the angles of the triangle.

Step 1∅   The data $\hat{C} - \hat{B} = 36°$ leads to the equation $y - x = 36 \ldots (1)$

Step 2∅   Since $\hat{A} + \hat{B} + \hat{C} = 180°$, $x + y + \hat{A} = 180°$

Step 3∅ $\hat{A} = 180 - (x + y)$

Step 4∅   Data $\hat{A} = 2\hat{B}$ leads to $180 - (x + y) = 2x \ldots (2)$

Step 5∅   The two simultaneous equations are $y - x = 36 \ldots (1)$
$$x + y + 2x = 180 \ldots (2)$$

Step 6∅   Solve the equations: $y - x = 36 \ldots (1)$
$$y + 3x = 180 \ldots (2)$$

Subtract: $-4x = -144$
$$x = 36°$$
$$\Rightarrow y = 72° \ldots \text{from (1)}$$

Step 7∅   Check that the results fit the problem.

    Does $\hat{A} = 2\hat{B}$?   Yes

    Does $\hat{C} - \hat{B} = 36°$?   Yes

Step 8∅   END

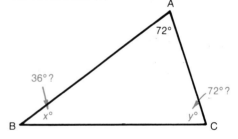

Exercise 8·4

A   **1**   I think of two numbers. Their sum is 19, their difference is 5. What are the numbers?

    2   Find two numbers whose sum is 39 and difference is 11.

    3   I think of two numbers. If I add 11 to the first I get twice the second. If I add 20 to the second I get twice the first. What are the numbers?

    4   One number is double another and also 12 more than it. What are the two numbers?

    5   In △ABC, $\hat{A} = 3\hat{B}$ and $\hat{C} = \hat{B} + 20°$. Find $\hat{A}$, $\hat{B}$ and C.

    6   5 kg of salt and 2 kg of sugar cost £3·55. 1 kg of salt and 3 kg of sugar cost £2·40. What is the cost of 1 kg of sugar?

B   **1**   In 4 years' time a father will be three times as old as his son will be. 4 years ago he was 5 times as old as his son was. Find their present ages. (*Hint:* let their present ages be *f* years and *s* years.)

    2   The ages of Miranda and Gill add to 28 years. Miranda is two years older than Gill. How old are the girls?

3 A heap of 10p and 5p coins is worth £2. If there were 3 times as many 10p coins and half as many 5p coins the heap would be worth £2·25. How many 5p coins are there in the heap?

4 Two cars are driven by A and B at steady speeds. If they were driving in opposite directions, their approaching speed would be 120 km/h. If they were driving in the same direction A would overtake B at 6 km/h. What are their speeds?

5 At the Burger World restaurant, the Jones family had 4 Eggburgers and 3 Double Beefburgers. The Smith family had 2 Eggburgers and 4 Double Beefburgers and paid £1 less than the Jones's. Eggburgers cost £1·40 each. How much does one Double Beefburger cost?

6 Mr Dawa bought 7 lb of potatoes and 3 lb of apples at a shop for £1·45. Mrs Evans bought 5 lb of potatoes and 2 lb of apples at the same shop. She paid exactly £1. How much per lb were the apples and potatoes?

Note: The problems above are really exercises in technique and not real problems. For example, in Question B.4 it would be much easier to measure the speed of each car than the speed of approach of the two cars. However, these exercises do give practice in changing problems into equations.

It is also good practice to make up some problems of your own to give to other people in the class.

C Make up some problems leading to simultaneous equations, to give to your friends. Make sure you can solve them for yourself first.

D *Examination questions* (These questions are adapted from examination questions to give you an idea of what to expect.)

1

x	-6	0	6
y	-3	-1	1

The table shows coordinates on the line $x - 3y = 3$

(a) Copy and complete the table below for $y = x + 2$

x	-6	0	6
y			

(b) Use the tables to draw graphs and solve the simultaneous equations

$$x - 3y = 3$$
$$x - y = -2$$

2 Solve $\quad 5x + 4y = 5$
$\qquad\qquad 2x + 3y = 9$

3 Solve $\quad 4x + 3y = -4$
$\qquad\qquad 6x - 2y = 7$

Note: In questions 2 and 3 both equations must be changed before x or y can be eliminated.

4 The simultaneous equations $\begin{array}{l} x + 3y = 7 \\ x - y = 3 \end{array}$ have as solution:

(a) $x = 4$, $y = 1$ (b) $x = 5$, $y = 2$ (c) $x = 1$, $y = 2$ (d) Many solutions

5 Solve the simultaneous equations $\quad x + 2y = 0$
$\qquad\qquad\qquad\qquad\qquad\qquad\quad 2x + y = 3$

6 Solve the equations $\quad 2p - 3q = 7$
$\qquad\qquad\qquad\qquad\quad 4p + q = 0$

7 The coach from London to Manchester had 28 passengers with return tickets and 12 with single tickets. The total fare value was £222. On the return coach, 20 people had singles and 16 had returns. The value of this fare was £192. What are the single and return fares?

8·5 The inverse of a matrix

The rule for multiplying two matrices is given in Unit 18 (M1/N1). It is given again here to remind you.

$$\begin{bmatrix} a & b \\ c & d \end{bmatrix} \begin{bmatrix} p & q \\ r & s \end{bmatrix} = \begin{bmatrix} ap + br & aq + bs \\ cp + dr & cq + ds \end{bmatrix}$$

The unit matrix **I** is $\begin{bmatrix} 1 & 0 \\ 0 & 1 \end{bmatrix}$

If two matrices multiply to a product **I**, then the matrices are inverses.
AB = I $\Rightarrow$ B is the inverse of **A** and **A** is the inverse of **B**

The inverse of matrix $\begin{bmatrix} a & b \\ c & d \end{bmatrix}$ is $\begin{bmatrix} d/\Delta & -b/\Delta \\ -c/\Delta & a/\Delta \end{bmatrix}$, $\Delta = ad - bc$

To form the inverse:
1. The d and a swap places
2. The b and c become negative
3. All four numbers are divided by Δ

Exercise 8·5

A Multiply the following pairs of matrices:

1 $\begin{bmatrix} 2 & 3 \\ 1 & 4 \end{bmatrix} \begin{bmatrix} 0 & 4 \\ 2 & 0 \end{bmatrix}$ **2** $\begin{bmatrix} 1 & 3 \\ 2 & 0 \end{bmatrix} \begin{bmatrix} 1 & 0 \\ 1 & -1 \end{bmatrix}$ **3** $\begin{bmatrix} 4 & 2 \\ -3 & 3 \end{bmatrix} \begin{bmatrix} 3 & 1 \\ 1 & 3 \end{bmatrix}$

4 $\begin{bmatrix} -1 & 1 \\ 1 & -1 \end{bmatrix} \begin{bmatrix} 1 & 2 \\ 3 & 4 \end{bmatrix}$ **5** $\begin{bmatrix} 7 & 2 \\ -1 & 4 \end{bmatrix} \begin{bmatrix} 6 & 5 \\ 3 & 1 \end{bmatrix}$ **6** $\begin{bmatrix} 2 & 7 \\ 1 & 4 \end{bmatrix} \begin{bmatrix} 4 & -7 \\ -1 & 2 \end{bmatrix}$

B **1** Write down the value of Δ for the following matrices:

(a) $\begin{bmatrix} 2 & 7 \\ 4 & 13 \end{bmatrix}$ (b) $\begin{bmatrix} 3 & 4 \\ 2 & 3 \end{bmatrix}$ (c) $\begin{bmatrix} 1 & 0 \\ 0 & 1 \end{bmatrix}$ (d) $\begin{bmatrix} -1 & 0 \\ 0 & 1 \end{bmatrix}$

(e) $\begin{bmatrix} 4 & 3 \\ 2 & 1 \end{bmatrix}$ (f) $\begin{bmatrix} 2 & 1 \\ 1 & 1 \end{bmatrix}$ (g) $\begin{bmatrix} -2 & 3 \\ 1 & -2 \end{bmatrix}$ (h) $\begin{bmatrix} -1 & 0 \\ 1 & -1 \end{bmatrix}$

2 Use the values of Δ you have found, and the rule for finding inverses, to write down the inverses of the matrices in question 1.

3 Check that each matrix times its inverse gives $\mathbf{I} = \begin{bmatrix} 1 & 0 \\ 0 & 1 \end{bmatrix}$

4 Show that $\begin{bmatrix} a & b \\ c & d \end{bmatrix} \begin{bmatrix} d/\Delta & -b/\Delta \\ -c/\Delta & a/\Delta \end{bmatrix} = \mathbf{I}$ by direct multiplication.

5 Show that $\begin{bmatrix} d/\Delta & -b/\Delta \\ -c/\Delta & a/\Delta \end{bmatrix} \begin{bmatrix} a & b \\ c & d \end{bmatrix} = \mathbf{I}$ by direct multiplication.

C The sections which follow explore the mathematics of 2×2 matrices. Read the sections carefully, and discuss them with a friend to make sure you understand what is going on.
1 The unit matrix **I** This is a matrix that leaves any other matrix unchanged when it is multiplied by **I**. It is like the number 1 in this respect. So:

Any matrix   **I**   The matrix unchanged

$$\begin{bmatrix} a & b \\ c & d \end{bmatrix} \times \begin{bmatrix} ? & ? \\ ? & ? \end{bmatrix} = \begin{bmatrix} a & b \\ c & d \end{bmatrix}$$

We can find I in several ways. Suppose $I = \begin{bmatrix} p & q \\ r & s \end{bmatrix}$

Then $\begin{bmatrix} a & b \\ c & d \end{bmatrix} \begin{bmatrix} p & q \\ r & s \end{bmatrix} = \begin{bmatrix} a & b \\ c & d \end{bmatrix}$

Multiplying out the left-hand side gives:

$\begin{bmatrix} ap + br & aq + bs \\ cp + dr & cq + ds \end{bmatrix}$ which equals $\begin{bmatrix} a & b \\ c & d \end{bmatrix}$

So: $ap + br = a$ You can see that $p = 1$, $r = 0$, $q = 0$, $s = 1$
$\quad\ \ aq + bs = b$ makes all these equations true.
$\quad\ \ cp + dr = c$ This shows that I can be $\begin{bmatrix} 1 & 0 \\ 0 & 1 \end{bmatrix}$ but we
$\quad\ \ cq + ds = d$

still need to prove that this is the only possible form for I.

Proof ... that there is only one unit matrix

1∅   Data I is a unit matrix

2∅   Data   Suppose I' is another unit matrix

3∅   Deduction $AI = A$ for every matrix A ..... from 1∅

4∅   Deduction $I'A = A$ for every matrix A ..... from 2∅

5∅   Deduction $I'I = I'$ .... from 3∅

6∅   Deduction $I'I = I$ .... from 4∅

7∅   Deduction $I' = I$ .... from 5∅, 6∅

8∅   END

Any comments?

2   (a)   Matrices obey the associative law for multiplication: $A(BC) = (AB)C$
       Choose particular matrices for A, B and C to show that this is so. If you want to show
       that it is true for all matrices you will have to start with

       $A = \begin{bmatrix} a_1 & a_2 \\ a_3 & a_4 \end{bmatrix}$, $B = \begin{bmatrix} b_1 & b_2 \\ b_3 & b_4 \end{bmatrix}$ and $C = \begin{bmatrix} c_1 & c_2 \\ c_3 & c_4 \end{bmatrix}$

   (b)   Matrices do not usually obey the commutative law, i.e. $AB \neq BA$
       You can demonstrate this by choosing any two matrices for A and B. Do so! Can you
       think of any times when AB and BA will be equal?

3   The proof below shows that if $AB = I$ then BA is also equal to I.

   1∅   Data $AB = I$

   2∅   Data   Suppose $BA = C$

   3∅   Deduction $BAB = B(AB) = BI = B$ ..... from 1∅

   4∅   Deduction $BAB = (BA)B = CB$ .... from 2∅

   5∅   Deduction $CB = B$ .... from 3∅, 4∅

   6∅   Deduction $C = I$ there is only one unit matrix!

   7∅   Deduction $BA = I$

   8∅   END

This shows that **AB** and **BA** can be equal if **A** and **B** are inverses. It does not tell you whether **AB** and **BA** can be equal without being inverses. What do you think? Investigate.

4 In Exercise 8·5B you have shown that $\begin{bmatrix} d/\Delta & -b/\Delta \\ -c/\Delta & a/\Delta \end{bmatrix}$

is an inverse of $\begin{bmatrix} a & b \\ c & d \end{bmatrix}$. Can you find a way to prove that it is the only inverse?

Note: (i) The inverse of **A** is usually written **A⁻¹**
(ii) If $\Delta = 0$ the matrix has no inverse

8·6 Simultaneous equations and matrices

A pair of equations can be written in matrix–vector form and then solved.

Example:

$$\left. \begin{array}{r} 2x + y = 3 \\ x + 3y = 2 \end{array} \right\} \Leftrightarrow \begin{bmatrix} 2 & 1 \\ 1 & 3 \end{bmatrix} \begin{bmatrix} x \\ y \end{bmatrix} = \begin{bmatrix} 3 \\ 2 \end{bmatrix}$$

The equations can be solved by finding the inverse of the matrix.

Step 1∅ The inverse of $\begin{bmatrix} 2 & 1 \\ 1 & 3 \end{bmatrix}$ is $\begin{bmatrix} \frac{3}{5} & -\frac{1}{5} \\ -\frac{1}{5} & \frac{2}{5} \end{bmatrix}$ since $\Delta = 5$

Step 2∅ Multiply both sides of the matrix equation by this inverse:

$$\begin{bmatrix} \frac{3}{5} & -\frac{1}{5} \\ -\frac{1}{5} & \frac{2}{5} \end{bmatrix} \begin{bmatrix} 2 & 1 \\ 1 & 3 \end{bmatrix} \begin{bmatrix} x \\ y \end{bmatrix} = \begin{bmatrix} \frac{3}{5} & -\frac{1}{5} \\ -\frac{1}{5} & \frac{2}{5} \end{bmatrix} \begin{bmatrix} 3 \\ 2 \end{bmatrix}$$

Step 3∅ Work out the multiplications: this is easier than it looks, as the left-hand side must now be $\begin{bmatrix} x \\ y \end{bmatrix}$:

$$\begin{bmatrix} 1 & 0 \\ 0 & 1 \end{bmatrix} \begin{bmatrix} x \\ y \end{bmatrix} = \begin{bmatrix} \frac{7}{5} \\ \frac{1}{5} \end{bmatrix} \qquad \text{i.e.} \quad \begin{bmatrix} x \\ y \end{bmatrix} = \begin{bmatrix} \frac{7}{5} \\ \frac{1}{5} \end{bmatrix}$$

Step 4∅ $x = \frac{7}{5}$, $y = \frac{1}{5}$

Note: In matrix algebra, the above example is simply . . .

$$\mathbf{AX = B}$$
$$\Rightarrow \mathbf{A^{-1}AX = A^{-1}B}$$
$$\Rightarrow \mathbf{X = A^{-1}B}$$

Exercise 8·6

A 1 Express the following pairs of equations in matrix–vector form:

(a) $x + y = 2$
$x + 2y = 3$

(b) $x + 3 = 4$
$x - y = 3$

(c) $2x - 5y = 13$
$x + 2y = 6$

(d) $2x - 3y = 5$
$y = 2x + 1$

(e) $x - y + 6 = 0$
$2x = 3y$

(f) $3x = 2y - 5$
$y = 3x + 6$

2 Write out these matrix–vector equations as ordinary simultaneous equations

(a) $\begin{bmatrix} 3 & 4 \\ 5 & 6 \end{bmatrix} \begin{bmatrix} x \\ y \end{bmatrix} = \begin{bmatrix} 4 \\ 2 \end{bmatrix}$

(b) $\begin{bmatrix} 2 & -3 \\ 1 & -1 \end{bmatrix} \begin{bmatrix} p \\ q \end{bmatrix} = \begin{bmatrix} -2 \\ -3 \end{bmatrix}$

(c) $\begin{bmatrix} -3 & 5 \\ 2 & -1 \end{bmatrix} \begin{bmatrix} x \\ y \end{bmatrix} = \begin{bmatrix} 7 \\ 0 \end{bmatrix}$

(d) $\begin{bmatrix} -1 & 3 \\ 0 & 0.5 \end{bmatrix} \begin{bmatrix} a \\ b \end{bmatrix} = \begin{bmatrix} 1.5 \\ 2.2 \end{bmatrix}$

3 Write the following equations in matrix–vector form. Find the inverse of the matrix in each case.

(a) $2x + y = 7$
  $x - y = 5$

(b) $2x - y = 5$
  $y = 3x - 8$

(c) $2x + y = 7$
  $x + y = 2$

(d) $2x - 3y = 3$
  $x = y - 1$

(e) $4x - 2y = 30$
  $3x - 2y = 11$

(f) $3x + 4y = 5$
  $x - 2y = 5$

4 Solve the equations in question 3 using the inverse matrices. Compare your solutions with those obtained by elimination.

B If the numbers in simultaneous equations are not simple, the best method of solution is to use a matrix and a calculator to find Δ and the values of x and y. Follow this example carefully and then solve the four pairs of equations given. Find a neat way to set out your work and take care to be accurate with the calculator.

Example:

Solve the equations $1.2x + 3.7y = 7.1$
  $0.4x + 2.2y = 6.8$

Matrix form: $\begin{bmatrix} 1.2 & 3.7 \\ 0.4 & 2.2 \end{bmatrix} \begin{bmatrix} x \\ y \end{bmatrix} = \begin{bmatrix} 7.1 \\ 6.8 \end{bmatrix}$

$\Delta = (1.2 \times 2.2) - (3.7 \times 0.4) = 1.16$

Inverse: $\begin{bmatrix} \frac{2.2}{1.16} & -\frac{3.7}{1.16} \\ -\frac{0.4}{1.16} & \frac{1.2}{1.16} \end{bmatrix}$

so $\begin{bmatrix} x \\ y \end{bmatrix} = \begin{bmatrix} \frac{2.2}{1.16} & -\frac{3.7}{1.16} \\ -\frac{0.4}{1.16} & \frac{1.2}{1.16} \end{bmatrix} \begin{bmatrix} 7.1 \\ 6.8 \end{bmatrix}$

$x = (\frac{2.2}{1.16} \times 7.1) - (\frac{3.7}{1.16} \times 6.8)$
$y = (-\frac{0.4}{1.16} \times 7.1) + (\frac{1.2}{1.16} \times 6.8)$

Calculator * gives $x = -8.2241$ $y = 4.5862$

* The calculator sequence will depend on what calculator you have. On mine you get
x from $\boxed{C}$ 2.2 $\boxed{\times}$ 7.1 $\boxed{-}$ 3.7 $\boxed{\times}$ 6.8 $\boxed{=}$ $\boxed{\div}$ 1.16 $\boxed{=}$
and y from $\boxed{C}$ 1.2 $\boxed{\times}$ 6.8 $\boxed{-}$ 0.4 $\boxed{\times}$ 7.1 $\boxed{=}$ $\boxed{\div}$ 1.16 $\boxed{=}$

Solve the following equations. Take your time!

1 $27x + 35y = 168$
  $19x - 7y = 44$

2 $3x - 1.1y = 14.2$
  $1.7x + 3y = 28$

3 $2.9x + 1.4y = 77$
  $1.8x - 3.5y = 18$

4 $4.5x + 7.2y = 19.1$
  $6.8x + 10y = 44$

The ideas you are using are used in industry to solve whole groups of linear equations. The method is exactly the same.

Unit 9 Inequalities

9·1 Order (<, >)

Numbers have the special quality that you
can always put them in order.
The signs <, > are used to compare the
positions of two numbers.

It is not so easy to put
people in order of size.
Mr Jones may be taller than
Mr Green, but Mr Green may be
much heavier! Mr Jones might
be older, but Mr Green could
have the biggest feet!

Examples:
3 < 5 means 3 is less than 5
7 > 0 means 7 is more than 0

The positions of numbers are clearly shown on a number line:

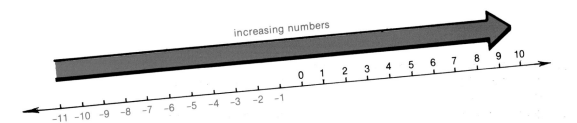

increasing numbers

−11 −10 −9 −8 −7 −6 −5 −4 −3 −2 −1 0 1 2 3 4 5 6 7 8 9 10

Note: (i) 0 is below all positive numbers.
(ii) All negative numbers are below all positive numbers.
(iii) Large negative numbers are below smaller negative
numbers.
(iv) Fractions lie in-between whole numbers, but still have their
own position.

Example:

x is a whole number such that $x > -4$ and $x < 3$ (i.e. $-4 < x < 3$)
What numbers could x be?

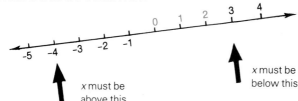

From the diagram, x can be any one of the numbers $-3, -2, -1, 0, 1$ or 2

x must be above this

x must be below this

Exercise 9·1

A 1 Insert the correct sign, $>$ or $<$, between the following pairs of numbers.

(a) 7, 12   (b) 10, 4   (c) 14, 3
(d) 0, 18   (e) 22, 10   (f) 45, 40
(g) $-5, -2$ (h) $-4, -1$ (i) $-7, 0$
(j) $-3, 4$ (k) $-17, -5$ (l) $-6, -9$
(m) 4, -12 (n) $-18, 16$ (o) 22, -22

2 (a) n is a whole number such that $n < 16$ and $n > 4$. What numbers could n be?
(b) x is a whole number such that $-5 < x$ and $x < 2$. What numbers could x be?
(c) y is a whole number such that $-7 < y$ and $y < -2$. What numbers could y be?
(d) What whole numbers are greater than -5 but less than 1? Show them on a number line.
(e) n is a number such that $n > 4$ and $n < 5$. Suggest four possible values for n.
(f) Show on a number line the possible values for w, given that $w > 2$ and $w < 8$.

3 Pick out the true statements from the following:

(a) $-3 < 5$ (b) $-3 < -5$ (c) $5 < 0$ (d) $0 < -4$
(e) $-3 < 3$ (f) $6 < -10$ (g) $-18 > 10$ (h) $x < 2x$

4 Pick out the true implications from the following:

(a) $x < 6 \Rightarrow x < 7$ (b) $x > 0 \Rightarrow x > 5$ (c) $x > 3 \Rightarrow x > -3$
(d) $x > -5 \Rightarrow x > -3$ (e) $x > 6 \Rightarrow 2x > 12$ (f) $x > 5 \Rightarrow x^2 > 25$

B 1 Insert the correct sign, $>$ or $<$, between these pairs of fractions. (Use your calculator if you cannot tell any other way.)

(a) $\frac{1}{2}, \frac{3}{4}$ (b) $\frac{2}{3}, \frac{1}{2}$ (c) $\frac{4}{5}, \frac{3}{4}$ (d) $\frac{3}{8}, \frac{1}{4}$
(e) $\frac{2}{3}, \frac{3}{5}$ (f) $\frac{2}{3}, \frac{5}{8}$ (g) $\frac{7}{8}, \frac{4}{5}$ (h) $\frac{3}{4}, \frac{7}{10}$

2 The cross products for the pair of fractions $(\frac{1}{2}, \frac{3}{4})$ are 1×4 and 3×2 (multiply the top of the first by the bottom of the second and vice versa). Is it true that $\frac{1}{2} < \frac{3}{4}$ and $1 \times 4 < 3 \times 2$?
(a) Check the cross products for all the fraction pairs of question 1.
(b) Do your results agree with the following statements
$a/b < c/d \Rightarrow ad < bc$
$ad < bc \Rightarrow a/b < c/d$

3 Use cross products to check the truth of these inequalities

(a) $\frac{3}{19} < \frac{2}{15}$ (b) $\frac{7}{8} > \frac{10}{12}$ (c) $\frac{4}{7} < \frac{5}{8}$
(d) $\frac{5}{13} > \frac{8}{19}$ (e) $\frac{6}{11} < \frac{5}{9}$ (f) $\frac{12}{25} < \frac{1}{2}$

4 Choose simple numbers for a, b, c, k etc. to test the following statements about inequalities.

(a) $a > b \Rightarrow -b < -a$ (b) $a > 0 \Rightarrow -a < 0$ (c) $a > b \Rightarrow a + c > b + c$
(d) $a > b, c > 0 \Rightarrow ac > bc$ (e) $a < b, c < 0 \Rightarrow ac > bc$ (f) $a > b \Rightarrow a - k > b - k$

9·2 Inequations

An inequation is a statement about one number being more or less than
another. It is like an equation except that:
(i) $<$ and $>$ signs are used instead of $=$
(ii)   An inequation has a set of solutions rather than just one solution
(iii)   Great care must be taken with negative numbers

Example:
Find the solution set of the inequation $2x + 1 < 5$ and show the set on the number line.
1∅ $2x + 1 < 5$ ←——This is short for 'If $2x + 1$ is a number less than 5, then $2x$ must be
                            less than 4.' If $2x$ were more than 4, $2x + 1$ would be more than 5!
2∅ $2x < 4$ ←

3∅ $x < 2$ ←——This is short for 'If $2x$ is less than 4 then x must be less than 2.' If x
                            were more than 2, $2x$ would be more than 4.
4∅   End

The solution of $2x + 1 < 5$
is the set of numbers less
than 2.

$x < 2$

This set does not include 2 itself.

You can add the same number to both sides of an inequation without
changing the order relationship. You can also multiply or divide by the
same positive number. Dividing or multiplying by a negative number
reverses the order.

Examples:
   $3 > 2 \Rightarrow 5 > 4$ (adding $+ 2$ to both sides)
   $3 > 2 \Rightarrow 0 > -1$ (adding $- 3$ to both sides)
   $3 > 2 \Rightarrow 6 > 4$ (multiplying by $+ 2$)
but $3 > 2 \Rightarrow -9 < -6$ (multiplying by $- 3$)

Exercise 9·2

A   Find the solution sets for the following inequations. Show each solution set on a number line.

1 $x + 3 < 5$	**2** $x + 7 < 10$	**3** $x + 10 < 7$
4 $x + 5 < 0$	**5** $2x < 6$	**6** $3x < -3$
7 $4x < 0$	**8** $2x + 3 < 8$	**9** $3x - 2 < 1$

B   Find the solution sets for the following inequations.

1 $x + 5 > 10$	**2** $x + 7 > 0$	**3** $x + 8 > -2$
4 $x - 5 > 7$	**5** $3x > 6$	**6** $4x > -4$
7 $2x - 1 > 3$	**8** $5x - 4 > 6$	**9** $7 - x > 5$

C Write these 'stories' in inequation form. Suggest a solution set in each case.
1 I have enough money in my purse to buy something for £3 or £4, but not for £10.
2 The speed limit was 30 mph. Mr Williams was exceeding the speed limit. How fast was he going?
3 A ship needed 20 ft of water to float.
   (a) The ship was afloat. How deep was the water?
   (b) The ship was aground. How deep was the water?
4 A thermostat for central heating is set so that the heating comes on if the temperature falls below 15°C and goes off if the temperature rises above 21°C.
   (a) The heating is on: what is the temperature?
   (b) The heating is off: what is the temperature?
5 An aircraft was ordered to fly at an altitude between 29 000 and 35 000 feet.
6 The length of a field was measured to be 149·8 metres to the nearest 10 cm.
7 Describe two other situations in which inequalities could be used.

9·3 Graphs of inequalities

The inequality $y > x + 5$ appears on the graph below as the unshaded area above the line $y = x + 5$.

The point A is $(-2, 6)$: $y > x + 5$ and so the point satisfies the inequality.

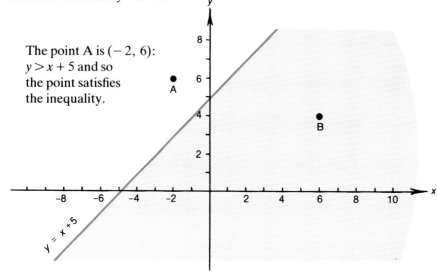

The point B is $(6, 4)$. It is not true for this point that $y > x + 5$. It is not a point that satisfies the inequality.

Thus the line $y = x + 5$ divides the plane into two regions. In one region (unshaded here) $y > x + 5$. In the other region $y < x + 5$.

Exercise 9·3

A 1 (a) Draw the lines $y = 3$ and $x = 2$ on the same graph.
   (b) Shade the areas corresponding to $x < 2$ and $y > 3$.
   (c) What combination of inequalities is represented by the unshaded area?
   (d) Which of these points lie in the unshaded area?
      $(0, 4)$ $(0, 0)$ $(-3, 4)$ $(-2, 1)$
   (e) List four points which satisfy both $x < 2$ and $y > 3$.
2 (a) Draw the graph of $y = x$ from $x = -3$ to $x = +3$.
   (b) Shade in the area corresponding to $y < x$.

(c) Which of the following points lie in the shaded area (i.e. satisfy $y < x$)?
(0, 2) (2, 0) (2, −1) (−1, 1)

(d) What area remains unshaded if $x + y > 1$ is shaded on the same graph?

(e) Give four points which satisfy the inequations
$$\left.\begin{array}{l} x + y < 1 \\ x > y \end{array}\right\} \text{simultaneously}$$

3 (a) Draw the lines $y = x + 1$ and $y = 3$ on the same graph.
(b) Shade in the areas for which $y > x + 1$ and $y > 3$.
(c) What inequations are represented by the unshaded area of your graph?
(d) Give four points which satisfy the inequations of (c).

4 (a) Draw a graph and shade the area which does not satisfy $y < x + 2$ and the area which does not satisfy $y > 2x − 1$.
(b) Choose four points which satisfy $y > x + 2$ and $y < 2x − 1$.

5 Investigate the areas which satisfy these pairs of inequalities.
(a) $x + y > 5$ and $x + y < 7$
(b) $2x + 3y < 8$ and $2x + 3y > 10$
(c) $y < 3x − 5$ and $y > 3x + 2$
(d) $2y − x < 5$ and $2y − x > 9$

B Write inequations which correspond to the unshaded areas in the graphs below.

1

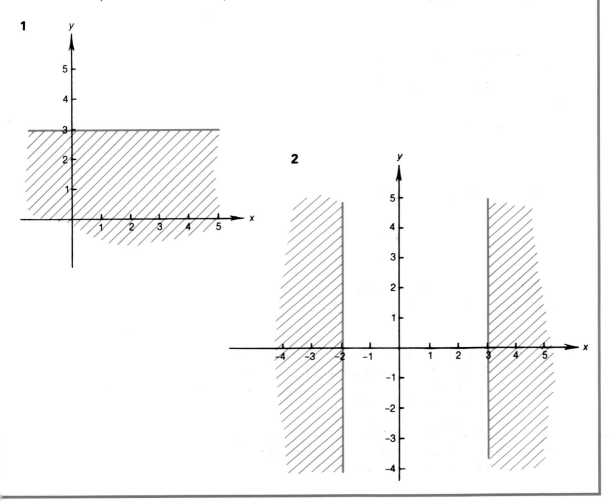

3

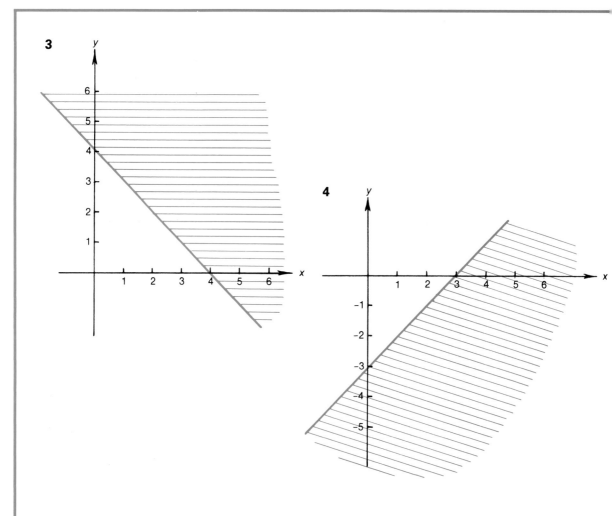

4

C Find pairs of inequations which correspond to the unshaded areas on the following graphs.

1

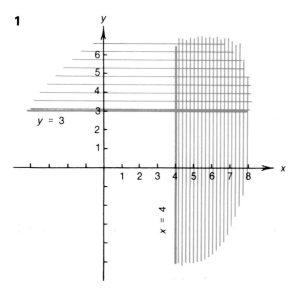

$y = 3$

$x = 4$

2

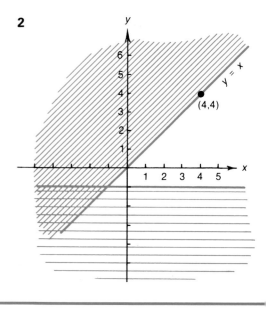

$y = x$

(4,4)

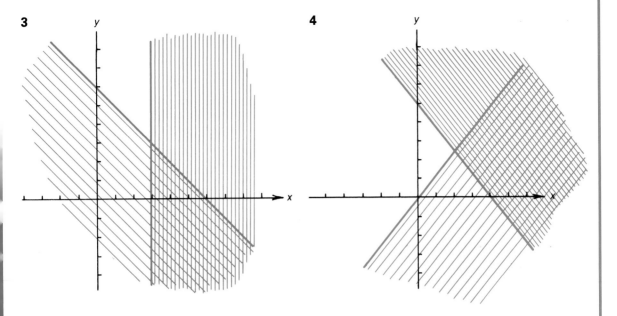

D *Some investigations*

1 The size (or magnitude) of a vector **a** is written $|\mathbf{a}|$. Investigate $|\mathbf{a}+\mathbf{b}|$ and $|\mathbf{a}-\mathbf{b}|$. Is it true that $|\mathbf{a}+\mathbf{b}| < |\mathbf{a}| + |\mathbf{b}|$?

2 It is said that in any triangle the greatest side is opposite the greatest angle. Do you agree? Can you prove your conclusions?

3 Inequalities can be converted to equality statements using the idea of a variable difference.

e.g. $3 < 5$ can be stated as $5 = 3 + n$

$a > b$ can be stated as $a = b + n$ where n is positive

Use this idea to prove these rules for inequalities

$a > b \Rightarrow a + k > b + k$

$a > b \Rightarrow ka > kb$ if k is positive

4 Investigate the relationship between the arithmetic mean and the geometric mean of sets of numbers.

Arithmetic mean of two numbers (m, n) is $\dfrac{m+n}{2}$

Geometric mean of m and n is $\sqrt{mn}$

Extend the definition to more than two numbers.

Is it true that AM > GM in all cases?

5 Investigate the following for a pair of fractions $\dfrac{a}{b}, \dfrac{c}{d}$

(a) $\dfrac{a+c}{b+d}$ (b) $\dfrac{ac}{bd}$

Look for inequalities.

6 A rectangle is measured carefully and it is found that its length is between 11·3 mm and 11·5 mm. Its breadth lies between 5·4 mm and 5·7 mm.

(a) What are the maximum and minimum possible values for its area?

(b) Suggest other situations where this type of problem is met.

Unit 10 Quadratics

10·1 Introduction

A quadratic expression has the form $ax^2 + bx + c$ where a, b and c are numbers.

What matters is whether x^2 is present or not: if $a = 0$, the expression becomes $bx + c$, which is linear, not quadratic

---

Examples of quadratics:

$2x^2 + 3x + 5$ here $a = 2$, $b = 3$, $c = 5$

$x^2 - x + 3$ here $a = 1$, $b = -1$, $c = 3$

$x^2 + 4x - 4$ here $a = 1$, $b = 4$, $c = -4$

Although the term in x^2 must always be present in a quadratic, the term in x or the pure number may be missing.

Examples:

$2x^2 - 3$ is a quadratic with $a = 2$, $b = 0$, $c = -3$

$x^2 + 5x$ is a quadratic with $a = 1$, $b = 5$, $c = 0$

$2x^2$ is a quadratic with $a = 2$, $b = 0$, $c = 0$

Exercise 10·1

A Which of the following are quadratic expressions?

1 $x^2 - 5$	**2** $2x + 6$	**3** $5 - 2x$	**4** $x^2 + 7x + 4$	**5** $2x^2 - 1$
6 $5x$	**7** $8x^2$	**8** $x - x^2$	**9** $x(x - 1)$	**10** $(x - 3)(x + 4)$

B The quadratics below are in the form $ax^2 + bx + c$: find a, b and c in each case.

1 $x^2 + 2x + 3$	**2** $x^2 - 3x + 2$	**3** $x^2 - 5x - 5$
4 $2x^2 - 3x - 7$	**5** $x^2 - 7x$	**6** $4x^2 - 5x$
7 $3x^2 + 5$	**8** $2x^2 - 7$	**9** $-3x^2$

C Rearrange the following expressions into the quadratic form $ax^2 + bx + c$. Give the values of a, b and c each time.

1 $x^2 + 5 - 2x$	**2** $3x - 2 - x^2$	**3** $-4 - x + 2x^2$
4 $1 - 3x^2 + x$	**5** $x^2 + 2 - 2x$	**6** $(x - 3)(2x + 4)$
7 $x(x - 2) + 2$	**8** $x(1 - x) - 1$	**9** $x(x - 4) + 2(x - 4)$

10·2   Quadratic equations

Equations in which a quadratic expression equals some number (usually zero) are called quadratic equations. The general quadratic equation
is $ax^2 + bx + c = 0$
If $b = 0$ or $c = 0$ the equation is easy to solve.

Examples:
Solve **1** $2x^2 - 3 = 0$ **2** $3x^2 - 2x = 0$ **3** $x^2 + 5x = 0$
1 $2x^2 - 3 = 0$ $1\emptyset$ $2x^2 - 3 = 0$

$2\emptyset$ $2x^2 = 3 \ldots$ from $1\emptyset$

$3\emptyset$ $x^2 = 1{\cdot}5 \ldots$ from $2\emptyset$

$4\emptyset$ $x = \sqrt{1{\cdot}5}$ or $x = -\sqrt{1{\cdot}5}$

$5\emptyset$ $x = 1{\cdot}2247$ or $x = -1{\cdot}2247$

$6\emptyset$ END

Notes: (i) There are two solutions, which can be expressed as $\pm 1{\cdot}2247$
(ii) The solutions can be checked by the calculator sequence:
  $1{\cdot}2247$ $\boxed{\times}$ $\boxed{=}$ $\boxed{\times}$ 2 $\boxed{-}$ 3 $\boxed{=}$

2 $x^2 + 5x = 0$ $1\emptyset$ $x^2 + 5x = 0$

$2\emptyset$ $x(x + 5) = 0 \ldots$ from $1\emptyset$

$3\emptyset$ $x = 0$ or $x + 5 = 0$

$4\emptyset$ $x = 0$ or -5

Notes: (i) $2\emptyset$ factorises the quadratic
(ii) $3\emptyset$ follows from $2\emptyset$ because if the product of two numbers is zero, one or the other of the numbers must be zero

Check: x $\boxed{\times}$ $\boxed{=}$ $\boxed{M_{in}}$ x $\boxed{\times}$ 5 $\boxed{=}$ $\boxed{+}$ $\boxed{M_R}$ $\boxed{=}$

3 $3x^2 - 2x = 0$ $1\emptyset$ $3x^2 - 2x = 0$

$2\emptyset$ $x(3x - 2) = 0 \ldots$ factorising

$3\emptyset$ $x = 0$ or $3x - 2 = 0 \ldots$ since one factor equals zero

$4\emptyset$ $x = 0$ or $3x = 2$

$5\emptyset$ $x = 0$ or $x = \frac{2}{3}$

Exercise 10·2

A Solve the following equations. Check your solutions.

1 $x^2 - 25 = 0$	**2** $x^2 - 81 = 0$	**3** $x^2 - 0{\cdot}64 = 0$
4 $x^2 - 15 = 0$	**5** $x^2 - 21 = 6$	**6** $x^2 - 3{\cdot}4 = 0$
7 $x^2 - 1000 = 0$	**8** $x^2 - 729 = 0$	**9** $x^2 - 200 = 44$

B Solve the following equations. Check your solutions.

1 $2x^2 - 40 = 0$	**2** $3x^2 - 18 = 0$	**3** $5x^2 - 20 = 30$
4 $3x^2 - 5 = x^2$	**5** $3x^2 - 8 = 1 - x^2$	**6** $3(x^2 - 6) = 18$

C Solve the following equations:

1 $x^2 - x = 0$ **2** $x^2 + 3x = 0$ **3** $2x^2 - 5 = 0$

4 $4x^2 + 7x = 0$ **5** $x^2 = 2x$ **6** $2x^2 = 5x$

7 $2x^2 = x^2 - 5x$ **8** $3x = 4x^2 - x$ **9** $x(x - 5) = 2x$

D **1** Solve the following problems. Form quadratic equations first.

(a) The square of a number is double the number. What is the number?

(b) The square of a number plus the number itself equals zero. What is the number?

(c) Twice the square of a number is two thirds of the number itself. Find the number.

2 Can you find a solution to these equations?

(a) $x^2 + 5 = 0$ (b) $2x^2 + 3 = 0$

Check any solution carefully on a calculator and comment.

3 Find solutions to the following equations, any way you like.

(a) $x^2 - 3x + 2 = 0$ (b) $x^2 + 4x - 5 = 0$

(Do not worry if you don't succeed. I want you to try for yourself before showing you the methods of the next section.)

10·3   Solving the general quadratic equation

We have seen that quadratic equations have two solutions

Example:

Show that $x = 2$ and $x = 3$ are both solutions of the equation $x^2 - 5x + 6 = 0$

Put $x = 2$ into $x^2 - 5x + 6$ Put $x = 3$ into $x^2 - 5x + 6$

                  ↓   ↓   ↓   ↓   ↓   ↓

          $4 - 10 + 6 \to 0$ $9 - 15 + 6 \to 0$

So both $x = 2$ and $x = 3$ are solutions of $x^2 - 5x + 6 = 0$

If the quadratic factorises, the solutions can be found by the following steps:

Step 1∅ $ax^2 + bx + c$ is replaced by two linear factors multiplied together

Step 2∅   Since the factors' product is zero, one or other of the factors must be zero

Step 3∅   Step 2∅ leads to two linear equations which are easy to solve

---

Example:

Solve $2x^2 - x - 6 = 0$

Step 1∅ $2x^2 - x - 6$ must be written as the product of two factors

         $2x^2 - x - 6 = (2x + \;?)(x + \;?)$

List all possible pairs of whole numbers whose product is -6

$-6 \times +1$.....would give $(2x - 6)(x + 1)$
$-3 \times +2$.....would give $(2x - 3)(x + 2)$
$-2 \times +3$.....would give $(2x - 2)(x + 3)$
$-1 \times +6$.....would give $(2x - 1)(x + 6)$
$+1 \times -6$.....would give $(2x + 1)(x - 6)$
$+2 \times -3$.....would give $(2x + 2)(x - 3)$
$+3 \times -2$.....would give $(2x + 3)(x - 2)$
$+6 \times -1$.....would give $(2x + 6)(x - 1)$

Only $(2x + 3)(x - 2)$ multiplies out to $2x^2 - x - 6$*
(Try the others and see)

Step 2∅ $(2x + 3)(x - 2) = 0$

Step 3∅   Either $2x + 3 = 0$ or $x - 2 = 0$.....from 2∅

Step 4∅   Either $x = -1\frac{1}{2}$ or $x = 2$.....from 3∅

Note: When checking a solution with a calculator you may save time by changing the form of the quadratic. Compare the calculator sequences for putting $x = -1\frac{1}{2}$ into
(a) $2x^2 - x - 6$ and   (b) $2x(x - 1) - 6$

(a) 1·5 $\boxed{+/-}$ $\boxed{\times}$ $\boxed{=}$ $\boxed{\times}$ 2 $\boxed{+}$ 1·5 $\boxed{-}$ 6 $\boxed{=}$ (b) 1·5 $\boxed{+/-}$ $\boxed{-}$ 1 $\boxed{\times}$ 1·5 $\boxed{+/-}$ $\boxed{\times}$ 2 $\boxed{-}$ 6 $\boxed{=}$

*This work is covered in M1 and N1

Exercise 10·3

A   Check that one correct solution has been given for each of the following quadratic equations. Find the other solution in each case.

1 $x^2 + 3x + 2 = 0$ solution: $x = -1$ **2** $x^2 - 5x + 6 = 0$ solution: $x = 3$
3 $x^2 + 4x + 4 = 0$ solution: $x = 2$ **4** $x^2 - x - 12 = 0$ solution: $x = 4$
5 $2x^2 - 3x - 2 = 0$ solution: $x = 2$ **6** $2x^2 - 5x + 3 = 0$ solution: $x = 1\frac{1}{2}$
7 $2x^2 - 3x + 1 = 0$ solution: $x = 1$ **8** $3x^2 - 7x + 2 = 0$ solution: $x = 2$

B   Factorise the following quadratics and find solutions to the equations.
1 $x^2 - 3x + 2 = 0$ **2** $x^2 - 6x + 9 = 0$ **3** $x^2 - 2x - 3 = 0$ **4** $x^2 - x - 2 = 0$
5 $x^2 - 7x + 12 = 0$ **6** $2x^2 - x - 1 = 0$ **7** $2x^2 - x - 3 = 0$ **8** $2x^2 - x - 15 = 0$

C   Rearrange the following quadratic equations into standard form. Then find their solutions. Check each solution in the original equation.
1 $2x^2 = x + 1$ **2** $x^2 = 5x - 6$ **3** $x = x^2 - 2$
4 $2x^2 = x + 3$ **5** $x^2 + 3 = 2x + 6$ **6** $3x - 5 = x^2 - 3$

10·4   Solution by drawing

Simple quadratic equations may be solved by drawing. The method is known as completing the square
x^2 is represented by a square.
x is represented by a strip.
Numbers are represented by unit squares.

Example:

Solve $x^2 + 4x + 3 = 0$

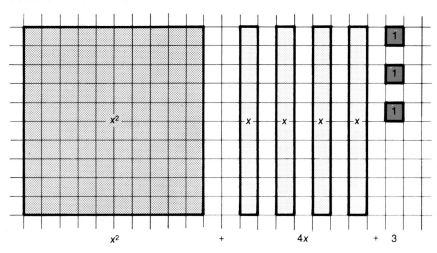

$$x^2 \qquad + \qquad 4x \qquad + \ 3$$

The shapes are rearranged to form a square.

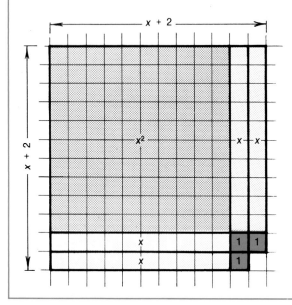

Clearly $x^2 + 4x + 3 = (x + 2)^2 - 1$
The equation $x^2 + 4x + 3 = 0$
becomes $(x + 2)^2 - 1 = 0$
$\Rightarrow (x + 2)^2 = 1$
$\Rightarrow x + 2 = +1$ or -1
$\Rightarrow x = -1$ or -3

Exercise 10·4

A Solve the following quadratic equations by 'completing the square'. Draw a careful diagram in each case. Work on $\frac{1}{2}$-cm-square paper.

1 $x^2 + 4x + 3 = 0$	**2** $x^2 + 6x + 8 = 0$	**3** $x^2 + 8x + 15 = 0$
4 $x^2 + 10x + 21 = 0$	**5** $x^2 + 12x + 35 = 0$	**6** $x^2 + 2x - 3 = 0$

B If the x term is odd, one of the x-strips will have to be divided to form the square. Use this idea to solve the following equations.

1 $x^2 + 3x + 2 = 0$	**2** $x^2 + 5x + 4 = 0$	**3** $x^2 + 5x + 6 = 0$
4 $x^2 + 7x + 10 = 0$	**5** $x^2 + 9x + 20 = 0$	**6** $x^2 + 9x + 14 = 0$

C All the equations in exercises **A** and **B** can be solved by factorisation. The equations which follow cannot be solved by factorisation. They can be solved by completing the square! Solve the equations carefully and check that each solution is correct by substituting in the equation.

1 $x^2 + 4x + 2 = 0$ 2 $x^2 + 6x + 4 = 0$ 3 $x^2 + 8x + 2 = 0$

4 $x^2 + 10x + 5 = 0$ 5 $x^2 + 3x + 1 = 0$ 6 $x^2 + x - 1 = 0$

D *Investigations*

1 Try to find a method of solution by drawing if the x-term is negative or the number is negative,
   e.g. $x^2 - 2x + 1 = 0$ or $x^2 - 2x - 3 = 0$

2 Find a method of solving equations in which the x^2 term is $2x^2$ or $3x^2$ rather than just x^2. Show your method working on four different quadratic equations.

10·5 Solution by graphs

The graph of $y = x^2$ can be drawn from a table of values of squares.

x	y
$-3 \cdot 0$	$9 \cdot 0$
$-2 \cdot 5$	$6 \cdot 25$
$-2 \cdot 0$	$4 \cdot 0$
$-1 \cdot 5$	$2 \cdot 25$
$-1 \cdot 0$	$1 \cdot 0$
$-0 \cdot 5$	$0 \cdot 25$
0	0
$0 \cdot 5$	$0 \cdot 25$
$1 \cdot 0$	$1 \cdot 0$
$1 \cdot 5$	$2 \cdot 25$
$2 \cdot 0$	$4 \cdot 0$
$2 \cdot 5$	$6 \cdot 25$
$3 \cdot 0$	$9 \cdot 0$

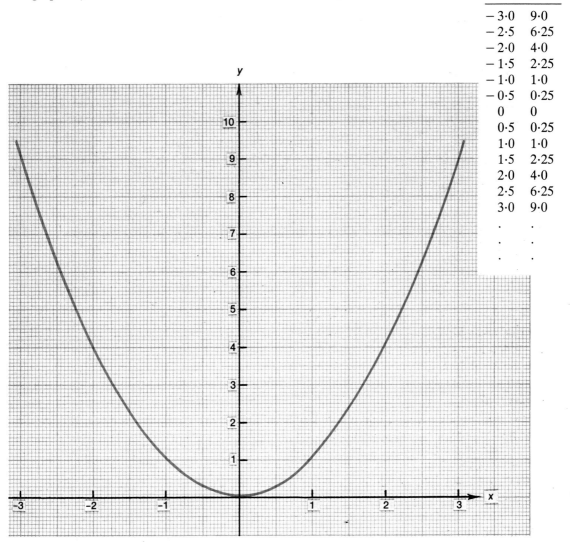

Notes: (i) We have used half-scale for *y* because *y* grows so fast. This has the effect of widening the graph. (Sketch the graph using same scale for *x* and *y* to see the difference.)
(ii) The graph touches the *x*-axis at the point (0, 0).
(iii) The *y*-axis is an axis of symmetry for the graph.

This graph may be used to find solutions to quadratic equations very quickly: this is extremely useful as a 'check' method.

Examples:

Use the graph of $y = x^2$ to solve   **1** $x^2 - 5 = 0$ **2** $x^2 - 2x = 0$
                                    3 $x^2 - x - 3 = 0$ **4** $x^2 + 2x + 5 = 0$

1 $x^2 - 5 = 0$

$x^2 - 5 = 0$
$\Rightarrow x^2 = 5$
so the solutions are
found where $y = 5$
cuts $y = x^2$

i.e. $x = \pm 2 \cdot 2$

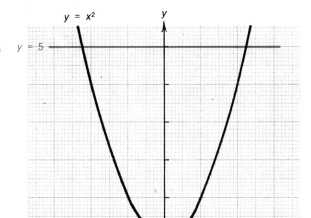

2 $x^2 - 2x = 0$

$x^2 - 2x = 0$
$\Rightarrow x^2 = 2x$
so the solutions are
found where the line
$y = 2x$ cuts $y = x^2$

i.e. $x = 0$ or 2

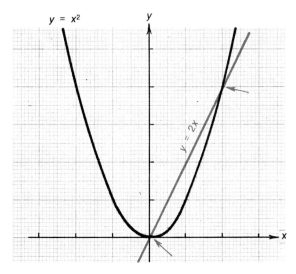

3 $x^2 - x - 3 = 0$

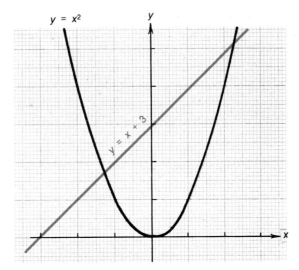

$x^2 - x - 3 = 0$
$\Rightarrow x^2 = x + 3$

So the solutions are found where
$y = x + 3$ cuts $y = x^2$

i.e. $x = 2 \cdot 3$ or $-1 \cdot 3$

4 $x^2 + 2x + 5 = 0$

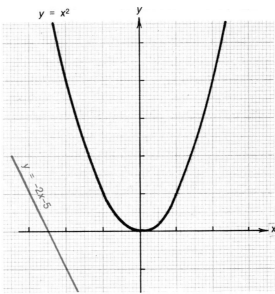

$x^2 + 2x + 5 = 0$
$\Rightarrow x^2 = -2x - 5$

The solutions would be found where
$y = x^2$ cuts $y = -2x - 5$
Clearly the curves do not meet, so the equation cannot be solved.

No solutions

Exercise 10·5

A 1 Draw carefully a graph of $y = x^2$ from $x = -3$ to $x = +3$ and stick the graph into the back of your exercise book.

   2 Draw a straight line on tracing paper. By placing this line over the graph of $y = x^2$ in the right place, solve the following equations.

(a) $x^2 - 4 = 0$	(b) $x^2 - 9 = 0$	(c) $x^2 - 5 \cdot 5 = 0$
(d) $x^2 + x = 0$	(e) $x^2 - 1 \cdot 5x = 0$	(f) $x^2 + 2x = 0$
(g) $3x^2 + 8x = 0$	(h) $x^2 - x - 3 = 0$	(i) $x^2 - 2x - 4 = 0$

B Investigate the following theorems.
   1 The sum of the solutions of a quadratic equation in the form $x^2 + px + q = 0$ is $-p$
   2 The product of the solutions of a quadratic equation in the form $x^2 + px + q = 0$ is q
   Use equations you have already solved for your investigation.

10·6　Graph of the quadratic function

A table of values can be made up for a quadratic function and the graph can be drawn, as shown in the example.
In making the table look for patterns in the values rather than calculating y for every separate value of x. See example. Note the symmetry which appears in the pattern of numbers.
In drawing the graph choose a scale which 'spreads' the graph to make it easier to read accurately.
The graph will give solutions to the corresponding quadratic equation where it cuts the x-axis. See example.

Example:

Draw the graph of $y = x^2 - x - 3$ and use your graph to solve the equation $x^2 - x - 3 = 0$.

Write $x^2 - x - 3$
as $x(x - 1) - 3$
and construct the
table of values.

x	-3	-2	-1	0	1	2	3	4
$x - 1$	-4	-3	-2	-1	0	1	2	3
$x(x - 1)$	12	5	2	0	0	2	6	12
-3	-3	-3	-3	-3	-3	-3	-3	-3
y	9	3	-1	-3	-3	-1	3	9

$y = 0$ between $x = -1$
and $x = -2$

$y = 0$ between $x = 2$
and $x = 3$

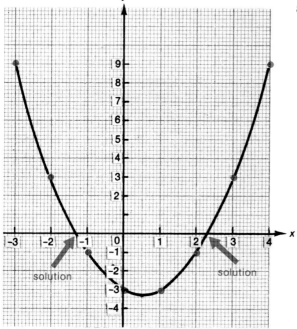

Draw the graph from the table of values
The solutions of $x^2 - x - 3 = 0$ are roughly
$x = -1\cdot3$ and $x = 2\cdot3$
Note: This is a much less efficient method than that shown in Section 10·5 (especially if $y = x^2$ is already drawn).

Exercise 10·6

A Solve the following quadratic equations by making a table of values of the function and then drawing a graph. Indicate which equations have no real solutions.
(Treat this exercise as an investigation)

1 $x^2 - x - 2 = 0$ **2** $x^2 + 2x + 3 = 0$ **3** $x^2 - 6x - 8 = 0$

4 $x^2 - 2x - 5 = 0$ **5** $x^2 + 3x - 7 = 0$ **6** $x^2 + x + 4 = 0$

B Investigate how the graph of $y = x^2 - x - 2$ could be used to solve the following equations.

1 $x^2 - x - 3 = 0$ **2** $x^2 - 2x - 2 = 0$ **3** $x^2 + x - 4 = 0$

Comment on the remark ... 'The graph of any quadratic can be used to solve all quadratic equations.'

10·7 Solution by formula

All quadratic equations can be solved by completing the square (see Section 10·4). This method leads to a formula which gives solutions of the equation $x^2 + px + q = 0$.
The following flow charts and examples explain the method.

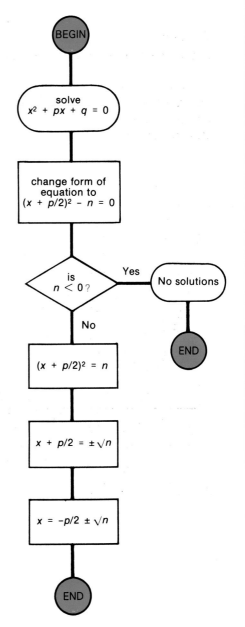

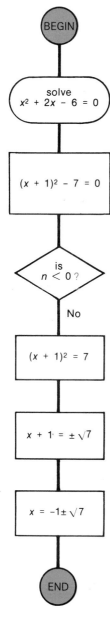

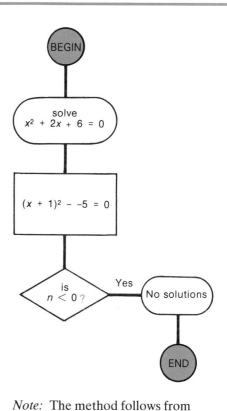

Note: The method follows from the expansion of $(x + a)^2$ to $x^2 + 2ax + a^2$

You must be **fluent** with the squaring of sums and differences

Check both solutions by substituting them in the function (use a calculator)

Exercise 10·7

Use the above method to solve the following quadratic equations. Indicate where there are no solutions.

1 $x^2 + 8x - 7 = 0$ **2** $x^2 - 6x + 5 = 0$ **3** $x^2 + 10x - 3 = 0$ **4** $x^2 + 8x + 8 = 0$

5 $x^2 + 3x + 2 = 0$ **6** $x^2 + 5x + 5 = 0$ **7** $x^2 + 9x + 7 = 0$ **8** $x^2 + 9x - 3 = 0$

Check the solutions on your calculator.

10·8   General formula

In completing the square, we do the following:
Step $1\emptyset$ change $x^2 + px + q$ into $(x + p/2)^2 - n$
Step $2\emptyset$ $x^2 + px + q = x^2 + px + p^2/4 - n$ (from $1\emptyset$)
Step $3\emptyset$ $q = p^2/4 - n$ (from $2\emptyset$)
Step $4\emptyset$ $n = p^2/4 - q$ (from $3\emptyset$)
Step $5\emptyset$ Thus in finding the general solution to
        $x^2 + px + q = 0$ we know $(x + p/2)^2 - n = 0$ (from $1\emptyset$)
Step $6\emptyset$ $(x + p/2)^2 = n$ (from $5\emptyset$)
Step $7\emptyset$ $x + p/2 = \pm \sqrt{n}$ (from $6\emptyset$)
Step $8\emptyset$ $x = - p/2 \pm \sqrt{n}$ (from $7\emptyset$)
Step $9\emptyset$ now substitute $n = p^2/4 - q$ (from $4\emptyset$)
Step $1\emptyset\emptyset$ to get $x = - p/2 \pm \sqrt{p^2/4 - q}$

If we started with the even more general equation $ax^2 + bx + c = 0$ the

formula would become $\dfrac{- b \pm \sqrt{b^2 - 4ac}}{2a}$ This formula must be learned.

Solving any quadratic equation is thus reduced to the simple process of deciding the values of a, b and c and then substituting them in the formula.
If $b^2 > 4ac$, the $(b^2 - 4ac)$ part of the formula is positive and the equation will have two solutions.
If $b^2 < 4ac$ there will be no real solutions.

Examples:
Solve the equations   **1** $x^2 + 3x - 5 = 0$ **2** $x^2 + 2x + 3 = 0$ **3** $2x^2 - 5x - 4 = 0$

1 $x^2 + 3x - 5 = 0$ $a = 1, \ b = 3, \ c = - 5$

   $x = \dfrac{- 3 \pm \sqrt{9 - (- 20)}}{2} = \dfrac{- 3 \pm \sqrt{29}}{2}$

   $x_1 = 1 \cdot 19; \ x_2 = - 4 \cdot 19$ Check the solutions: Does $x_1 + x_2 = - b/a$?
                                              does $x_1 x_2 = c/a$?
2 $x^2 + 2x + 3 = 0$ $a = 1, \ b = 2, \ c = 3$
   $b^2 < 4ac$ so $b^2 - 4ac$ is negative: the equation has no solutions
   (Your calculator will show 'E' if you try to find $\sqrt{- 8}$)
3 $2x^2 - 5x - 4 = 0$ $a = 2, \ b = - 5, \ c = - 4$

   $x = \dfrac{5 \pm \sqrt{25 + 32}}{4} = \dfrac{5 \pm \sqrt{57}}{4}$

   $x_1 = 3 \cdot 137; \ x_2 = - 0 \cdot 637$ Check: $x_1 + x_2 = 2 \cdot 5 = - b/a$
                                             $x_1 x_2 = - 2 = c/a$

A Use the formula $x = \dfrac{- b \pm \sqrt{b^2 - 4ac}}{2a}$ to find the solutions of the following equations. In each case check that the sum of the roots is $- b/a$ and the product c/a.
  1 $x^2 + 5x - 3 = 0$ **2** $2x^2 - 6x - 4 = 0$ **3** $5x^2 - 2x + 1 = 0$
  4 $x^2 + 7 = 0$ **5** $3x^2 - 2x = 0$ **6** $4x^2 - 3x - 2 = 0$

B Rearrange the following equations into the form $ax^2 + bx + c = 0$ and then solve them.
  1 $2x^2 = 3x + 5$ **2** $x^2 - 7x = 9 - x$ **3** $2 - x^2 = 5 - x$
  4 $x(x + 1) = 2x^2 - 3$ **5** $\frac{1}{x} + 3 = 3x$ **6** $x = 1 + \frac{1}{x}$ (Golden Section)

C Review all the different methods of solving quadratic equations studied in this unit. Choose any quadratic equation you like and show that all the methods lead to the same solutions.

Unit 11 Sets

11·1 Belonging: ∈ and ∉

A set is a collection of things picked out because they have something in common. The things are called members of the set.

Signs   ∈ means 'belongs to'
         ∉ means 'does not belong to'

A set is represented by a capital letter. The members may be listed, or a rule may be given which shows how the members are selected.

These people belong to the set {Christians}

Examples:

S = {1, 2, 3, 4}	The set S consists of the four numbers 1, 2, 3 and 4
S = {n: $0 < n < 5$}	Since n is the letter used to represent whole numbers, this set consists of the numbers 1, 2, 3 and 4
X = {x: x is a square}	The set of all squares

Diagrams

A set is usually shown by a circle or other closed curve.
Things which belong to the set are shown as points inside the circle.
It is clear from the diagram that the point x belongs to set A, so $x \in A$.
It is also clear that y does not belong to the set A so $y \notin A$

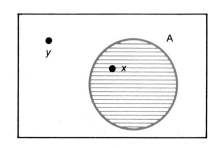

Exercise 11·1

1 Give three members of each of the following sets.
   (a) A = {the capital letters}
   (b) B = {capital letters with one axis of symmetry}
   (c) S = {s: s is a type of snake}
   (d) C = {c: c is a country of Europe}
   (e) G = {g: g is a sport}

2 Which of the following are true, given that A, B, S, C and G are the sets in question 1.

   (a) $b \in A$ (b) $M \in A$ (c) $M \in B$ (d) $p \in B$
   (e) Viper $\in$ S   (f) Coypu $\in$ S   (g) China $\in$ C   (h) .Soccer $\in$ G
   (i) Italy $\in$ C   (j) Maths $\in$ G

3 Which of the following are true of the figure?

   (a) $x \in P$ (b) $a \in P$
   (c) $z \notin P$ (d) $r \notin P$
   (e) $m \in P$ (f) $m \notin P$
   (g) $y \notin P$ (h) $y \in P$

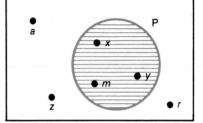

4 Draw a diagram which shows a set Q and the following points.

   (a) $x \in Q$ (b) $y \in Q$ (c) $m \notin Q$
   (d) $n \notin Q$ (e) $w \notin Q$ (f) $q \in Q$

5 The set X = {x: x = 3n}, where n is a whole number greater than zero, consists of the numbers 3, 6, 9, 12 ... etc.
   Write the following sets of numbers in a similar way:
   (a) {5, 10, 15, 20, ...}
   (b) {2, 3, 4, 5, ...}
   (c) {10, 20, 30, 40, ...}
   (d) {1, 3, 5, 7, 9, ...}
   (e) {2, 5, 8, 11, ...}
   (f) {1, 4, 9, 16, ...}

These sets of numbers cannot be listed as they go on for ever. Such sets are called **infinite sets**.

11·2   Universal set, complement and empty set

When we pick out the members of a set we choose them from a larger set. For example, we may pick out the even numbers from the set of all whole numbers, or the set of squares from the set of all quadrilaterals. The large set is called the universal set. It is given the symbol $\mathcal{E}$ which is just a big E, for 'Everything'.

As you have seen, we usually show a set as a circle (or other closed curve) inside a rectangle. The rectangle represents the universal set.

Examples:

1 G is the set of girl-students in a school

$\mathcal{E}$ is the set of all students in the school.

Clearly $m \in G$ $m \in \mathcal{E}$

       $p \notin G$ $p \in \mathcal{E}$

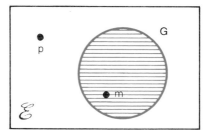

Mary (m) and Peter (p) are students at the same school.

2 T is the set of right-angled triangles

$\mathcal{E}$ is the set of all triangles.

Those members of the universal set which do not belong to the set A are said to belong to the complement of A, written A′.

The set G′ in example **1** is 'students of the school who are not girls', i.e. the boys. The set T′ in example **2** is the set of all non-right-angled triangles.

The idea of complement can be stated using the 'if . . then' arrow ($\Rightarrow$).

$x \in A \Rightarrow x \notin A'$ If x belongs to A it does not belong to A′

$x \in A' \Rightarrow x \notin A$ If x belongs to A′ it does not belong to A.

The set and its complement are best shown by dividing a rectangle.

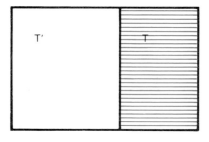

This diagram shows clearly that T and T′ between them take up the whole universal set. What is left after T and T′ are taken from $\mathcal{E}$ is called the empty set and given the symbol $\varnothing$. *pronounced ur as in hurt.*

Exercise 11·2

1 Suggest the universal set from which the following have been taken.
   (a) {apples, pears, bananas}
   (b) {grass, cabbages, emeralds}
   (c) {London, Paris, Hongkong, Lagos}
   (d) {jaguar, tiger, leopard}
   (e) {bad, cat, mug, ant}

2 Explain why the universal sets given for the following sets are *not* correct. Suggest a correct universal set in each case.

	Set		Universal set

(a) {a, b, d, g, 3, z} . . . . (letters)

(b) {   } . . . . (triangles)

(c) {   } . . . . (quadrilaterals)

(d) {1, 2, 4, 8, 16, 32} . . . . (multiples of 2)

(e) {2, 3, 4, 5, 6} . . . . (factors of 36)

3 Name three members of A′ in each case

A $\mathscr{E}$

(a) {pig, dog}   (domestic animals)

(b) {1, 4, 9, 16}   (the square numbers)

(c) {x: $x<3$}   (all numbers)

(d) {xyz: xyz is a three letter word}   (all words)

4 Which of the following statements are true?

(a) $a \in A'$ (e) $a \in A$

(b) $b \in A'$ (f) $b \in A$

(c) $c \in A'$ (g) $c \in A$

(d) $d \in A'$ (h) $d \in A$

5 The diagram shows two sets A and B drawn from a universal set $\mathscr{E} = \{1, 2, 3 \ldots\}$

(a) Given that $x \in A'$, where would x be marked on the diagram?

(b) Given that $y \notin B'$ where would y be marked on the diagram?

(c) Explain why A = B′ and B = A′

(d) If A is the set of even numbers, what is B?

(e) If B is the set of multiples of 7, what is A?

(f) If A is the set of whole numbers less than 50, what is B?

(g) If B = {x: $x>100$} what is B′ and what is A?

(h) Suggest another pair of sets A and B that fit the diagram. What is the universal set?

11·3 Intersection and union

Sometimes two sets overlap, i.e. there are some members that belong to both sets. This collection of things that belong to A and belong to B is called the intersection of A and B. The set is given the symbol A ∩ B
This is clearly shown on a diagram.

The point x is in A and in B
so it belongs to $A \cap B$
$x \in A \cap B \Rightarrow x \in A$ and $x \in B$

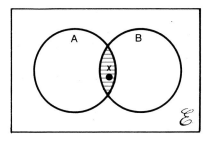

The shaded area
represents $A \cap B$

If you combine two sets to form a new one which contains all the
members of both sets, the new set is the union of A and B. This is shown
clearly on a diagram.

All three points a, b and c
belong to $A \cup B$
$x \in A$ or $x \in B \Rightarrow x \in A \cup B$

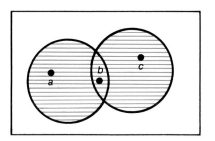

The shaded area
represents $A \cup B$

Examples:

1 The set A is the odd numbers under 20, i.e. {1, 3, 5, 7 ... 19}
The set B is the multiples of 3 under 20 {3, 5, 9, ... 18}
$A \cap B$ is the set {3, 9, 15} ... the odd multiples of 3 from set B
$A \cup B$ is the set {1, 3, 5, 6, 7, 9, 11, 12, 13, 15, 17, 18, 19}
i.e. all the members of A plus all the members of B.

2 Of 50 families who went camping, 16 took caravans and 20 took tents (5 took both). How
many took neither?
If A = {families who took caravans} then n(A) = 16
If B = {families who took tents} then n(B) = 20
$n(A \cap B) = 5$
$n(A \cup B) = 11 + 5 + 15 = 31$
$\Rightarrow n(A \cup B)' = 19$
i.e. 19 families took neither

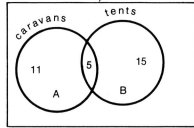

Note: You may have arrived at the same answer by different reasoning.

Exercise 11·3

1 At Lonsdale Comprehensive School there is a first-eleven cricket team and a first-eleven
soccer team. There are 20 first-eleven players altogether. How many boys are in both teams?

2 At the same school eight girls are in the school swimming team and there is a first-eleven
hockey team. Altogether fifteen girls swim or play hockey for the school. How many are in
both teams?

3 Set A = {1, 2, 4, 8, 16, 32}. Set B = {2, 4, 6, 8, 10 ... 32}.
   (a) How many members are there in set A, how many in set B?
   (b) What is the set A∩B? How many members does it have?
   (c) List the members of the set A∪B.

4 R is the set of right-handed people, L is the set of left-handed people.
   (a) Do you belong to R'?
   (b) Do you belong to L'?
   (c) What set is L∩R?
   (d) What set is L∪R?
   (e) What set is (L∪R)'?

5 R = {rectangles}, Q = {rhombuses}, S = {squares}, $\mathscr{E}$ = {parallelograms}
   (a) Draw one member of each of the sets R, Q and S.
   (b) Draw a member of $\mathscr{E}$ which does not belong to R, Q or S.
   (c) Draw a member of R∩Q.
   (d) Draw members of R', Q' and S'.
   (e) Is it true that $x \in S \Rightarrow x \in Q$?
   (f) Is it true that $x \in S \Rightarrow x \in R$?

6 A class arrived for mathematics. Twenty people had forgotten their rulers and 17 had forgotten their calculators. "Go and get them at once" said the teacher: 24 people left the room. How many had forgotten both?

7 Which of the following statements about the figure are true?

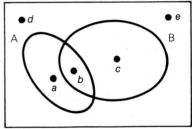

   (a) $a \in A$ (b) $a \in B$ (c) $e \notin B$
   (d) $b \notin A$ (e) $a \in A \cup B$ (f) $b \in A \cap B$
   (g) $c \notin A \cap B$ (h) $d \notin A \cup B$ (i) $e \in (A \cup B)'$
   (j) $d \in (A \cap B)'$ (k) $a \notin (A \cap B)'$ (l) $d \in A' \cap B'$

8 Draw a Venn diagram and mark in points to fit these pieces of information.
   (a) A, B are two sets such that A∩B = ∅
   (b) $c \in A \cup B$
   (c) $d \notin B'$
   (d) $e \in A' \cap B$
   (e) $f \in A' \cup B'$

11·4 Subsets

When a smaller set is picked from a larger one the smaller set is called a
subset of the larger one.

> **Examples:**
> The set {a, e, i, o, u} is a subset of the letters of the alphabet.
> The set of points {(4, 1), (5, 1), (6, 1)} is a subset of the line $y = 1$
> The set of children under 3 years old is a subset of {children under 5 years old}.

Signs and diagrams

If A is a subset of B we write $A \subset B$

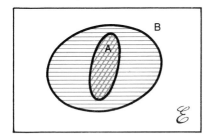

You can see from this diagram that
(i)   A is inside B
(ii) Every point of A is a point of B
(iii) $x \in B' \Rightarrow x \in A'$

Note: $\subset$ reminds you of the sign $<$ used for numbers.

Exercise 11·4

A 1 Write down a *subset* of each of these sets.
   (a) {a, b, c, d, e, f, g, h}
   (b) {10, 20, 30, 40, 50, 60}
   (c) {I, you, me, they, them, him, her, us, it, we}
   (d) {(1, 1), (2, 2), (3, 3), (4, 4), (5, 5)}

2 (a) Find two words whose letters are subsets of {A, E, R, S, T}
   (b) Find two words whose letters are subsets of {M, A, T, H, E, I, C, S} and which belong
        to {w: w is a five-letter word}.

3 $A = \{a, b, c, d, e, f, g, o\}$
   Find words, whose letters are subsets of A, to fit these clues.
   (a) not good   (b) soggy ground   (c) 'can't hear too well'
   (d) poem   (e) to disappear slowly (f) secret message

4 Make up a question of your own like question 3.

5 Which of the following sets are subsets of the set of odd numbers:
   (a) {prime numbers}   (b) {square numbers}   (c) $\{x: x = 2n + 1\}$
   (d) $\{x: x = 3n\}$ (e) $\{x: x = 5n + 1\}$ (f) {squares of odd numbers}
   Explain your answers.

6 T = {Triangles} R = {Right-angled triangles} I = {Isosceles triangles}
   Which of these statements are true? Give your reasons.
   (a) $R \subset T$ (b) $I \subset T$ (c) $I \subset R$
   (d) $(I \cap R) \subset R$ (e) $(I \cap R) \subset I$

B 1 Show, by means of a diagram, that for any two sets A and B:
   (a) $(A \cap B) \subset A$ (b) $(A \cap B) \subset B$ (c) $A \subset (A \cup B)$ (d) $B \subset (A \cup B)$

2 A = {left-handed people} B = {old people}
   C = {males}   D = {females}
   (a) Describe each of these sets in words:
        $A \cap B, A \cup D, B \cap D, C \cup D$
   (b) Show in a diagram that $(A \cap B) \subset (A \cup B)$
   (c) Show in a diagram that $(A \cup B) \subset (C \cup D)$

3 Choose any two sets you like for A and B and show that:

(a) $(A \cap B)' = A' \cup B'$

(b) $(A \cup B)' = A' \cap B'$

Can you demonstrate this on a diagram?

(*Note:* Two sets are equal if they have exactly the same membership.)

11·5 Set algebra

Sets behave like numbers in some ways but not in others. Their 'algebra' is important as it is the same as the algebra of logic. It is very useful in circuit design in computers, and in the theory of probability.

Investigations

1 Explore the list of properties and theorems given below.

Set properties	Number properties
$A \cup B = B \cup A$ $A \cap B = B \cap A$ } commutative laws	{ $a + b = b + a$ $ab = ba$
$A \cap A = A$	$a \times a = a^2$
$A \cup A = A$	$a + a = 2a$
$A \cap (B \cup C) = (A \cap B) \cup (A \cap C)$	$a(b + c) = ab + ac$
$A \cup (B \cap C) = (A \cup B) \cap (A \cup C)$	No equivalent law for numbers

2 Can you find a set which behaves like the number zero, i.e. $a + 0 = a$, $a \times 0 = 0$?

Can you find a number which behaves like the universal set?

3 Compare negative numbers and the complements of sets.

4 Two very important laws of sets are De Morgan's Laws

$(A \cap B)' = A' \cup B'$ and $(A \cup B)' = A' \cap B'$

Show that these laws are true. Can you find similar laws in the rules of arithmetic?

5ᐟ An interesting way of showing sets was invented by Karnaugh. A square is divided into four regions marked A, B, A', B' as shown.

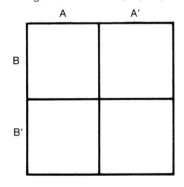

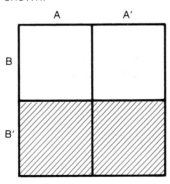

B' is shaded

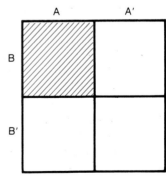

A∩B is shaded

(a) Draw Karnaugh maps which show the following

A', $(A \cap B)'$, $(A \cup B)'$, $A \cap B'$, $A' \cup B$, $A' \cap B'$ and $A' \cup B'$.

(b) Use Karnaugh maps to demonstrate De Morgan's Laws (see question 4).

(c) Can you find other 'laws' using the maps?

(d) Can you suggest a way in which this idea could be extended to three sets (or possibly even more)?

Unit 12   Graphs

12·1   Reading graphs

Graphs are widely used to present information. In science a graph is
used to give a picture of a relationship.
When you read a graph always make sure you understand which
variables are shown and also what scales have been used.

Example:

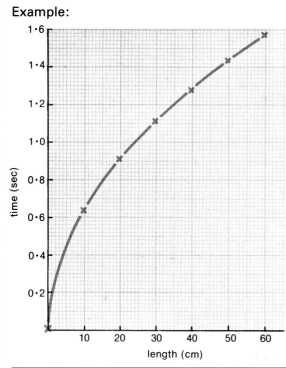

Time of a swing of a pendulum
Variables: Length in cm
               Time in seconds
Scale: Length 1 cm on graph: 10 cm
             Time 1 cm on graph: 0·2 sec

The graph was drawn from the results of
an experiment, given in the following
table.

The time for 10 complete swings (there
and back ten times) was measured: this
was divided by 10 to obtain T.

Length (cm)	0	10	20	30	40	50	60
Time (sec)	0	0·63	0·90	1·10	1·27	1·42	1·55

Note:
(i)   The graph shows that the relationship between time and length is not linear, but does get
       nearer to being linear for lengths over 40 cm.
(ii) The scales are carefully chosen so that all the data can be shown on the graph.
(iii) The points of the graph have been joined by a smooth curve. This means that 'in-
       between' values can be estimated from the graph. They can then be checked by
       experiment.

Exercise 12·1

A These questions refer to the example above.

1 What is the time of swing of a pendulum with length
  (a) 30 cm   (b) 50 cm   (c) 15 cm   (d) 35 cm
  (e) 12 cm   (f) 36 cm   (g) 21 cm   (h) 54 cm

2 What was the time for 10 swings for the lengths of question 1.

3 Sarah carried out an experiment and found that the time of a swing for a 28 cm pendulum was 1·4 seconds. Does this result fit with the relationship shown by the graph? What should Sarah do next?

4 Sandra, in studying the pendulum, measured the swing for 40 cm, 50 cm and 60 cm lengths only. She thought the graph should be a straight line through the three points and drew one. How would you show that she must be wrong?

5 Copy the graph onto 1 mm² paper and extend it. Use your extended graph to find the time for lengths (a) 70 cm   (b) 80 cm   (c) 100 cm.

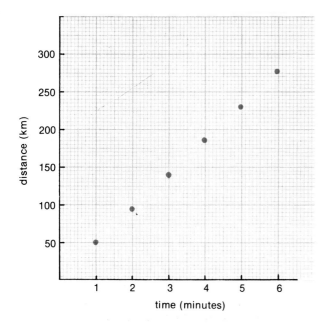

Distance travelled by a missile
travelling at 2700 km/h

B 1 What are the variables in the graph above?

2 What are the scales of the graph?

3 Could this graph be joined up in a straight line? (Think about what happens between zero and 1 minute.)
   Does the graph suggest that the relationship is linear?

4 What distance would be travelled by the missile in
  (a) 1·5 minutes
  (b) 3·2 minutes
  (c) 4·7 minutes

5 Do you think this graph could be extended to give reliable estimates for 10 minutes, or 1 hour? Give reasons for your answer.

C Study the following graphs, which come from newspapers. Comment on each graph, describing the variables and scales.

1

Divorce petitions in England and Wales

First divorce law 1857

Divorce Reform Act

Legal aid available

World War II

Reform of divorce law to include grounds of cruelty and desertion

World War I

2 Surge in shoe sales puts factories at full stretch

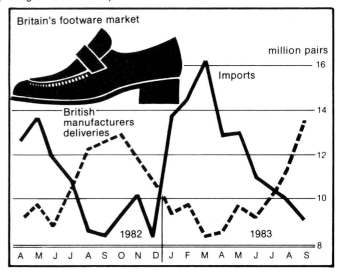

Britain's footware market

million pairs

Imports

British manufacturers deliveries

1982   1983

12·2 Drawing graphs: choosing axes and scales

The choice of axes and scales will make a big difference to a graph. In the example which follows, three different graphs are drawn from the same data.

The rules for choosing axes and scales are:

(i)   Choose a convenient scale for calculation (avoid fractions of a square, etc.).

(ii) Choose the largest possible scale that will allow you to show all the data but not waste graph paper.

(iii) Choose axes that make the best use of the graph paper.

Remember: A graph is a form of communication. It should be clear and simple to read.

Example:

Draw a graph to show how the length of a steel rail changes as its temperature rises (very important for railway lines and bridges). Use the data below.

Lengths (m)	100	100·012	100·024	100·036	100·048	100·060
Temp (°C)	0°	10°	20°	30°	40°	50°

GRAPH I

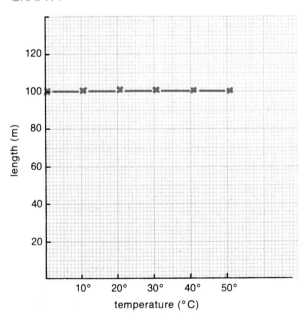

This graph shows that the change is very small indeed. In fact it does not show the change at all. It would be dangerous, however, for a builder or engineer to suppose that temperature did not affect steel.

GRAPH II

This graph shows clearly that the length of the rail increases with temperature. However, it is not very easy to make measurements on the graph, and most of the graph paper is not used.

The origin is drawn at 100 m and 0°C

The scales are 1 cm: 10°C

1 cm: 0·1 m

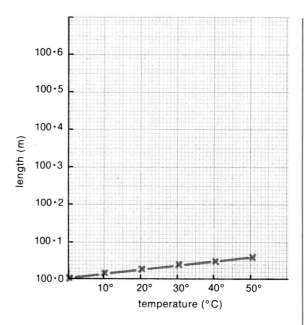

GRAPH III

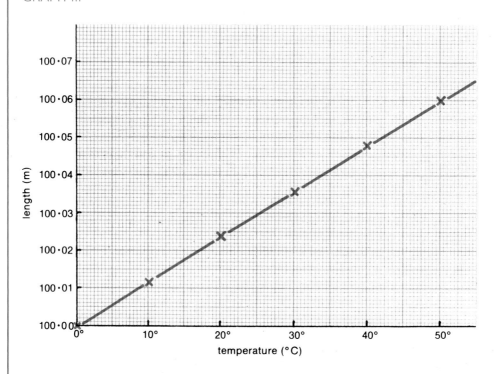

This graph is easier to read accurately, but it does give a misleading impression of the increasing length. This would be the best graph for estimating the size of the gap to be left between rails.

Exercise 12·2

A Draw graphs of the following sets of data. Think about the best scale and axes to use.

1 Height in thousands of feet, and air temperature.

Height (10³ ft)	39	30	24	18	10	5
Temperature (°C)	− 57	− 44	− 29	− 17	− 1	+ 8

2 Stopping distances for a car travelling at different speeds.

Speed (mph)	10	20	30	40	50	60	70	80
Stopping distance (feet)	10	40	70	120	180	260	350	450

Many drivers travel (illegally) at 80 mph on the motorway. What would be a safe distance to keep from the car in front at this speed?

3 Population of Britain at ten-year intervals from 1901 to 1971.

Year	1901	1911	1921	1931	1941	1951	1961	1971
Population (10⁶)	39	39·5	42	44	....	50	52·7	55·5

No census was taken in 1941 because of the war. Estimate the 1941 population.

4 The air pressure on a particular day.

Time	0900	1000	1100	1200	1300	1400	1500	1600
Pressure (mm Hg)	750·4	754·4	756	754	759	755	740	735

Estimate the maximum pressure for the day.

5 A healthy calf should increase in weight as follows:

Age (weeks)	3	12	16	20	24	30	36
Weight (kg)	10	25	40	60	85	110	122

B 1 Draw the graph of $y = x^2$ for the following values

x	0·1	0·2	0·3	0·4	0·5	0·6	0·7	0·8	0·9	1·0
y	0·01	0·04	0·09	0·16	0·25	0·36	0·49	0·64	0·81	1·0

Use the graph to find (a) $\sqrt{0·8}$ (b) $\sqrt{0·08}$ (These will be solutions of $x^2 = 0·8$ and $x^2 = 0·08$.)

2 Draw the graph of $y = x^2$ for the following values

x	31	32	33	34	35	36	37	38	39
y	961	1024	1089	1156	1225	1296	1369	1444	1521

Use your graph to estimate $\sqrt{1000}$ and $\sqrt{1200}$

Which of the graphs above is almost straight?

3 Draw the graph of $y = \sin x$ from the following pairs of values

$x°$	0°	10°	20°	30°	40°	50°	60°	70°	80°	90°
$y = \sin x$	0	0·17	0·34	0·5	0·64	0·77	0·87	0·93	0·98	1

Comment on the shape of the curve.

4 Draw the graph of $y = 2x + 9$ for values of x from 201 to 210.

5 Show by drawing the graph of $y = 2x$ that
   (a) This graph is a straight line whatever scale you use.
   (b) The graph is a straight line for negative values of x.
   (c) The graph is a straight line even if $x > 1000$.
   (d) The graph will pass through the point (0, 0).

6 Find the values of y for which $x^2 + y^2 = 100$ *and* $x = 1$, $x = 2$, ... $x = 10$. Use these values to draw the graph of $y = 100 - x^2$ from $x = 0$ to $x = 10$.
   (a) What is the shape of the graph if the scales for x and y are the same?
   (b) What is the shape if the scale chosen for x is double the scale chosen for y?

12·3   Graphs of time, distance and speed

A graph can be plotted showing the distance moved by an object at particular times. Such a graph can give a lot of information about the speed of the object.

If speed is then plotted against time, the graph will show changes in speed, i.e. acceleration and deceleration (speeding up and slowing down). Time is always measured along the horizontal axis.

Example 1:

Distance–time and speed–time graphs for a marathon walker.

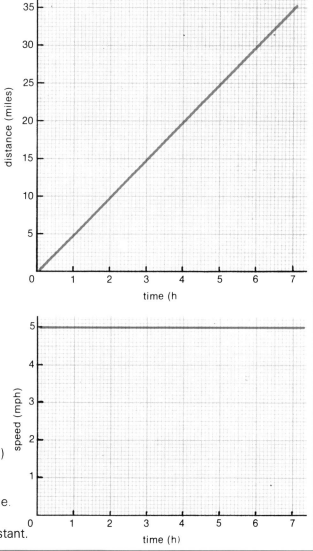

You can see from the distance–time graph that the distance travelled in each hour is 5 miles. (This is the slope.) The speed–time graph also shows a steady, unchanging speed. The slope of the speed graph is zero, i.e. no increase or decrease in speed takes place: the walker's speed is constant.

Example 2:

Distance–time graph for a mountain walk.

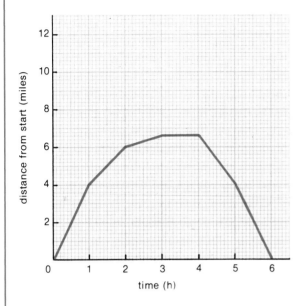

The graph shows that:
(i) The walk started and finished at the same place.
(ii) The speed was greater in the first hour than in the second hour (why?)
(iii) A rest was taken in the fourth hour.
(iv) The furthest distance of the walk from the starting point was 6·6 miles, so the total distance travelled was 13·2 miles.

The speed–time graph tells the same story in a different way. Note that the sudden changes of slope in the distance–time graph produce breaks in the speed graph.

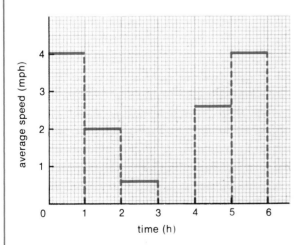

Distance travelled = speed × time
This is shown as the **area** under the speed–time graph. (Check for yourself.)

Exercise 12·3

A **1** The graph shows the distance from shore of someone swimming out to sea and back.

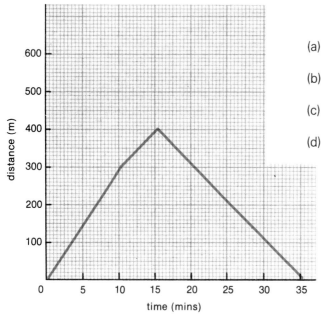

(a) After what time did the swimmer turn back?
(b) What was the swimmer's speed during the first 10 minutes?
(c) How long was the swimmer in the water altogether?
(d) What other information can you obtain from the graph?

2 The graph shows a **coach** travelling from Glasgow towards London and a **car** travelling from London to Glasgow.

(a) Write down all the facts you can find from the graph.
(b) Where and when did the car and coach pass one another?
(c) What was the average speed (for the whole journey) of the car?
(d) What was the average speed (not counting stops) of the coach?
(e) Find the speeds of the car and the coach while they were travelling.

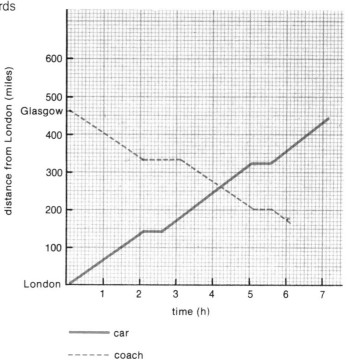

—————— car

------ coach

3 The graph shows speed against time for the first 8 seconds of a buggy race.

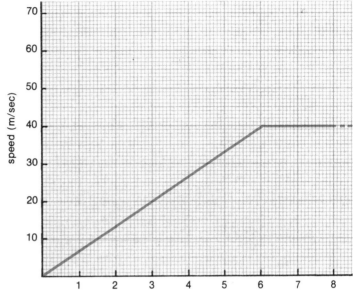

(a) What is the speed at the end of
    (i) the 3rd second?
    (ii) the 6th second?
    (iii) the 8th second?
(b) What is the acceleration over the first 6 seconds?
(c) What is the acceleration during the 7th and 8th second?
(d) Use the graph to find the distance travelled by the buggy in
    (i) the 8th second   (ii) the 7th and 8th seconds   (iii) the first 6 seconds
    (Remember: distance travelled is represented by the area below the speed–time graph.)

4 The graph shows the velocity* of a cricket ball thrown vertically upwards, during the time it is in the air.

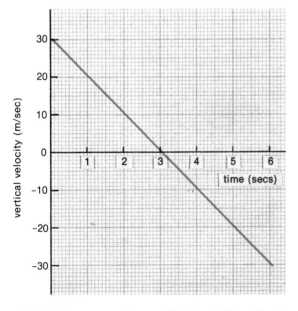

(a) The graph shows zero upward velocity at 3 seconds and from then on the velocity is negative. What can this mean?
(b) What is the distance of the ball from its starting point
    (i) after 1 second?
    (ii) after 2 seconds?
    (iii) after 3 seconds?
    (iv) after 4 seconds?
(c) Describe the flight of the ball, second by second.

* 'Velocity' is a more precise word for 'speed': it includes 'direction'.

B When an object falls freely, its speed v (in metres/sec) is given by the formula $v = 9 \cdot 8\,t$ where t is the time in seconds from the moment it starts to fall.

The distance fallen d (in metres) is given by the formula $d = 4 \cdot 9\,t^2$

1 Find the speed in m/sec of a parachutist who does not use his parachute 5 seconds after jumping.

2 Another parachutist jumps, waits for 12 seconds, and then pulls the rip cord. The parachute takes another 3 seconds to operate. What is his speed when the parachute opens?

3 An aircraft goes out of control at 10 000 metres and falls. What is its speed after it has fallen for 20 seconds?

4 How far does the parachutist in question 1 fall in the 5 seconds before his parachute opens.

5 How far does the aircraft in question 3 fall in 20 seconds?

6 How long would it take the aircraft to fall the full 10 000 metres?

7 What would be its speed on striking the ground?

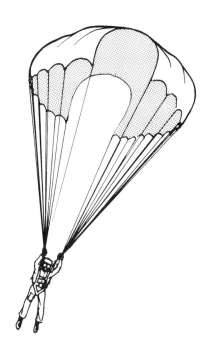

8 Kevin knocks a flowerpot off the balcony of his 17th-floor flat (50 metres from the ground).
  (a) How long does it take to reach the ground?
  (b) What is its speed when it strikes the ground?
  (c) What speed is this in km/h?

C *An investigation into braking*

It is never possible to stop a car or bike instantly. Even runners have to slow down gradually. It is important to leave a safe distance so that a car or bike can be stopped in time to avoid hitting the vehicle in front. The safe distance can be found using a speed–time graph.

Example:

The graph gives the speed a car travelling at 30 mph (44 ft/sec) which comes to a stop in exactly 6 seconds.

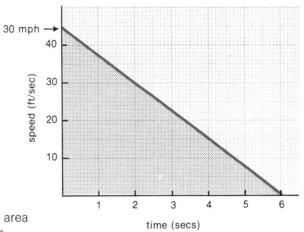

30 mph →

The stopping distance is shown as the area under the graph $= \frac{1}{2} \times 44 \times 6 = 132$ feet

Draw speed–time graphs for the following examples and find the stopping distance in each case.

1 A car with the same braking power as the one in the example, but travelling at:
   (a) 70 mph (= 103 ft/sec)
   (b) 90 mph (= 132 ft/sec)
   (c) 50 mph (= 73 ft/sec)

2 A bike (which can reduce its speed at the rate of 10 ft/sec/sec) travelling at:
   (a) 15 mph (= 22 ft/sec)
   (b) 25 mph (= 37 ft/sec)

3 (a) What happens if a cyclist loses speed too quickly?
   (b) What happens to the speed if a car crashes into a wall?

4 A train can reduce speed by 2 feet per second every second. How long would the train take to stop from a speed of 120 mph (176 ft/sec)? What distance would the train cover in this time?

5 A jet aircraft travels at 600 mph in the air. It lands on the runway at a maximum speed of 120 mph. The pilot can safely reduce speed in the air by 60 mph every minute. How long does it take to reduce speed in preparation for landing? How far does the aircraft travel in this time?

6 *Reaction time*
When a driver sees something going wrong ahead, it takes time for him to decide what to do and do it. This time is called reaction time. During this time his car is travelling at full speed. Investigate how the reaction time affects the safe stopping distances in questions 1 and 2.

D Some problems in which speed–time and distance–time graphs may be used to help find solutions.

1 Two people live 10 km apart and one has a bicycle. They set out at the same time ($t = 0$) and go directly towards each other, one walking at 6 km/h and the other riding at 20 km/h. When and where will they meet?

2 Two country girls want to get to the nearest town as quickly as possible. They have one bicycle between them and cannot both ride it together. How should they organize the journey? (Assume the bike may be left at the roadside without being stolen!)

3 Extend the above problem to:
(a) three girls with one bicycle.
(b) three girls with two bicycles.
(c) x girls with y bicycles.

4 A coach leaves London at 4.45 p.m. and travels North up the M1 at 60 mph. A car follows the same route at 70 mph, starting 1 hour later. When and where does the car overtake the coach?

5 Investigate the problems of firing anti-aircraft shells (speed 4000 ft/sec) at aircraft travelling at a speed of 800 ft/sec.

6 Investigate the problem of intercepting missiles.

Unit 13   Polygons

13·1   Definitions

Any closed shape made up of straight lines is called a polygon. Special names for particular polygons are given below.

Number of sides	Name	Number of sides	Name
1	doesn't exist	6	hexagon
2	doesn't exist	7	heptagon
3	triangle	8	octagon
4	quadrilateral	10	decagon
5	pentagon	n	n-gon

'The Pentagon': Washington D.C.

Other words connected with polygons are shown in the diagrams below.

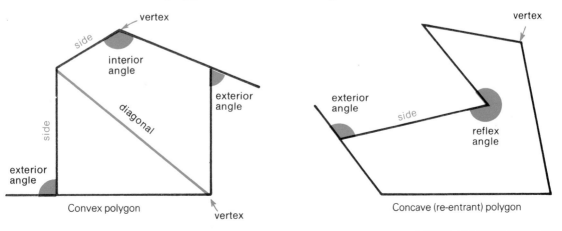

Convex polygon   Concave (re-entrant) polygon

The perimeter is the sum of the lengths of the sides. The perimeter encloses the area of the polygon.

Lines joining two vertices are either sides or diagonals of the polygon.

At least one diagonal of a re-entrant polygon will lie outside the polygon.

Exercise 13·1

1 Give the correct name for each of the figures drawn below.

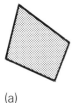  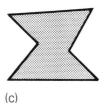 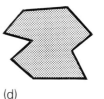 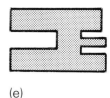

(a) (b) (c) (d) (e)

2 (a) How many vertices has a hexagon?
   (b) How many vertices has an octagon?
   (c) How many vertices has a re-entrant octagon?
   (d) Is it true to say that 'every polygon has the same number of vertices as it has sides'? Give reasons.
   (e) Prove that a 2400-gon (2400 sides) must have 2400 vertices. Drawing won't help!

(f)

3

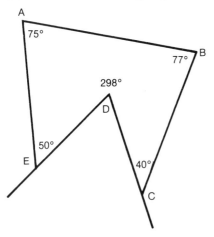

(a) What is the size of the largest interior angle of this pentagon?
(b) What are the sizes of the two exterior angles shown?
(c) What is the size of the re-entrant external angle?

4 (a) Measure the pentagon above and calculate its perimeter.
   (b) What is the length of the external diagonal of the pentagon?

5 A quadrilateral must have two diagonals, as shown below.

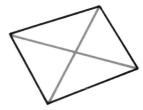 

(a) How many diagonals does a pentagon have? Does a re-entrant pentagon have the same number of diagonals as a convex one?

(b) How many diagonals does a convex hexagon have?

(c) How many diagonals does a convex octagon have?

(d) Can you find a pattern which relates the number of diagonals to the number of vertices?

(e) Use your pattern to find how many diagonals a 100-gon would have.

6 List the different polygons that can be found in the designs below. Can you find a shape that no one else in your class has found?

1

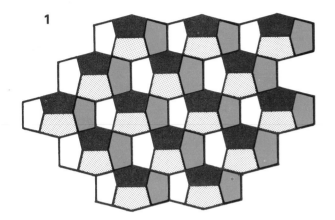

2

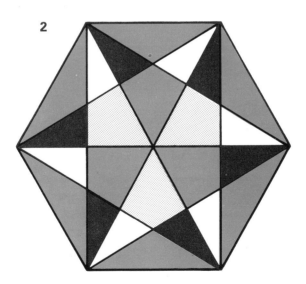

13·2 Angles in polygons

You remember that the angles of a triangle add up to 180°? From this fact we can deduce the sum of the angles in any polygon.

To prove that the angles of a triangle add up to 180°

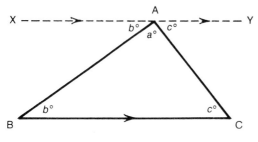

1∅	Data	ABC is any triangle. Its angles are $a°$, $b°$, $c°$
2∅	Data	The line XY has been drawn through A, parallel to BC
3∅	Deduction	$\widehat{XAB} = b°$ ... from 2∅
4∅	Deduction	$\widehat{YAC} = c°$ ... from 2∅
5∅	Deduction	$a° + b° + c° = 180°$ (XY is a straight line)
6∅	END	

The angles of a quadrilateral add up to 360°

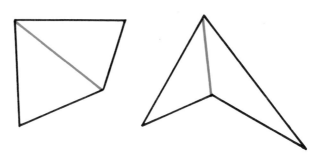

This follows from the fact that a quadrilateral can be divided into two triangles. Any polygon can be divided up into triangles. The two proofs given below are for a pentagon.

To prove that the angles in a pentagon add up to 540°

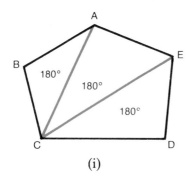

(i)

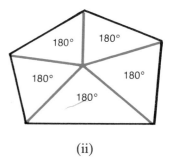

(ii)

(i) Every pentagon can be divided into three triangles by drawing all the diagonals from one vertex.
Total of angles $= 3 \times 180° = 540°$
$(= 6$ right angles$)$

(ii) Choose any point inside the pentagon. Five triangles can be formed by joining the point to the five vertices. An extra 360° is formed at the point.
Total of vertex
angles $= (5 \times 180°) - 360° = 540°$
$(= (10 - 4)$ right angles$)$

Exercise 13·2

A 1 Calculate the angles marked ? in the figures below

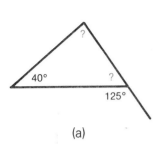

(a)

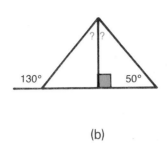

(b)

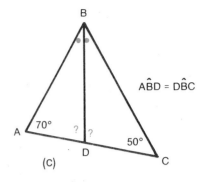

AB̂D = DB̂C

(c)

2 Prove that, for any triangle, any exterior angle is equal to the sum of the opposite interior angles.

3 Prove that a quadrilateral with all angles equal must be a rectangle.

4 Calculate the angles marked ? in the figures below.

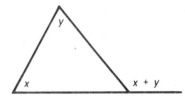

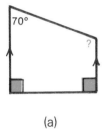

(a)

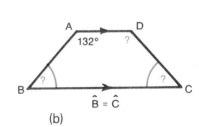

(b)

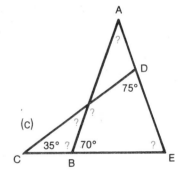

(c)

5 Each side of a quadrilateral is extended, to produce four exterior angles. What is the sum of these angles? Give reasons for your answer.

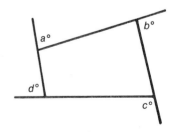

6 Attempt to draw a quadrilateral whose angles are 100°, 120°, 120° and 150°. Comment.

B 1 Prove that the angles of a hexagon add up to 720°.

2 Draw any hexagon and confirm by measurement that its angles add up to 720°.

3 Find the total of the angles in   (a) an octagon
                                     (b) a decagon
                                       (c) a 25-gon

4 The sides of a pentagon are extended to form exterior angles. Calculate the sum of these exterior angles. If a person walked right round a pentagonal path, through what angle would he or she turn altogether?

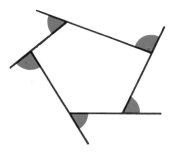

5 Draw a pentagon and all its diagonals. How many are there? Do all pentagons have the same number of diagonals?

6 Investigate the number of diagonals that different polygons have. Can you find a formula that gives the number of diagonals for an *n*-gon?
If you manage to find a formula, check it on a 15-gon. Does it still work if the polygon is re-entrant?

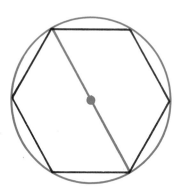

A re-entrant polygon

13·3   Regular polygons

Regular polygons have all sides and angles equal. They have a centre, and there is a circle which passes through all the vertices. If the number of sides is even, a maximum diagonal will be a diameter of the circle.

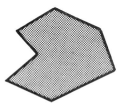

A regular hexagon. The diameter of its circle is a diagonal of the hexagon.

The circle can be used to calculate the angles, and also to draw the polygon. This is shown in the example.

Example:

To draw a regular heptagon (seven sides)

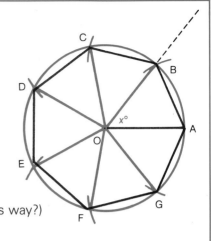

Step 1∅　The 360° angle at the centre must
　　　　　be divided into seven equal parts
　　　　　$x° = 360° ÷ 7 = 51·4°$

Step 2∅　One radius OA is drawn, then another
　　　　　OB is drawn so that
　　　　　$\hat{BOA} = 51·4°$ (as near as possible)

Step 3∅　Arc AB is 'stepped' round the circle
　　　　　　　A → B → C → D
　　　　　then A → G → F → E → D ... (why is it done this way?)

Step 4∅　Join AB, BC, CD, DE, EF, FG and GA

The construction gives a method of calculating the angle at each vertex
of a regular heptagon.

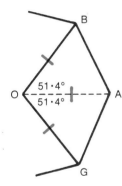

1∅	Data	△ OAB is isosceles
2∅	Data	$\hat{OBA} + \hat{OAB} + 51·4° = 180°$
3∅	Deduction	$\hat{OBA} = \hat{OAB}$ ....(from 1∅)
4∅	Deduction	$\hat{OBA} + \hat{OAB} = 128·6°$ ... (from 2∅)
5∅	Deduction	$\hat{OBA} = \hat{OAB} = 64·3°$ .... (from 3∅, 4∅)
6∅	Deduction	$\hat{BAG} = 128·6°$

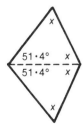

Shorter proof (I)
$102·8° + 4x = 360°$
$4x = 257·2°$
$2x = 128·6°$
(This proof is the same in principle as the one above)

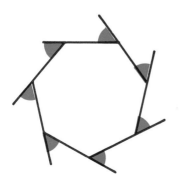

Shorter proof (II)
The seven exterior angles add up to 360°
... (why?)
If the heptagon is regular all the exterior angles
are equal (51·4°).
Each interior angle is $180° − 51·4° = 128·6°$

Exercise 13·3

A Draw a complete set of regular polygons from 3-gons to 10-gons. Use a circle of 5 cm radius as a starting point for each polygon. Draw as accurately as you can.

Measure each polygon carefully and complete the data table which is begun below. Check your measurement by calculation.

Polygon		Number of sides	Vertex angle	Length of side	Largest diagonal
Equilateral triangle		3	60°	8·66 cm	7·5 cm *
Square		4			

Keep your polygons for reference

B 1 Calculate the vertex angles for regular polygons with: (a) 10 sides (b) 20 sides (c) 50 sides (d) 100 sides

2 Draw a graph with 'number of sides' along the *x*-axis and 'size of vertex angle' along the *y*-axis.

3 The size of a vertex angle of a regular *n*-gon is given by the formula:
$$\frac{(2n-4)}{n} \text{ right angles}$$
Confirm that this formula is correct for *n* = 4, 6, 8, 12

13·4 Tessellations with regular polygons

A tiling pattern which leaves no spaces is called a tessellation.
Tessellations with regular polygons are often used in design and have always been used by artists.

Exercise 13·4

Investigate the tessellations given below. Draw them for yourself. Develop them in interesting ways. Vary the colouring. Find 'rules'. Each tessellation is accompanied by questions.

1 *Squares*

A tessellation with squares. Useful but a little dull.

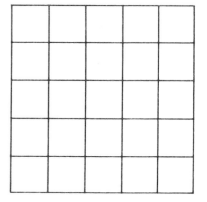

* axis of symmetry but not a diagonal

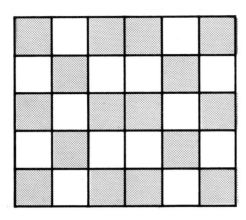

Tessellation with two different-coloured
squares. (Will this need equal numbers of both
colours?)

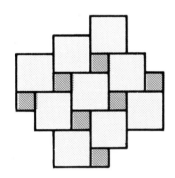

In this case the side of the small square is half
the side of the large square.
Note that each node has the same angle
structure: 90°, 90°, 180°

Design a tessellation using *three* different
sizes of square.

2 *Regular hexagons*

Can you find a tessellation which makes use of
two different sizes of hexagon?

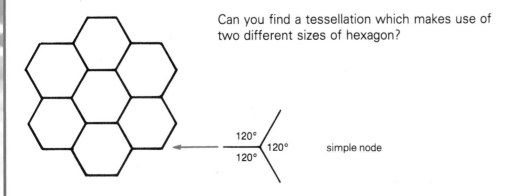

simple node

The centres of the hexagons are joined. This shows up a tessellation of equilateral triangles. The basic shape is an interesting quadrilateral:

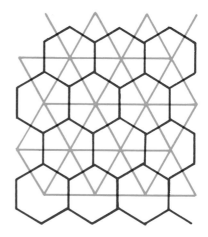

(a) Draw the three different types of nodes in this tessellation.
(b) Copy the tessellation (use isometric paper) and colour to make designs.

3 Investigate the two tessellations below. How are they constructed? What is the basic shape? How would you draw them? How are the nodes constructed? What are the main differences between the two tessellations?

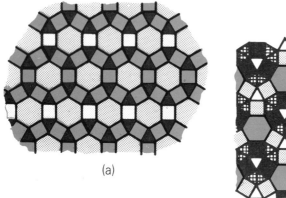

(a)

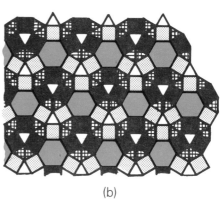

(b)

4 Make a collection of the tile designs which can be found at your local tile shop or decorator's shop. You will find that wallpaper designs are also often tessellations.

13·5   Perimeter and area of regular polygons

If the radius of a regular polygon is known, the length of a side (and hence the perimeter) can be calculated.

Example:
A regular pentagon is drawn in a circle of radius 5 cm. What are its perimeter and area?

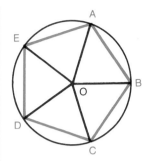

The pentagon consists of five triangles congruent to OAB.

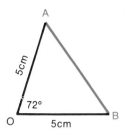

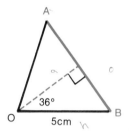

$$AB = 2 \times 5 \sin 36° = 5.88 \text{ cm}$$
$$\text{Area of } \triangle OAB = \tfrac{1}{2} \times 25 \times \sin 72°$$
$$= 11.888 \text{ cm}^2$$

Thus the perimeter of the pentagon $= 5 \times 5.88 = 29.4 \text{ cm}$
Area of the pentagon $= 5 \times 11.888 = 59.44 \text{ cm}^2$

Exercise 13·5

A **1** Find the perimeter and area of a regular pentagon:
    (a) with radius 1 metre
    (b) with radius 14·2 metres

2 A building in the shape of a regular pentagon covers an area of 1800 m². Calculate the radius of the pentagon and find the length of the outside wall of the building.

3 Find the radius of a regular pentagon whose sides are 8 cm in length. What is the area of the pentagon?

4 Find the areas and perimeters of regular hexagons of radius: (a) 10 cm (b) 25 cm (c) 36 cm (d) 50 cm

5 Find the radius of a regular hexagon whose area is 112 cm².

6 A mosque is built in the shape of a perfect hexagon. The distance around the inside walls of the mosque is 240 metres. What is the area of the space inside the mosque?

7 A room 10 m long and 12 m wide is to be tiled with hexagonal tiles, side 30 cm. How many tiles are needed to cover the floor?

8 An emerald is cut to fit a regular octagonal mount.
The sides of the mount are each 5 mm long.
What is the area of the cut surface of the emerald which fits into the mount?

B 1 Use the formula
Area $= \frac{1}{2}nr^2 \sin C$
(where r is the radius of the n-gon
and C is the angle each side subtends at the centre)
to find the ratio   area ÷ (radius)²
for regular polygons of n sides, where $n = 5, 10, 20, 100, 360, 3600, 36\,000$.
Show that the sequence of values for this ratio approaches
a special number. (What is it?)

2 Investigate the perimeter/radius ratio for regular polygons.

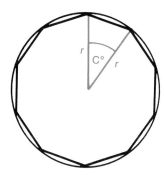

3 Investigate the perimeter/diagonal ratios for regular n-gons where n is an odd number less than 10.
Note: The pentagon will have only one ratio to investigate, but the heptagon will have three and the nonagon will have five.

Unit 14 Geometry through transformations

14·1 Straight lines

The transformations translation, reflection, rotation and enlargement can change straight lines in certain ways.

Examples:

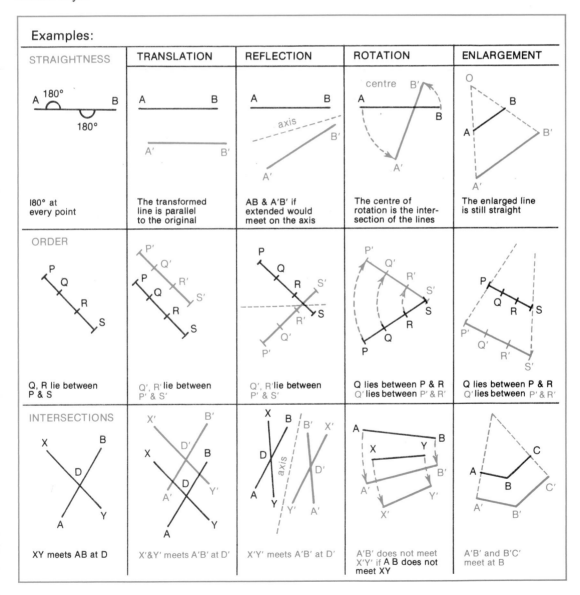

STRAIGHTNESS	TRANSLATION	REFLECTION	ROTATION	ENLARGEMENT
180° at every point	The transformed line is parallel to the original	AB & A'B' if extended would meet on the axis	The centre of rotation is the inter-section of the lines	The enlarged line is still straight
ORDER				
Q, R lie between P & S	Q', R' lie between P' & S'	Q', R' lie between P' & S'	Q lies between P & R Q' lies between P' & R'	Q lies between P & R Q' lies between P' & R'
INTERSECTIONS				
XY meets AB at D	X'&Y' meets A'B' at D'	X'Y' meets A'B' at D'	A'B' does not meet X'Y' if A B does not meet XY	A'B' and B'C' meet at B

Some things however do not change. These are:
  (i)   the straightness of lines
  (ii) the order of points on a line
  (iii) the intersections of a line with others: i.e. the angles are
        unchanged

Exercise 14·1

A These questions refer to the examples above.
  1 Copy the diagrams which show:
    (a) A line AB reflected into A′B′
    (b) A line AB enlarged into A′B′
    (c) A line PQ rotated into P′Q′
    (d) Two lines with just one point in common enlarged to two lines with just one point in common.
  2 Copy the diagram which shows most clearly that the order of points on a line is not changed by transformations.
  3 Which of the following are true for all the translations in the example?
    (a) All points move the same distance.
    (b) All points move in the same direction.
    (c) Some points do not move at all.
    (d) Points of intersection move the same distance and direction as other points.
  4 Which of the following are true for all the reflections in the example?
    (a) All points move the same distance.
    (b) All points move in the same direction.
    (c) Some points do not move at all.
    (d) Points of intersection do not move.
    (e) A reflection can be performed by rotation, provided you pick the right centre.
  5 Which of the following are true for all the rotations in the example?
    (a) All points move the same distance.
    (b) All points move in the same direction.
    (c) Some points do not move at all.
    (d) Every rotation has a centre.
    (e) If two intersection lines are rotated, the resulting lines will also intersect.
  6 Which of the following are true for all enlargements?
    (a) Straight lines can be enlarged to form curved lines.
    (b) All points move the same distance.
    (c) All lines are enlarged by the same length.
    (d) All lines are enlarged in the same proportion.

B **1**

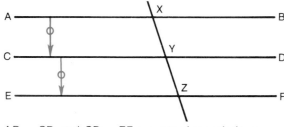

    AB → CD and CD → EF are equal translations
    (a) What can be said about XY and YZ?
    (b) Is it true that AB//CD and CD//EF?

(c) Investigate this theorem:
A straight line cuts three parallel
lines at X, Y and Z. It is found
that XY = YZ. Any other line crossing the lines
will be cut in the same way, i.e. two equal
parts will be cut from the line
by the three parallel ones.

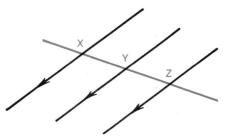

Note: This is called the
equal intercepts theorem

2 (a) Which lines are parallel to AW?
(b) Which lines are equal to AB?
(c) Which lines are equal to AC?
(d) Which lines are equal to WX?
(e) Which lines are equal to XZ?
(f) Is it true that WY = $\frac{2}{3}$WZ?

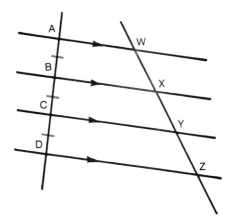

3 In △ ABC, AX = XB. What other equal
lengths can be found in the figure?
Give your reasons.

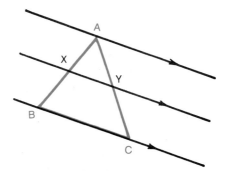

4 Follow these instructions:

1∅ Draw any straight line AB 12 cm long.

2∅ Draw another line AC about 15 cm long, so that BÂC is over 30° but under 40°

3∅ Use compasses to mark out three equal distances along AC: AX, XY, YZ

4∅ Join ZB with a ruler

5∅ Draw lines through X and Y parallel to ZB, cutting AB at P and Q

6∅ Measure AP, PQ and QB

7∅ END

5 The instructions of question 4 give a very accurate method of dividing a line into three equal parts. Write a similar program which will divide a line into five equal parts and show that it works. How do these programs connect with questions 1 and 2 of this exercise?

6 Practise dividing lines into seven, eight and nine equal parts using compasses and ruler only. Check by measurement.

C 1 Two straight lines meet at X.
   (a) Use rotation to explain why
       (i) $C\hat{X}B = A\hat{X}D$
       (ii) $C\hat{X}A = B\hat{X}D$
   (b) Find another argument to prove the pairs of angles equal.

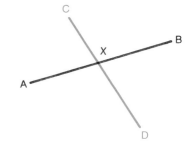

2 A pair of parallel lines is cut by a transversal LXYM.
   (a) Use rotation of XY to explain why:
       (i) $L\hat{X}B = L\hat{Y}D$
       (ii) $L\hat{X}B = A\hat{X}Y$
       (iii) $B\hat{X}Y = X\hat{Y}C$
   (b) Write down all the angles equal to $L\hat{X}B$.
   (c) Write down all the angles equal to $D\hat{Y}M$.
   (d) What is the value of:
       (i) $A\hat{X}L + L\hat{X}B$
       (ii) $A\hat{X}Y + X\hat{Y}C$
       (iii) $B\hat{X}Y + Y\hat{X}D$

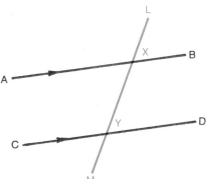

3 The figure ABCD is made from two pairs of parallel lines.
   Prove that $D\hat{A}B = B\hat{C}D$
            and $A\hat{B}C = A\hat{D}C$

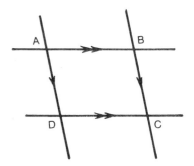

4 A stick the length of AB is rotated around the $\triangle ABC$; first about A, then about C, and finally about B.
   Explain why this shows that the sum of the angles of a triangle is 180°.

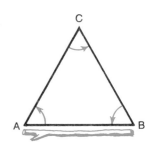

5 Study the following argument. It proves that the lines PR and P′R′ must have the same number of points, even though P′R′ is longer than PR.

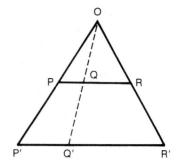

Proof:

1∅ P′R′ is an enlargement of PR

2∅ O is the centre of enlargement

3∅ Every point of PR has a corresponding point on P′R′ (Example: Q′ is the point for Q)

4∅ Every point of P′R′ must have come from a point of PR by enlargement

5∅ PR and P′R′ have exactly matching points

6∅ END

What do you think?

14·2 Quadrilaterals

Most of the geometry of quadrilaterals can be understood by appealing to the transformations listed in section 14.1.

Examples:
1. The diagonals of a parallelogram bisect each other.
2. The diagonals of a rhombus are perpendicular.

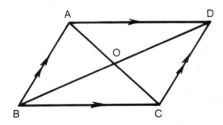

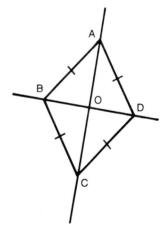

O is a centre of symmetry for the parallelogram. When the parallelogram is rotated through 180° about O, OD fits over OB and OA fits over OC.

Thus the diagonals bisect each other.

The rhombus has two axes of symmetry (the diagonals).
Thus $A\hat{O}B = A\hat{O}D$, so both are 90°
($\angle$s on straight line)
also $A\hat{O}D = D\hat{O}C$, so both are 90°
($\angle$s on straight line)
This proof uses reflection

Exercise 14·2

A *General properties of parallelograms and rectangles*
Explain how transformations can account for the following properties of parallelograms. Draw a clear diagram for each question.
1 Opposite sides of a parallelogram are equal.
2 Opposite angles of a parallelogram are equal.
3 The area of a parallelogram is calculated as 'base times height'.

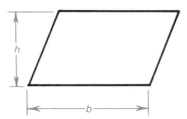

4 The diagonals of a rectangle are equal.
5 A parallelogram with one right angle must be a rectangle.
6 A quadrilateral with opposite sides equal must be a parallelogram.

B *Properties of other quadrilaterals* Prove the following theorems (questions 1–5):
1 A quadrilateral with all sides equal must be a parallelogram.
2 The diagonals of the quadrilateral in question 1 are perpendicular.
3 A quadrilateral with all angles equal must be a parallelogram.
4 The diagonals of the quadrilateral in question 3 are equal.
5 The angles of a quadrilateral add up to 360°.
6 A quadrilateral has one pair of sides parallel and the other pair equal. Would you expect its diagonals to be equal?

C **1** A quadrilateral ABCD is drawn. The mid-points of its sides are P, Q, R, and S. Investigate PQRS for different quadrilaterals (squares, parallelograms, trapezia).
2 A quadrilateral ABCD is drawn. The angles A, B, C and D are bisected. Investigate the quadrilaterals formed by the bisectors when ABCD is   (a) a parallelogram   (b) a rectangle   (c) an isosceles trapezium (see question B6).

14·3 Circles

The properties of a circle follow from its symmetry under rotation and reflection.

The circle has an infinite number of axes of symmetry, but as soon as a radius is added there is only one axis of symmetry for the figure.

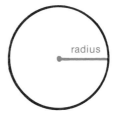

Examples:

1 All radii are equal.

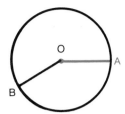

If the circle is rotated about O, OA will come over OB.
It follows that triangle OAB will be isosceles.

2 Equal chords are equidistant from the centre of the circle.

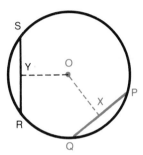

The circle could be rotated until PQ came over RS. At that point, OX would fit over OY.
So OX = OY.

Exercise 14·3

Investigate the following properties of circles. In each case find a proof of the property using symmetry or rotation. Make a careful drawing demonstrating each property, to check that it is always true.

1 The perpendicular bisector of any chord of a circle passes through the centre.
How would you use this property to find the centre of a circle?

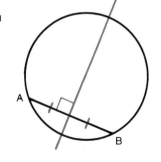

AB is any chord

2 Equal chords of a circle subtend equal angles at the centre.

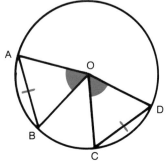

AÔB and CÔD are the angles subtended by AB and CD at the centre.

3 The angle in a semicircle is a right angle.
Hint: Join the right angle to the centre of the circle.

4 Equal chords of a circle subtend equal
angles at the circumference.
(You might have guessed this property.)

5 Opposite angles of a cyclic quadrilateral
add up to 180°.
Hint: Join the four vertices of the cyclic
quadrilateral to the centre of
the circle.

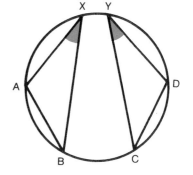

6 Angles in the same segment are equal.
7 The angle subtended by a chord at the centre
is twice the angle subtended at the
circumference.
Hint: Join X to O and produce it as
shown.

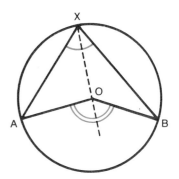

Note: Questions 6 and 7 can be taken in reverse order, if you like.

14·4 Some applications of enlargement

In an enlargement, lines are increased in proportion but angles stay the
same. If two triangles have the same three angles, one triangle must be
an enlargement of the other.
In fact, it is sufficient if they have two angles the same, because the third
angle must then add to 180° and will therefore be the same in both
triangles.

Example:

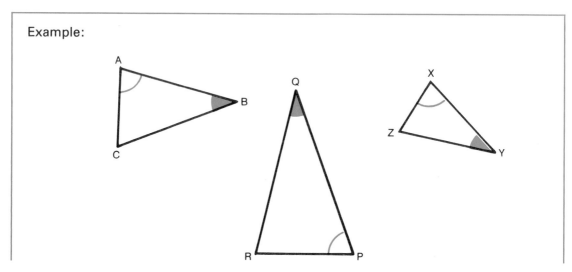

The three triangles are equi-angular. Thus △ PQR is an enlargement of △ XYZ, while △ ABC is an enlargement of both the other triangles. This can be seen by changing the position of the triangles to match △ ABC, as shown below. When the triangles are arranged like this it is easy to see the enlargement.

It is also easy to see the equal ratios such as

(i) $\dfrac{BX}{XZ} = \dfrac{QP}{PR} = \dfrac{YA}{AC}$

(ii) $\dfrac{BX}{QP} = \dfrac{BZ}{QR} = \dfrac{XZ}{PR}$

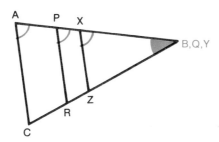

Exercise 14·4

1 Complete these ratios for the triangles of the above example:

(a) $\dfrac{BC}{AC} = \dfrac{YZ}{?} = \dfrac{?}{PR}$ (b) $\dfrac{XZ}{PR} = \dfrac{BX}{?} = \dfrac{?}{BR}$

2 Two quadrilaterals have the same four angles at the vertices. Does this mean that one quadrilateral is necessarily an enlargement of the other? Give examples to justify your answer.

3

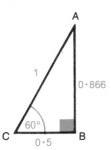

Every right-angled triangle with one angle equal to 60° is an enlargement of the triangle shown.

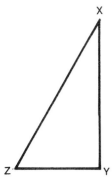

Check this by drawing several 30°/60°/90° triangles XYZ. For each triangle show that

(a) $\dfrac{XZ}{1} = \dfrac{XY}{0·866} = \dfrac{YZ}{0·5}$

(b) $\dfrac{XY}{XZ} = 0·866 = \sin 60°$

(c) $\dfrac{YZ}{XZ} = 0·5 = \cos 60°$

4 Show that every square is an enlargement of the unit square (i.e. the square whose side is 1 unit).

Use this fact to deduce that:

(a) The perimeter: diagonal ratio is the same for all squares.

(b) The enlargement of a square by a factor k enlarges its area by a factor k^2.

(c) The enlargement of any shape by a factor k enlarges the shape's area by a factor k^2.

5

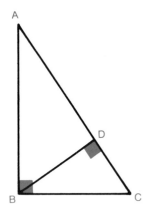

ABC is a right-angled triangle. BD is drawn perpendicular to AC.
(a) Show that
  (i) △s ABC, ABD are enlargements of △ BDC

  (ii) $\dfrac{AD}{AB} = \dfrac{AB}{AC}$ (ii) $\dfrac{DC}{BC} = \dfrac{BC}{AC}$

(b) Study the following proof of Pythagoras's Theorem

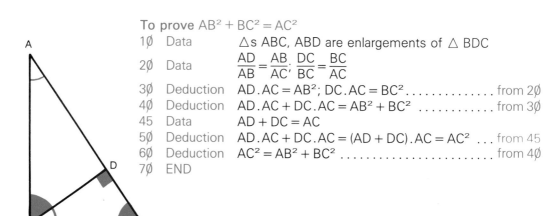

To prove $AB^2 + BC^2 = AC^2$

1∅	Data	△s ABC, ABD are enlargements of △ BDC
2∅	Data	$\dfrac{AD}{AB} = \dfrac{AB}{AC};\ \dfrac{DC}{BC} = \dfrac{BC}{AC}$
3∅	Deduction	$AD.AC = AB^2;\ DC.AC = BC^2$ .... from 2∅
4∅	Deduction	$AD.AC + DC.AC = AB^2 + BC^2$ .... from 3∅
45	Data	$AD + DC = AC$
5∅	Deduction	$AD.AC + DC.AC = (AD + DC).AC = AC^2$ ... from 45
6∅	Deduction	$AC^2 = AB^2 + BC^2$ .... from 4∅
7∅	END	

6

AB, DC are any chords of the circle. They meet at Y.

(a) Copy the figure and mark in all angles which must be equal.
(b) What enlargements can you find in this figure?
(c) Investigate the following:
    (i) $YA.YB = YC.YD$
    (ii) $AX.XC = BX.XD$
Can you extend the figure to find more relationships?

14·5 Algebra of transformations

Movements can be represented by symbols. There are rules of transformation algebra which can be discovered through experiment: these rules are rather different from the rules that apply when the symbols represent numbers.

Example:

Consider the movement instructions **R** = right turn

L = left turn

A = about turn

I = stay where you are

The symbols are **R L A I**
As soon as we combine symbols an algebra is obtained

In this example, we consider **R, L, A, I** as applied to one of the four points of the compass (although there are other ways of looking at turning). So **R**(N) means 'face North, then turn right'. You can check that you end up facing East.

So **R**(N) = E

Here are some examples: **R**(E) = S
L(S) = E
I(W) = W
A(S) = N

If movements are combined a relationship can be found between them.

RR(E) means 'face East, turn right, then turn right again'

R(E)   **RR**(E)

It can be seen that **RR**(E) = W

This suggests that **RR** = **A**

This theory can be tested on all four starting points:
RR(N) = S = **A**(N)
RR(E) = W = **A**(E)
RR(S) = N = **A**(S)
RR(W) = E = **A**(W)
So we have established the rule   RR = A   for all the possible cases.

Exercise 14·5

A   These questions refer to the example above.

1   Check that these relationships are true:
   (a) **RL** = **I**   (b) **AA** = **I**   (c) **LL** = **A**   (d) **AL** = **R**

2   Complete the double-entry table below.

	R	L	A	I
R	A	?	L	?
L	?	A	?	?
A	?	?	I	?
I	?	?	?	I

3   Investigate the following relationships in the **R, L, A, I** system. **X, Y, Z** will be one of **R, L, A** or **I** every time.

   (a) **XY** = **YX**   (b) **X²** = **X** ⇒ **X** = **A**   (c) **XYZ** = **ZYX**
   (d) **RX** = **I** ⇒ **X** = **L**   (e) **X⁴** = **I**   (f)   **X⁵** = **X**

B   Investigate the algebra of rotations, translations and reflections in a similar way to the example above.

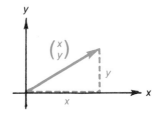

Start with a vector $\begin{bmatrix} x \\ y \end{bmatrix}$ and see how

it responds to the following transformations:
R⁺   rotation, anticlockwise, through an angle of 90°
T$_v$ translation by a vector **v**
R$_x$ reflection in the x-axis
R$_y$ reflection in the y-axis.

C   The following matrices all produce transformations. Combinations of transformations can be treated the same way as matrix multiplications. Investigate.

$\begin{bmatrix} 1 & 0 \\ 0 & 1 \end{bmatrix}$ The unit matrix: no change $\begin{bmatrix} -1 & 0 \\ 0 & -1 \end{bmatrix}$ Rotation through 180°

$\begin{bmatrix} -1 & 0 \\ 0 & 1 \end{bmatrix}$ Reflection in the x-axis $\begin{bmatrix} 0 & -1 \\ 1 & 0 \end{bmatrix}$ Anticlockwise rotation through 90°

$\begin{bmatrix} 1 & 0 \\ 0 & -1 \end{bmatrix}$ Reflection in the y-axis $\begin{bmatrix} 0 & 1 \\ -1 & 0 \end{bmatrix}$ Clockwise rotation through 90°

Compare your results with the **R L A I** system.

Unit 15   Problem solving

15·1   Real problems

Mathematics is often used in solving problems. In real life the problems are much more complicated but the answer does not have to be exactly right.

An approximate solution may be found first and then a better solution found at a later stage.

The first step is a careful study of the problem itself. During this study we try to establish:

(a) What is important.
(b) What things can be changed in our attempt to solve the problem.
(c) How accurate we need to be.
(d) The weak spots where guesses have to be made.

Example:

A student at school found that he was always getting behind with his homework. He never seemed to have enough time to do all the things he wanted to do.

He made a list of all the activities in one week. Since time is the most important variable, times should be listed with the activities.

Activity	Time (hours)	Notes
Sleep	63	(7 × 9)
School	35	(7 × 5)
Travel	5	(5 × 1)
Meals	14	(7 × 2)
TV	14	(7 × 2)
Sport	9	Practice and Sat. morning
Homework	9	1 h per day + 2 extra hours at weekends
Girlfriend	12	3 evenings per week
Total:	**161**	

Note: (i)   It would not be sufficient to consider just one day.
(ii) The total comes to 161 hours out of the possible maximum of 168.

This first stage, the collection of information, is basic in all problem solving.
The figures in the table are estimated for the week. Some times (school for example) can be calculated exactly. Others vary from day to day and from week to week.
The data are called a model of the problem.
To help us think about the problem, the data can be presented in visual form as a graph, pie chart or diagram, whichever is the most suitable.

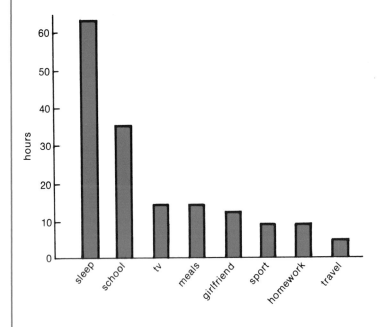

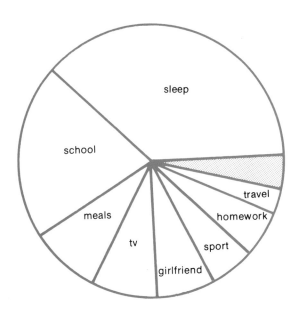

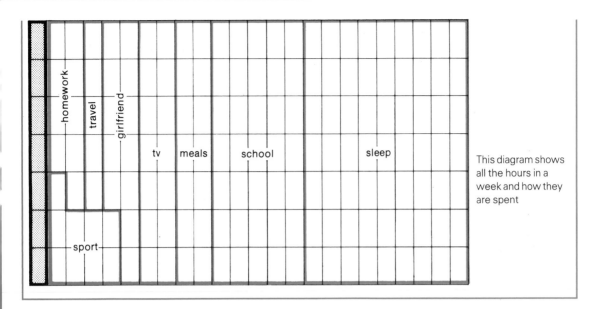

This diagram shows all the hours in a week and how they are spent

Exercise 15·1

A These questions refer to the example above.
1. Place the activities in order of importance (in your opinion).
2. How would you set about measuring the times spent on the different activities? What level of accuracy is possible?
3. What would it mean if the total came to more than 168 hours per week?
4. Which of the activities can have their time altered?
5. Which of the activities could be reduced without changing the student's life too much?
6. Where are the 'weak spots' in the data, i.e. what parts are not reliable?
7. Write out three different suggestions which would enable the student to increase his homework time.
8. Make an analysis of the way you spend your own time.

B Explore the following problems (I don't expect you to solve them).
1. You want to organise a 16th birthday party for a friend but you have only £10. The birthday is in four weeks' time.
2. Six friends want to get as quickly as possible from one town to another 15 miles away for a football match. They have three bicycles but each can only be used by one person at a time. Three of the friends are fast walkers, the others are much slower.
3. Two friends have a job delivering leaflets in a block of flats on an estate. The flats are arranged as shown in the plan.

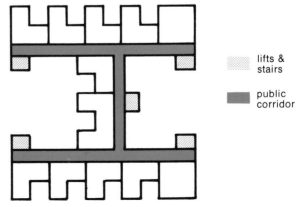

lifts & stairs

public corridor

There are 12 flats on each floor, and 12 floors altogether. How should the friends share the job?

4 You are trying to decide what to do after the fifth year in secondary school. Will you stay on at school, go to work, go to college, go on a training scheme or what?

15·2 Mathematical models

When a mathematician is called in to solve a real problem he makes a model of the problem. This is usually much simpler than the problem itself: it concentrates on just part of the problem. This process, called mathematical modelling, is a very important part of a mathematician's work.

Example: Insuring bikes

It is well known that bikes are stolen and that you can insure against losing yours. But how do the insurance companies know what to charge for insuring the bike?

First question: If 1000 people had bikes, how many would be likely to have them stolen in a year?

Since nobody knows the answer to this question, the insurer has to guess. He asks a sample of 100 cyclists how many of them have had their bikes stolen in the year, and how many times. His findings are put in a table:

Number of times bike was stolen (f)	Number of cyclists (n)	Number of thefts ($n \times f$)
0	85	0
1	10	10
2	4	8
3	1	3
Totals:	**100**	**21**

Number of thefts per cyclist = 0·21
Number of thefts per 1000 cyclists = 210

Second question: How much would the stolen bikes cost to replace?

Here the insurance company returns to its sample: in fact, the cyclists should have been asked this question at the same time to save expense. The results are again put into a table. As you can see, an average value is needed for each class.

Value of bike stolen	Average value for class ($£v$)	Number stolen (s)	Total value ($£v \times s$)
0–£50	25	2	50
£51–£60	55	4	220
£61–£70	65	3	195
£71–£80	75	0	0
£81–£90	85	4	340
£91–£100	95	5	475
£101–£200	150	3	450
Totals:		**21**	**1730**

Third question: How much should a cyclist be charged, and how should it relate to the value of the bike?

This question will be answered in Exercise 15·2A.

Exercise 15·2

A These questions relate to the above example.
   1 The data showed that there were 21 thefts.
   (a) What does 0·21 thefts per cyclist mean?
   (b) How has the insurer arrived at the figure of 210 thefts per 1000 cyclists?
   2 (a) How many bikes worth between £51 and £60 were stolen?
   (b) Where does the figure of £55 come from?
   (c) Where does the figure of £220 in the last column come from?
   3 (a) What is the average value of the stolen bikes?
   (b) Since £1730 was paid out to the 100 cyclists in the sample, what should the average premium be?
   (c) What would the company expect to pay out to 1000 cyclists?
   4 Do you think a more valuable bike should cost more to insure? Suggest a scale of charges that would allow for:
   (a) The value of the bike insured.
   (b) The number of thefts a cyclist has in a year.
   (c) A 10% profit for the insurance company.
   5 Compare your scale of charges with those of a real bike insurance company (obtainable from any insurance agent). Would it be better to organise a bike insurance for your own school than use a real bike insurance company?

B Select one of the problems listed and make a model in the way that we did with bike insurance. Work with a friend.
   1 Organise a draughts competition so that better players have a handicap.
   2 Pick a team to represent your school in athletics.
   3 Plan an outing for old people living in a local old people's home. You will have to raise the money to pay for it.
   4 Make an emergency plan for a fire in your school.
   5 (a) Share out the housework in a family with three children aged 17, 14 and 12, where father and mother both have jobs.
   (b) Consider the equivalent problem in a one-parent family.

C Make a model of a problem of your own choice.

15·3 Mathematical toolbox

The main mathematical tools used to solve problems are:
1 Data investigation (observation and measurement)
2 Thinking and planning
3 Patterns
4 Predictions and checks

The exercises which follow give examples of all four of these activities.
Remember that in this section you are learning about the process of
solving problems

Exercise15·3

A *Data investigation exercises*
    1 Make a study of a traffic-flow problem.

Collect the data after school or during the weekend. Prepare a report of your work when
you bring the data back to school. Some suggestions are:
(a) Choose a busy crossroads with traffic lights and study how long cars wait, how
     difficult it is for people to cross, etc.
(b) Study a multi-storey car park. How long do cars have to queue to get in? How many
     spaces are empty?
(c) Study the parking problems in town on Saturday morning. How many illegally parked
     cars are there? How often do you find cars parked so that crossing roads becomes
     dangerous?

(d) Study a petrol station (ask permission first). What is the pattern of queueing, using pumps, etc.?

2 An experiment with drawing pins
Put 20 drawing pins into a cup and investigate what happens when you shake the cup and tip the pins on to a flat surface.
It has been suggested that the pins are equally likely to land point up or point down.  Do you agree?

3 Observation of triangles
(a) A triangle ABC is drawn, as shown, with a right angle at B
(b) Points P_1, P_2, P_3, P_4, P_5
are chosen on AC
(c) Lines P_1Q_1, P_2Q_2, etc. are drawn parallel to CB
(d) Measure P_1Q_1, P_2Q_2, etc. and AP_1, AP_2, etc.
(e) Investigate the ratios $\dfrac{P_1Q_1}{AP_1}$, $\dfrac{P_2Q_2}{AP_2}$, ..., $\dfrac{BC}{AB}$

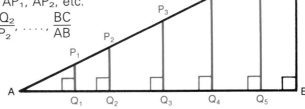

(f) What does the experiment tell you about angle A? (think trig!)
(g) What could you predict as the result of your experiment?

4 Observation of rectangles
Draw accurately a number of rectangles. Measure their long sides, short sides and diagonals.

5 Observation of numbers (Use your calculator)
(a) Make a study of the decimal part of the result when numbers are divided by 7.
(b) Make a study of the decimal part of the result when numbers are divided by 17.
You may wish to continue this investigation with other numbers (or on a computer).

B *Thinking and planning*

You have learned mathematical ways of thinking and planning. In particular, you know how to use a flow chart, a Venn diagram and a tree diagram. It is also useful to work backwards from facts to reasons as well as to write a proof.

1 Two friends went from London to Liverpool to see Liverpool play Arsenal. They arrived very early for the match and took a bus to the city centre, where they got lost. Make a flow chart to show how they might continue.

2 Use Venn diagrams to solve these problems.
  (a) In a class of 30 people, 16 play tennis and 18 play badminton. How many play both?
  (b) In an election with only a Tory and a Labour candidate, 17 800 people didn't vote Tory and 24 900 people didn't vote Labour. Altogether, 30 000 people had the vote: how many didn't use it?

3 (a) Mr Jackson loves gambling. He does the pools every week, bets on the horses every week and goes to a gambling club on Thursdays. Use a tree diagram to show the different 'wins' that he could have in a week.
  (b) A social worker hears that Mr and Mrs Banstead have five children. Use a tree diagram to find the most likely combination of boys and girls in the family.
  (c) Draw your own family tree. How many great-great-grandparents does each person have? Is this certain?

4 A carpenter building a door frame checks that it is a perfect rectangle by measuring the diagonals. If the diagonals are equal he assumes the frame is correct. Is he right?

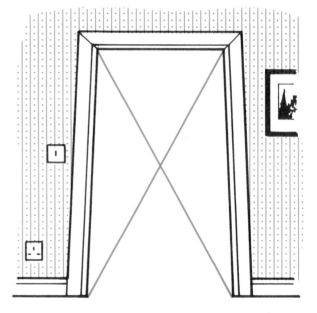

5 (a) A box contains three sticks. Their lengths are an exact number of centimetres, and they can be formed into a triangle. Say as much as you can about the sticks.
  (b) Another box contains five sticks. Their lengths are an exact number of centimetres, and any three of them will form a triangle. Say as much as you can about them.

C *Patterns*

Relations often show up as patterns of numbers or shapes. The pattern can sometimes be expressed as a formula or equation. Sometimes the number pattern is only revealed if differences are studied.

Example:

Numbers: 2─┬─5─┬─8─┬─11─┬─14 . . .

Differences: 3   3   3   3 . . .

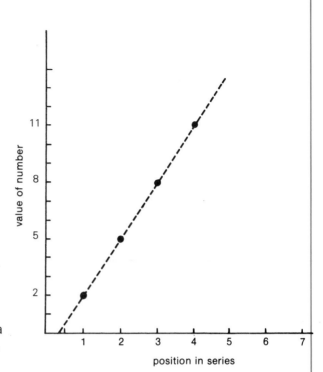

A picture of this pattern can be seen on a graph. All the points lie on a straight line, which has the equation $y = 3x - 1$

1   Find out all you can about these number patterns. How would you find the 100th number? What does the pattern look like as a graph?
(a) 3, 5, 7, 9, . . .
(b) 3, 6, 9, 12, . . .
(c) 1, 4, 7, 10, . . .
(d) 1, 3, 6, 10, . . .
(e) 1, 4, 9, 16, 25, . . .
(f) 2, 4, 8, 16, 32, . . .
(g) 1·1, 1·21, 1·331, 1·4641, . . .
(h) 1, 1, 2, 3, 5, 8, 13, . . .
(i) $\frac{1}{1}, \frac{2}{1}, \frac{3}{2}, \frac{5}{3}, \frac{8}{5}$, . . .
(j) $\frac{4}{7}, \frac{7}{11}, \frac{11}{18}, \frac{18}{29}$, . . .

2   Find the pattern connecting these number pairs: (0, 5); (1, 4·899); (1·414, 4·796); (1·732, 4·69); (2, 4·58); (2·236, 4·472); (2·45, 4·359); (2·646, 4·242); (2·828, 4·123); (3, 4). Once you have found the connection, find three more number pairs.

3 What pattern can you find connecting the three diagrams?

4 What pattern can you see linking the points P, Q, R and S, T, U?

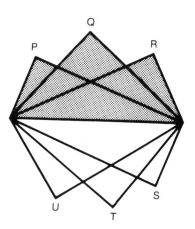

5 How is this pattern constructed?

What is the basic shape of the pattern?

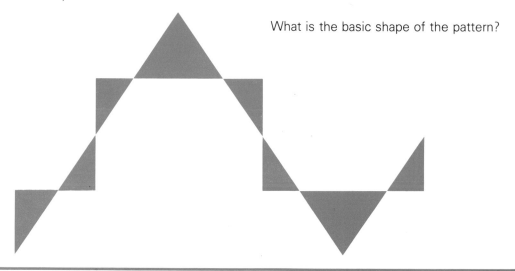

Unit 16 Polyhedra

16·1 Regular tetrahedron and cube

A regular polyhedron is a solid with all its faces congruent, all its edges equal, and all its angles equal

The two simplest regular polyhedra are the regular tetrahedron, whose faces are equilateral triangles, and the cube, whose faces are squares.

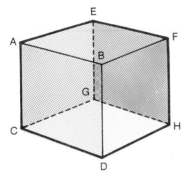

Cube

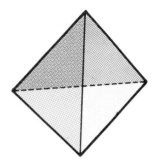

Tetrahedron

A model cube can be made from a set of six equal squares.

A model tetrahedron can be made from four equilateral triangles.

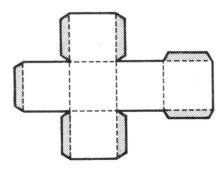

Net of a cube
Score along the dotted lines with a biro to assist folding. Cut carefully. Glue flaps.

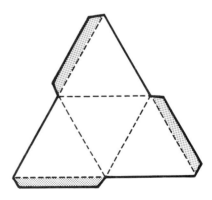

Net of a tetrahedron

165

Exercise 16·1 (Use thin card for these models)

A 1 Make a set of model cubes with edges 30, 40, 50 and 60 mm long. Use a different net arrangement for each cube. Colour your cubes and keep them.
Note that the 60 mm cube would hold 8 times as much sand as the 30 mm cube.

2 Make a set of regular tetrahedra, with edges of 42 mm, 56 mm, 70 mm and 84 mm. Colour the tetrahedra. They should fit inside the cubes of question 1.

3 Use your models to answer the following questions.
(a) How many vertices has each cube and each tetrahedron?
(b) How many faces has each cube and each tetrahedron?
(c) How many edges has each cube and each tetrahedron?

4 How many different ways can a cube be coloured with two colours if only one colour can be used on each face and no vertex is completely one colour?

5 How many different ways can a tetrahedron be coloured with two colours if only one colour can be used on each face?

6 A tetrahedron is coloured red, blue, green and yellow – one colour for each face. Can there be two different colour arrangements which cannot be made the same by moving the tetrahedron?

B 1 How many different routes (along edges) could be taken from one vertex of a cube to the next (A to E in the diagram at the start of the unit). List them.

2 How many different routes could be taken from one vertex to another on a tetrahedron?

3 Measure the longest diagonals of each of your cubes and check that the length is
$\sqrt{x^2 + x^2 + x^2}$, where x is the length of an edge.
How many 'longest diagonals' are there altogether in each cube?

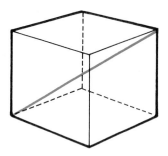

4 Measure the height of each tetrahedron in question **A2**.
Check that the height is the same whichever face is horizontal.
Show that the height is

$$\frac{\sqrt{2}}{\sqrt{3}} x$$

where x is the length of the side.

The calculator sequence to give $\frac{\sqrt{2}}{\sqrt{3}} x$ is:

2 $\boxed{\sqrt{}}$ $\boxed{\div}$ 3 $\boxed{\sqrt{}}$ $\boxed{=}$ $\boxed{\times}$ x $\boxed{=}$

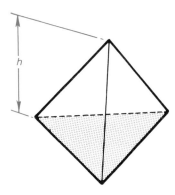

5 The space in an 8 cm cube can be filled exactly with one regular tetrahedron and four congruent tetrahedra like the one shown below.

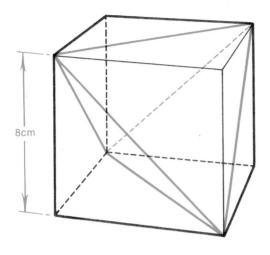 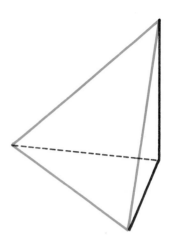

Work out the dimensions of the four congruent tetrahedra and then draw their nets. Make models of the cube, the regular tetrahedron and the four congruent tetrahedra. Colour your models and pack the tetrahedra into the cube.

C *Angles and packing*
Spaces can be filled without gaps by packing cubes together. What other shapes can be packed together in this way? Investigate!

16·2   Octahedron and dodecahedron

These two regular solids have 8 faces and 12 faces.

The 8 faces of the octahedron are all equilateral triangles.

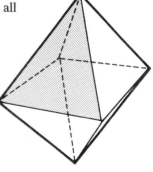

The 12 faces of the dodecahedron are all regular pentagons.

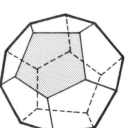

Exercise 16·2

A **1** The octahedron can be made from two pyramids: each pyramid has a square base, with four equilateral triangles making the sides of the pyramid.

Work out the nets of these pyramids and make a pair of them. Glue them together to make a complete octahedron. Then answer these questions:
  (a) How many vertices, edges and faces does the octahedron have?
  (b) Can the octahedron fill space without gaps? (Share models with other people to answer this question.)
  (c) How many different routes can you find from the top vertex to the bottom vertex of the octahedron?

2 The complete octahedron can be made from the net below.
  (a) Make it and compare it with the one you made from two pyramids. Add flaps where necessary.
  (b) Can you find another net of eight equilateral triangles that will fold into an octahedron?

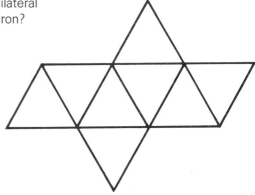

3 Make a set of regular octahedra and colour them in three different colours, one colour per face. How many different colour arrangements can you find if:
  (a) No adjacent sides have the same colour?
  (b) Two pairs of adjacent sides have the same colour?
  How could the above colouring problem be solved without making models?

B **1** Drawing a regular pentagon. It is necessary to draw a regular pentagon before further models can be made. Two methods are given below. Try them both.

Method I

1∅ Draw a circle and one radius

2∅ Draw another radius at 72° to the first

3∅ Step off equal intervals around the circumference, two clockwise and two anticlockwise

4∅ Join the step marks

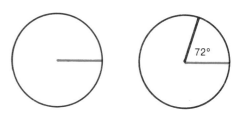

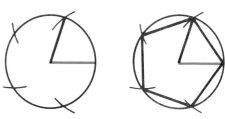

168

Method II

1 mm² graph paper.
Suppose you want the side to be 4 cm.

1∅ Draw the base line AB so that there is a clear axis of symmetry

2∅ Construct an angle of 108° by adding 18° to the right angle at A: use tan 18° = 0·325

3∅ Measure 4 cm up from A to find the 3rd vertex (E) of the pentagon

4∅ Find the 4th vertex (C) by symmetry

5∅ Find the 5th vertex: it will be on the axis of symmetry of the base and 4 cm from C and E

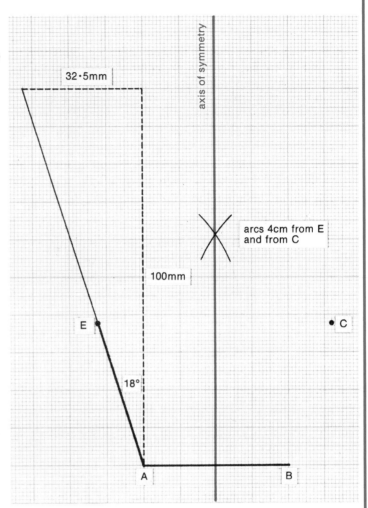

32·5mm

axis of symmetry

arcs 4cm from E and from C

100mm

E

C

18°

A   B

2 Enlarging a regular pentagon
Once you have an exact regular pentagon it can be used to draw another with a different length of side.

1∅ Draw radial lines AB, AC, AD, AE

2∅ Measure the required length along AB

3∅ Draw lines parallel to the sides of the first pentagon to form the new one

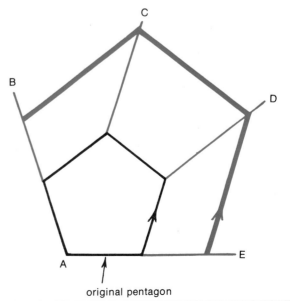

original pentagon

(a) Draw an accurate regular pentagon of side 4 cm.

(b) Extend your pentagon to form one with sides 6·5 cm long. Check the equality of its sides with a ruler.

3 Show that any polygon can be enlarged by the method described in question 2 by giving an example of your own choice.

4 (a) A net for a regular dodecahedron is given below. Make a copy of the net (but enlarge the pentagons), cut it out and fold it into a model.

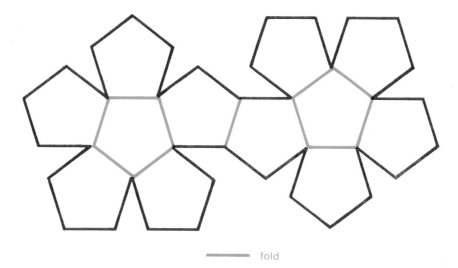

— fold

(b) Use your model to decide the best places for tabs on the net. Make a new net with tabs, and a new model: it should be stronger than the first, especially if you glue the tabs.

5 Colour your model dodecahedra so that the pattern of colouring is the same at every vertex.

6 Use your models to answer these questions about the regular dodecahedron.

(a) How many faces, edges and vertices does the dodecahedron have?

(b) What is the total distance from one vertex to the opposite vertex by the shortest route along edges?

(c) What sizes of angles can be found on the dodecahedron?

(d) Estimate the total surface area of the dodecahedron.

16·3 The regular icosahedron

It may surprise you to learn that there are only five regular polyhedra. (After all, it is possible to draw a regular polygon with any number of sides.) The five were known to the ancient Greeks more than 2000 years ago and are known as the Platonic solids.

The icosahedron is made up of 20 equilateral triangles, with five of them meeting at every vertex. Its net is very simple to draw.

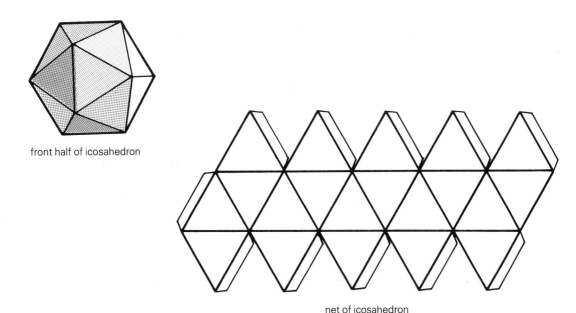

front half of icosahedron

net of icosahedron

Exercise 16·3

Make a model of an icosahedron. You will have to draw very carefully, and perhaps make two or more attempts. When you have made the model, colour it and answer the following questions.

1 How many edges and vertices does an icosahedron have?

2 Find regular pentagonal points (sets of points which would form pentagons if joined), square points, and regular hexagonal points on the model.

3 Estimate the surface area of the icosahedron and also its radius (r), which is half its diameter. (The diameter is the distance between opposite vertices.) Do you agree that surface area is approximately $12r^2$?

4 A planet in another galaxy is icosahedral in shape. Suggest some of the differences from Earth landscape that you would expect. (Think about the sea and the mountains.)

5 What would be the greatest possible distance between two vertices of the icosahedron? Aircraft and ships travel in great circles on the Earth. Can you find routes like great circles on the icosahedron?

6 Modern dance uses the vertices of an icosahedron as reference points for a dancer. If you want to know more about this, ask your dance teacher.

Unit 17 Statistics

17·1 More about averages

Averages 'iron out' differences. For this reason they are useful in finding underlying laws or trends.

Example:

The heights of the girls and boys in one class were all measured on the 1st of October in 1981, 1982, 1983 and 1984. (In 1981 the children were all 11 years old.) Find the average heights for boys and for girls, for each year. What do the averages show?

Name	Height (inches)			
	1981	1982	1983	1984
Joanne Andover	64	65	67	68
Susan Bass	61	63	64	66
Jeni Devi	58	60	61	62
Christine Elton	67	68	70	72
Dolly Fulson	61	62	64	65
Ruth Gordini	55	56	58	62
Sue Hall	59	60	62	64
Elisabeth Jones	69	69	70	70
Alison Khan	62	64	64	66
Pat Miller	57	58	61	64
Marilyn O'Leary	59	60	62	64
Doreen Penn	66	67	67	67
Ravu Singh	60	62	63	63
Sandra Tall	63	64	66	68
Brett Allen	63	63	65	68
Thomas Archway	61	61	62	64
Tim Bull	58	59	61	63
Simon Burns	54	55	56	57
Chris Crittall	62	63	66	69
John Dow	60	61	63	63
Kevin Foxton	56	58	59	60
Gary Hill	68	68	70	72
Mitch Howe	62	64	65	66
Taj Jamal	59	60	62	63
Vic Jones	55	56	56	60
Steven King	66	66	69	72

Average heights for girls
1981 61·5 in.
1982 62·7 in.
1983 64·2 in.
1984 65·8 in.

Average heights for boys
1981 60·1 in.
1982 60·9 in.
1983 62·6 in.
1984 64·7 in.

Name	Height (inches)			
	1981	1982	1983	1984
Brian Lennox	61	62	64	67
Ladi Naidoo	58	58	61	64
Charles Phillips	53	53	55	58
John Prince	65	66	68	70

The averages show that the girls were generally taller than the boys of the same age. The girls had a growth spurt in 1983 (when they were 13 years old) and left the boys behind. By 1984 the boys were catching up fast!

The averages alone would not tell you that some boys were taller than some girls, or show the wide differences in heights that exist among boys and girls.

Exercise 17·1

A These questions refer to the example above.
1 Which girl was tallest in   (a) 1981   (b) 1983   (c) 1984?
2 Which girl grew the greatest amount in one year?
3 Which boys were taller than Doreen Penn in 1981?
4 Which boys were taller than Doreen Penn in 1984?
5 Find the increases in average height for the boys and for the girls for 1981–82, 1982–83 and 1983–84. At what age do there appear to be growth spurts for boys and for girls?
6 Which boys were above the average in 1981 and in 1984?
7 Make an investigation into the heights of the people in your class.
   Or investigate the heights of 1st-year, 2nd-year, 3rd-year and 4th-year pupils in your school. There may be medical records for past pupils that can be used.

B Calculate averages for the following sets of data and discuss the way differences are 'ironed out' by averaging.
1 The number of hours a pupil spends on homework during the 30 weeks of a school year:
   Term 1:   4, 7, 7, 9, 6, 7, 5, 6, 3, 2
   Term 2:   5, 7, 10, 11, 7, 10, 6, 11, 9, 5
   Term 3:   6, 5, 8, 10, 8, 11, 7, 8, 3, 0
2 The length of life (in hours) of batteries used in cassette players, when tested at the factory:
   Batch 1:   7, 11, 12, 14, 10, 9, 13, 11, 14, 10
   Batch 2:   8, 7, 8, 11, 13, 9, 12, 13, 15, 7
   Batch 3:   9, 11, 10, 14, 14, 12, 13, 10, 11, 9
   Batch 4:   13, 14, 10, 8, 14, 11, 15, 12, 11, 11
3 Twelve people in a club recorded three attempts each at the high jump. The heights (in cm) were:

	A	B	C	D	E	F	G	H	I	J	K	L
1st jump	193	188	183	178	180	185	190	175	180	185	172	183
2nd jump	190	190	180	178	185	183	188	183	180	183	174	188
3rd jump	190	193	183	178	175	183	190	188	185	175	172	185

(a) Find the average of the three jumps for each person (A, B, C, ... etc.).
(b) Find the average height for the first jump, the second and the third.
(c) Would you agree that 'on the whole, the jumpers did best with their first jump'?

4 A dentist recorded the number of fillings in the teeth of 100 teenagers aged 14–17.

14 years: 5, 8, 4, 0, 2, 8, 3, 7, 5, 8, 12, 4, 0, 2, 1, 6, 9, 10, 12, 8, 6, 10, 0, 6, 3

15 years: 2, 0, 8, 6, 10, 13, 11, 5, 7, 13, 10, 5, 8, 6, 4, 9, 10, 8, 6, 7, 5, 8, 12, 6, 10

16 years: 4, 5, 7, 12, 10, 14, 8, 4, 8, 6, 8, 0, 6, 4, 8, 9, 11, 10, 13, 3, 5, 8, 0, 6, 10

17 years: 12, 3, 2, 0, 5, 0, 7, 8, 3, 11, 5, 8, 6, 14, 10, 6, 9, 5, 10, 9, 13, 2, 5, 6, 0

Find the average for each age-group and comment.

5 A class noted the price per pound of apples and tomatoes over the course of a year and found the average price for each month.

	Jan	Feb	Mar	Apr	May	Jun	Jul	Aug	Sep	Oct	Nov	Dec
Tomatoes	65	60	58	48	40	42	35	30	28	35	45	52
Apples	35	38	35	37	36	34	28	25	20	15	22	29

(a) Find the average price of each fruit over the year. What factors cause the changes in price?

(b) Compare the average price of each fruit for the six winter months (Jan–Mar + Oct–Dec) with the average for the six months April–September.

6 A survey by a police radar device recorded the following speeds for particular coaches, lorries, cars and motor-bikes. The speeds are given in kilometres per hour (km/h).

 100, 120, 110, 105, 110, 100, 95, 102

 75, 80, 80, 85, 78, 85, 95, 110, 90, 110, 85, 90, 80, 84, 76, 82, 90, 88, 95, 100

 110, 120, 125, 110, 100, 106, 110, 120, 130, 106, 104, 98, 118, 122, 126, 118, 130, 112

 105, 95, 108, 110, 110, 112, 98, 122, 130

(a) Find the average speed for each type of vehicle.

(b) Do you agree with this order of average speeds?
Car > Bike > Coach > Lorry

C Sometimes the average of a set of data is known, but the raw data is not available. It is then possible to construct different models of raw data to fit the known facts.

Example:

The average of five numbers is 10. Suggest models for the set of numbers.

The numbers could be   10, 10, 10, 10, 10
    or   5, 10, 15, 10, 10
    or   3, 8, 21, 12, 6
    or   25, 25, 10, − 5, − 5
    or   3·5, 7·5, 18, 10·4, 10·6

In fact, the numbers could be any set of five numbers that add up to 50.

If more information is given, the number of alternative models is reduced. For example, if it is known that:

(a) all the numbers are whole numbers

and (b) all the numbers are greater than 7

and (c) all the numbers are less than 13

and (d) the average of the five numbers is 10

then the following models are possible:

(12 11 10 9 8)

(12 12 10 8 8)

(11 11 10 9 9)

(11 11 11 9 8)

(12 11 11 8 8)

(12 11 9 9 9)

(12 10 10 10 8)

(12 10 10 9 9)

(10 10 10 10 10)

And one more. Can you find it?

A further restriction, allowing only one pair, would eliminate all but the first model (12 11 10 9 8).

---

1   Four numbers have an average of 6. Suggest six different models for the set of numbers, if:
     (a) the numbers are all whole numbers
  and (b) the numbers are all different.

2   Five numbers have an average of zero. Suggest four different models for the numbers, if:
     (a) none of the numbers are integers (positive or negative whole numbers)
  and (b) none of the numbers is larger than 1.

3   (a) A die is thrown three times and the average score is 6. What can you say about the scores in the three throws? Give models.

    (b) A die is thrown four times. The average score is 4. What can you say about the four throws?

4   Two dice were thrown together four times. The average score was 10. Give models for the four throws.

5   (a) What would you expect the average of a large number of throws with a die to be? Give your reasons.

    (b) What would you expect the average of a large number of throws with a pair of dice to be? Give your reasons.

6   A train travels non-stop from Leeds to Plymouth in 5 hours, giving an average speed for the journey of 64 miles per hour.

    (a) Make a model of the journey in the form of a travel graph on graph paper.

    (b) Another train from Leeds to Plymouth stops at Sheffield, Birmingham and Bristol. Make a model of this journey.

    (c) Compare the two journeys if both trains have an average speed of 64 mph.

17·2 Moving averages

A different way of looking for trends in a set of data is to plot a 'moving average'. This is done in the two examples which follow.

Example 1:

The price of tomatoes was recorded monthly over a year:

Month	Jan	Feb	Mar	Apr	May	June	July	Aug	Sept	Oct	Nov	Dec
pence/lb	65	60	58	48	40	42	35	30	28	35	45	52

The first 6-month moving average is the average of the six months starting with January, the second is for the six months starting with February, then with March, etc. The averages work out as follows:

Jan–June	Feb–July	Mar–Aug	Apr–Sept	May–Oct	June–Nov	July–Dec
52·2	47·2	42·2	37·2			

The 'ironing-out' effect is shown clearly on a graph. The bar-chart shows the monthly averages, the coloured curve the 6-month moving averages.

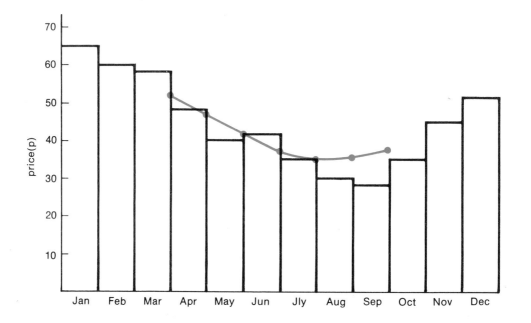

Note: The little jump in price in June has been smoothed out in the moving average. So has the minimum in September.

Example 2:

In a game of ludo, one player threw 5, 6, 2, 3, 3, 1, 5, 4, 6, 3, 2, 2, 4, 5, 1, 3, 6, 3, 2, 4, 5, 5, 3, 4, 1, 2, 6 in 27 throws of a die. The moving averages for five throws are 3·8, 3, 2·8, 3·2, 3·8, etc.

The single scores and the moving averages are shown on the graph below.

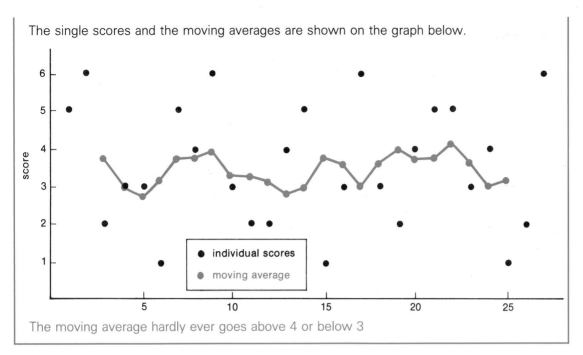

The moving average hardly ever goes above 4 or below 3

Exercise 17·2

A These questions refer to the data of the examples above.

1 Calculate the values of the last three moving averages of tomato prices from the data given.

2 What would you expect to happen to the moving average of tomato prices in October, November and December?

3 Calculate the remaining values of the moving average calculated over five throws of the die.

4 How would you expect the moving average score for the die to continue over the next 27 throws?

5 Calculate moving averages over ten throws of the die from the data given. Plot a new graph showing the ten-throw moving average in a third colour.

B Plot graphs to show the following sets of data.

1 A supermarket kept records of the amount of sugar sold each week. Draw a graph of the data and show the four-weekly moving average.

Week	1	2	3	4	5	6	7	8	9	10	11	12	13	14	15	16	17	18	19	20
Sugar sold (tonnes)	4	7	9	6	5	4	8	10	7	6	5	5	9	8	11	10	9	10	11	8

Would you say that the data showed an increasing trend?

2 The rainfall over England and Scotland in 1983 is given below in millimetres per month. Calculate a three-month moving average for England and one for Scotland and plot them, and the raw data, on the same graph. Comment.

	Jan	Feb	Mar	Apr	May	June	July	Aug	Sept	Oct	Nov	Dec
England	111	86	78	52	47	70	89	71	54	19	54	174
Scotland	158	104	166	52	40	69	90	110	177	99	198	156

3 The scores from throwing a pair of dice are given below. Plot the scores and a ten-throw moving average for the data. Then look back to your answer to Exercise 17·1 C, question 5b.

Scores (in order):7, 6, 6, 7, 8, 9, 7, 4, 9, 8, 5, 7, 6, 6, 8, 6, 5, 5, 8, 7, 5, 6, 5, 7, 10, 6, 5, 5, 7, 11, 9, 5, 6, 5, 8, 9, 3, 5, 6, 3, 5, 5, 6, 5, 8, 10, 2, 7, 7, 4

4 A newspaper shop sells *The Sun, The Mirror* and *The Guardian* and records the number sold each day. Calculate a simple average (sales per day) and a series of 6-day moving averages for each paper. Would you expect much difference between the two sorts of averages?

	M	Tu	W	Th	F	S		M	Tu	W	Th	F	S
Sun	50	60	45	70	70	35		48	55	70	65	80	60
Mirror	32	40	48	40	42	50		45	38	44	60	32	38
Guardian	12	18	22	14	16	30		14	22	—	36	24	26

	M	Tu	W	Th	F	S		M	Tu	W	Th	F	S
Sun	54	61	65	60	70	30		30	42	50	52	45	40
Mirror	42	36	—	—	60	72		40	32	42	44	34	39
Guardian	18	25	30	32	18	22		16	14	20	18	21	18

C The graph below gives 10-year moving averages for sunshine at the London Weather Centre (in central London) and at the Kew Observatory (on the edge of London). Given in the data are the average number of hours of sunshine each month from December to February.

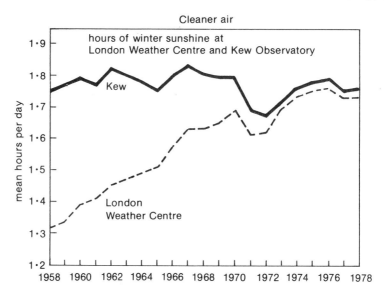

1 Why is a moving average used to show this data?
2 Why has the air become cleaner over the centre of London?
3 How many hours of sunshine would you expect altogether *from December to February in 1986* in London?
4 How does London compare with your area for hours of sunshine?

17·3 Cumulative frequency

This is a complicated name for a simple and useful idea. In the example below we calculate the ordinary frequency and the cumulative frequency of the same set of data.

Example:

The thirty people in class 4R wrote down the amount of their weekly pocket-money, including earnings from jobs. The list looked like this:

Joanne	£1·35	Marilyn	£1·40	Kevin	60p
Susan	60p	Doreen	£2·80	Gary	£1·80
Jeni	75p	Rava	£3·40	Mitch	£2·25
Christine	£1·20	Sandra	£1·75	Taj	£1·60
Dolly	£2·20	Brett	£1·20	Vic	£3·20
Ruth	£2·40	Tom	£1·60	Steven	£2·80
Sue	£1·85	Simon	80p	Brian	£2·10
Elspeth	90p	Tim	£2·30	Ladi	£1·90
Alison	£1·90	Chris	£1·80	Charles	£1·30
Pat	£2·35	John	£2·40	John	£1·10

This raw data is organised below into a frequency table. The third column gives the cumulative frequency (c.f.).

Amount of pocket money	Number of people (frequency)	Cumulative frequency
0–50p	0	0
51p–£1	5	5
£1·01–£1·50	6	11
£1·51–£2·00	8	19
£2·01–£2·50	7	26
£2·51–£3·00	2	28
£3·01–£3·50	2	30
	30	

The cumulative frequency keeps a running total of the frequency.

19 people $(0 + 5 + 6 + 8)$ have pocket-money of £2 or less, while

28 people have £3 or under.

The final cumulative frequency should equal the total frequency of the data, since all the people have been counted.

Exercise 17·3

Organise the following sets of raw data into frequency tables. Complete a cumulative frequency column in each case. (Work with a partner if possible.)

1 Number of exam subjects passed by 100 young people aged 16:

7 2 6 0 8 0 6 3 0 1 8 9 2 7 0 0 1 9 4 8 3 1 0 9 6 3 8
9 1 3 1 2 7 8 8 9 5 6 0 9 4 4 7 0 4 5 1 5 2 9 4 9 0 2
9 7 5 6 4 3 9 4 8 3 1 1 5 3 3 5 4 5 6 9 6 3 5 8 3 8 2
2 9 5 5 2 4 1 6 3 4 8 1 1 1 0 3 7 0 5

2 Hours of paid work done in a week by a sample of 50 school children (including baby-sitting):

```
5 0 2 1 2 4 4 2 0 0
0 1 2 0 4 3 0 2 6 0
5 0 0 3 0 2 4 0 2 3
0 3 0 2 3 0 3 0 0 2
1 0 0 3 2 0 0 3 0 4
```

How would this data compare with a similar set collected from your class?

3 Number of hours of TV watched by a sample of 60 students in one week:

```
17 22 14  9 13 21 23 26 27 16  8 15  0
13 20 23 14 24 19  7 10 17 22 25 20 18
 9 11 15 23 29 24 24 20 10 18 16 12  4
19 26 21 14 27 12  8 13 21  0 22 28  6
15 25 30 12 20  7  5 14
```

(Group the data 0–4, 5–9, 10–14, etc.)

4 Weekly rent paid by 50 families living in rented accommodation. Group the data 0–£9·99, £10–£19·99, £20–£29·99, etc.

£32·00	£15·50	£18·00	£9·50	£14·80	£36·50	£42·00	£21·00
£33·00	£40·00	£8·50	£17·00	£25·20	£36·00	£12·00	£19·00
£7·50	£16·70	£28·00	£31·50	£22·00	£18·60	£24·50	£44·00
£36·30	£25·00	£17·50	£28·50	£35·00	£8·50	£48·00	£12·50
£33·00	£21·00	£27·50	£18·00	£36·00	£34·20	£40·00	£15·50
£31·20	£14·50	£26·00	£28·00	£44·50	£19·00	£27·20	£26·50
£31·00	£37·20						

5 Make 100 throws with a pair of dice. Make up a frequency table with a cumulative-frequency column from for your own experimental data.

6 A sample of people were asked if they favoured unilateral nuclear disarmament. In response to

the statement by the CND that 'Britain should get rid of all her nuclear weapons', they were asked to choose one of these replies:

- strongly agree (SA)
- agree (A)
- uncertain (U)
- disagree (D)
- strongly disagree (SD)

The results were:
SA, U, D, SD, U, A, D, SA, D, A, D, U, SD, A, SA, U, SD, SD, SD, U, SA, A, A, SA, D, SA, SD, SA, A, U, SA, U, SD, D, SA, D, SD, A, SA, SD, D, A, SA, A, U, SA, D, SA, SD, D, A, SA, A, SA, SD, D, U, U, SA, D, SA, D, SD, U, U, A, D, SD, SA

Make a frequency table with a cumulative-frequency column and use it to answer these questions:

(a) How many people did not strongly agree with CND?
(b) How many people agreed or were uncertain?
(c) How do the results of this survey compare with the opinions of the people in your class?

Unit 18 Trigonometry

18·1 Sin, cos, tan (Revision)

These are the three important ratios found in a right-angled triangle.
They are functions of the angles: the values of sin θ, cos θ and tan θ
depend on the value of θ and nothing else.
The values can be obtained from a scientific calculator or a book of
tables.

Example:
Find the values of sin 42°, cos 36° and tan 27·4°

calculator
sin 42°   = 0·669 130 606
cos 36°   = 0·809 016 994
tan 27·4° = 0·518 350 765

tables
sin 42°   = 0·669
cos 36°   = 0·809
tan 27·4° = 0·518

The ratios are easily found in any right-angled triangle.
First find the hypotenuse (h in the figure).

$\sin \theta = y/h$ $\tan \theta = y/x$
$\cos \theta = x/h$

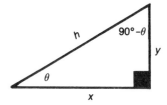

Note: $\cos \theta = \sin(90° - \theta)$
         $\sin \theta = \cos(90° - \theta)$
'cos' stands for cosine, sine of the co-angle (see M1 Unit 27·2).

Solving triangles

Sin, cos and tan can be used to 'solve' a right-angled triangle. This
means finding all the sides and angles, *given one side and one angle*.

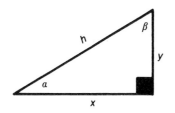

Two programs for solving a right-
angled triangle are given below.

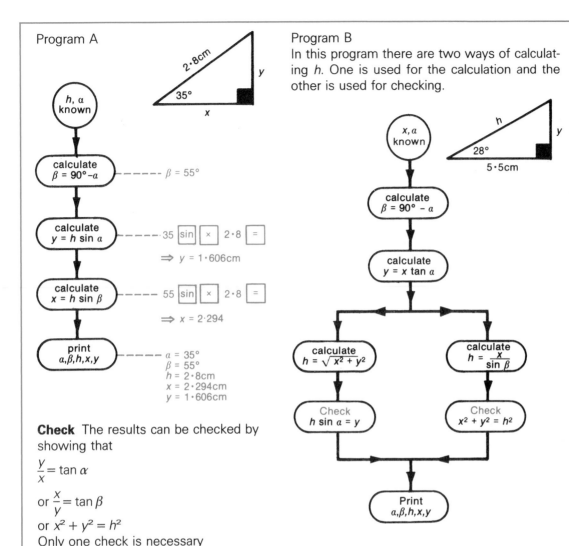

Program A

h, α known

calculate
β = 90° − α ------ β = 55°

calculate
y = h sin α ------ 35 $\boxed{\text{sin}}$ × 2·8 $\boxed{=}$

⟹ y = 1·606cm

calculate
x = h sin β ------ 55 $\boxed{\text{sin}}$ × 2·8 $\boxed{=}$

⟹ x = 2·294

print
a,β,h,x,y ------ α = 35°
β = 55°
h = 2·8cm
x = 2·294cm
y = 1·606cm

Check The results can be checked by showing that

$$\frac{y}{x} = \tan \alpha$$

or $\frac{x}{y} = \tan \beta$

or $x^2 + y^2 = h^2$

Only one check is necessary

In this case, $\frac{y}{x} = 0·700 = \tan \alpha$

Program B
In this program there are two ways of calculating h. One is used for the calculation and the other is used for checking.

x, α known

calculate
β = 90° − α

calculate
y = x tan α

calculate
h = √ x² + y²

Check
h sin α = y

calculate
h = $\frac{x}{\sin \beta}$

Check
x² + y² = h²

Print
a,β,h,x,y

Exercise 18·1

A 1 Work through program A above and check that you agree with the values found for β, x and y.

2 Work through the second program for x = 5·5 cm and α = 28°. Check that both routes give the same value for h. Check this example by drawing on 1 mm² paper.

3 Rewrite program A so that the check is included in the program. Then use it to solve a triangle for which h = 13 cm and α = 44°.

4 Modify program B to solve a triangle when y and α are known. Then work through your program for y = 5·5 cm and α = 31·2°.

5 (a) Construct a program for the solution of a triangle in which x and y are known, but neither α nor β.

(b) Use your program to find the angles of triangles (i) to (iv) on the next page.

183

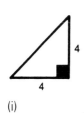
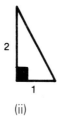

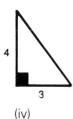

(i)   (ii)   (iii)   (iv)

B Solve the triangle for each set of data given below.
1   △ABC where $\hat{A} = 90°$, BC = 15 cm and $\hat{B} = 37°$.
2   △XYZ where XY = 43 cm, YZ = 27 cm, and $\hat{Y} = 90°$.
3   △PQR where $\hat{P} = 90°$, QR = 17 cm and $\hat{Q} = 44°$.
4   △LMN where LM = 12 cm, MN = 13 cm and $\hat{M} = 90°$.
5   △EFG where $\hat{F} = 37°$, $\hat{G} = 90°$ and EF = 2·6 metres.

C In the problems which follow it is not always necessary to solve the triangle completely. The best technique, however, is to solve the triangle and then select the values you want. This has the advantage that the checks are built in. Most of the questions are taken from past examination papers.

1   For the right-angled triangle shown, calculate the length w to the nearest millimetre. *(EA 1975)*

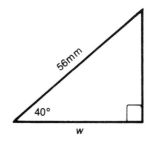

2

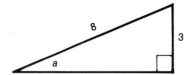

    The diagram represents a section of a steep road. All the measurements are in metres. Calculate the value of a to the nearest degree. *(YR 1978 (II))*

3   In the figure (which is not drawn to scale), AD is perpendicular to BD and is 100 metres high. If $A\hat{B}C = 30°$ and $A\hat{C}D = 45°$, calculate:
  (a) the lengths of CD and AB
  (b) the angle $B\hat{A}C$
  (c) the length of AC in square root form
  (d) the following ratios in square root form:
    (i) $\sin A\hat{C}D$ (ii) $\cos A\hat{B}D$ (iii) $\tan B\hat{A}D$ (iv) BC/AD
(EA 1972)

4 A rectangle ABCD is shown in the diagram below. Angle $\hat{BAC} = x°$, angle $\hat{ACB} = y°$, length AB = 3 cm, length BC = 7 cm.
Which of the following are true statements?
(a) $x + y = 90°$ (b) angle $\hat{ACD} = y°$ (c) the area of $\triangle$ ABC is 10·5 cm²   (d) $\tan x = \frac{3}{7}$
(e) $\cos x = 3/\sqrt{58}$

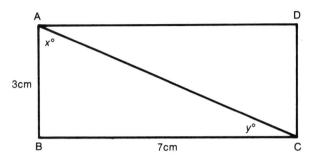

5 A telegraph pole is supported by a tight stretched wire. The wire is attached to a point 12 metres above the base of the pole. The other end is attached to an 'anchor' 5 metres from the base. Calculate the minimum length of the wire.

6 In the diagram, AD = DF = 10 cm, $\hat{DAC} = 20°$, $\hat{DFC} = 30°$.
Calculate the length of AC.

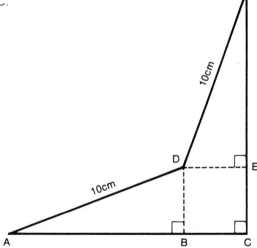

7 An aircraft climbs at an angle of 40° to the horizontal. Its speed is 280 miles an hour. How much height will the aircraft gain in one minute? (1 mile = 5280 feet)

8 A rocket travelling in a straight line at 1000 m/sec gains 40 000 m of height in one minute. What is the angle of climb of the rocket?

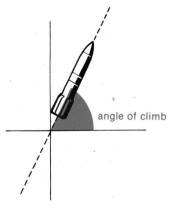

angle of climb

185

9 A circle has radius 6 cm. Calculate the length of a chord which subtends 140° at the centre. Calculate the length of another chord which also subtends 140° at the centre.

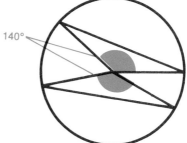

10 A bridge over a motorway is in three sections—two ramps sloping up at 9° to the horizontal, and a horizontal central section 8 m above the motorway. A car going from A to B over the bridge travels 180 m. Calculate:
(a) the length of each ramp
(b) the length of the central section (assume A and B are level with the motorway)

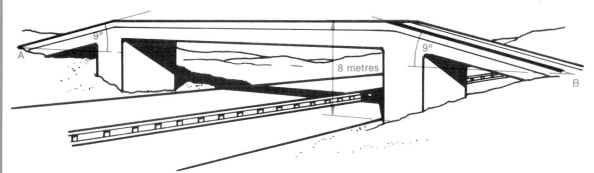

18·2 Elevation, depression and slope

Angles measured from the horizontal plane are given the special names angles of elevation **and** angles of depression.

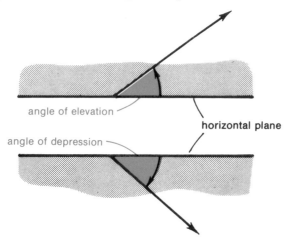

These angles are important in air-traffic control, surveying, navigation and warfare.

Example 1:

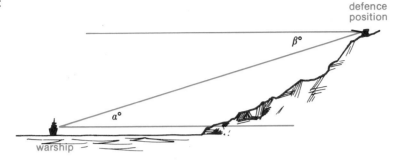

defence position

The angle of elevation of the defence position from the warship is $\alpha°$.
The angle of depression of the warship from the defence position is $\beta°$.
Clearly $\alpha = \beta$ in this example.

Example 2:

The angle of elevation of the top of
a tree from a point 12 metres from its
base is 72°. Find the height of the tree.

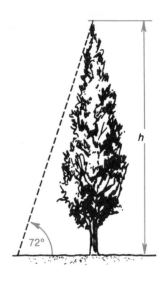

If the height of the tree is h metres,

$$\frac{h}{12} = \tan 72°$$
$$\Rightarrow h = 12 \tan 72°$$
$$\Rightarrow h = 36\cdot93 \text{ metres}$$

The slope of a line is measured by the tangent of the angle of elevation.
To find the slope of a straight
line, choose any points O and P
on the line.

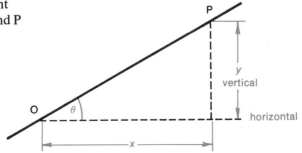

The slope is the ratio $\dfrac{y}{x}$

i.e. $\dfrac{\text{the distance moved up}}{\text{the distance moved along}}$ in moving from O to P.

Thus slope $= \tan \theta$

When the slope of a road is found, it is only possible to measure along the surface of the road. In this case the slope is indicated by sin θ. In the figure, sin $\theta = \frac{h}{d} = \frac{1}{3}$

(If θ is less than 10°, the difference between sin θ and tan θ is less than 0·003.)

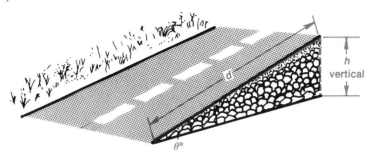

STEEP HILL
1 in 3

Exercise 18·2

A 1 Measure the angles of elevation and depression in each of the diagrams below.

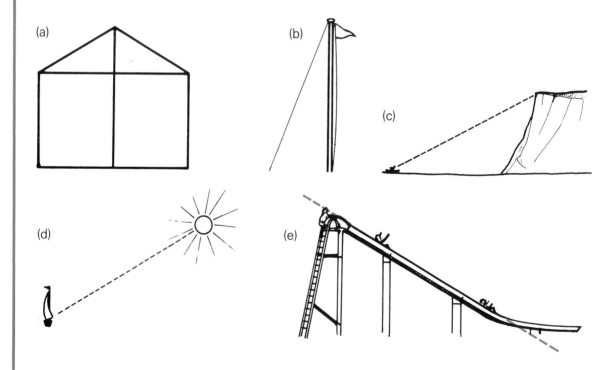

(a) (b) (c) (d) (e)

2 A radar system detects an unidentified flying object (UFO). The angle of elevation is 14° and its distance is 45 km. Calculate the height of the UFO above the ground.

3 A ship in trouble is spotted by a coastguard, directly out to sea. The angle of depression is 4·5°. Calculate the distance from the coastguard station to the ship if the station is at a height of 200 m above sea level.

4 An aircraft coming in to land is flying along a beam from the control tower. At 02.30 the angle of elevation is 24°, the distance 72 km. At 02.35 the angle of elevation is 30° and its distance 40 km. How much height has been lost during the five minutes of flight? (Solve the problem by making an accurate drawing.)

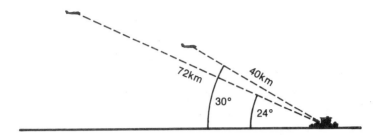

5 A garage is built with a sloping roof. Calculate the angle of slope of the roof, given that the centre ridge is 4·4 metres high, the walls are 5 metres apart, and the walls are 2·1 metres high.

6 A UFO shows up on a radar screen at a distance of 200 km and an angle of elevation of 16°. Is the object more likely to be an aircraft (maximum height 16 km), a weather satellite (height 50–100 km) or a TV satellite (height 200–300 km)?

7 An aircraft crashed in the desert but just before it did so it was picked up on two radars 60 km apart. The angles of elevation were 14° on the first radar and 17° on the second at the moment when the pilot reported his height as 12 000 metres. Suggest how these angles of elevation could help in the search for survivors. Draw a plan of the radar stations and show where you think searches should be made.

8 An aircraft's altimeter is faulty. However, the pilot measures the angle of depression to the control tower to be 17° when his horizontal distance from it is 1400 metres. What is his height?

B The angles of elevation of the sun and the stars are used in navigation. Discuss the following ideas and find out more from the library.

1 It is possible to find out your latitude by observing the angle of elevation of:
(a) the sun at its highest point during the day
(b) the Pole Star

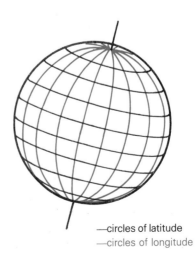

—circles of latitude
—circles of longitude

2 It is possible to find your longitude if you know Greenwich time when the sun rises.

3 Find some way of measuring the elevation of the Pole Star on a clear night at your home.
(If you were at the North Pole the elevation would be 90°.)
Compare your result with the latitude of your home read from an atlas.

4 Suggest how you could use a sextant to find your exact position at sea, using two tall objects on land and a map.

C *Slope*

1 A path up a hill has a slope of 0·4. What angle does the path make with the horizontal?

2 A train travels 7 kilometres downhill along a track with a slope of 1 : 141. How much height is lost by the train as it travels this section of the line?

3 The angle of a ski-slope is 36° to the horizontal. What is its gradient?

4 The centre ridge of a roof is 2·4 metres above the lower edges (see diagram). The total width of the roof is 8 metres.
(a) What is the slope of the roof?
(b) What is the angle of elevation from edge to ridge?

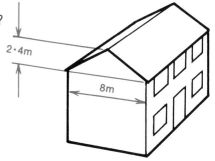

2·4m

8m

5 A steeple 35 metres high is built on a tower 20 metres high whose diameter is 10 metres.
  (a) Find the slope of the sides of the steeple.
  (b) What is the angle between the sides of the steeple and the vertical axis?
  (c) What is the angle of elevation of the top of the steeple from a point 100 metres from the base of the tower on the same horizontal plane?

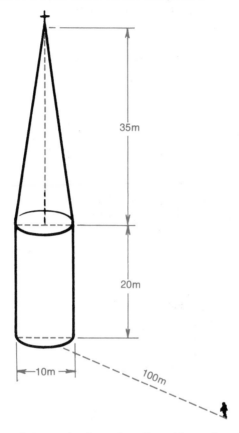

6 (a) Calculate the slope of the paths from A to B and from A to C on the contour map of a hill below.
  (b) Which part of the hill is steepest and which part has the gentlest slope?
      Look at a 1:50 000 map of your own area and find the steepest hill on the map.

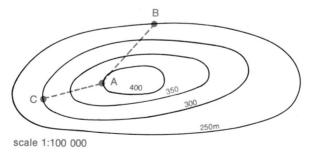

7 Show that the slope of the straight line joining PQ, where P is (3,5) and Q is (13,11), is 0·6. Deduce the angle between PQ (extended) and the x-axis.

8 · Use coordinates to find the slopes of AB, BC and CA in the diagram.
Note: The slopes of both BC and AC are negative because the line is going down as *x* increases.
What do you notice about the product of all three slopes?
(Multiply them together.)
Investigate further by choosing three other points as A, B and C.

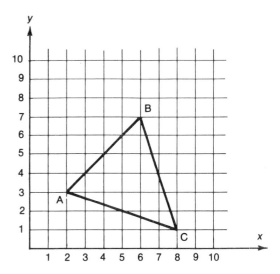

9 Draw a pair of axes and find a set of points A, B, X, Y such that the lines AB and XY are perpendicular. What connection can you find between their slopes?

10

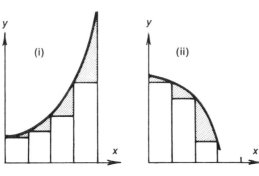

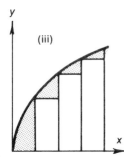

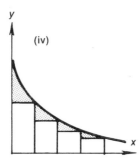

It is simple to find the slope of a straight line. On a curve, however, the slope is different at different points.

Match the following descriptions to the above diagrams:
(a) The slope is increasing as *x* increases
(b) The slope is negative but getting less (steep) as *x* increases
(c) The slope is positive but getting less (steep) as *x* increases
(d) The slope is negative and is getting more steep as *x* increases
Note: This type of graph is often used in newspapers to describe increasing unemployment, the fall in the rate of interest, etc. See if you can find some examples in a newspaper or magazine.

18·3 Angles over 90°

It is not possible to form a right-angled triangle when θ is more than 90°.
In spite of this, values can still be found for sin θ, cos θ and tan θ.

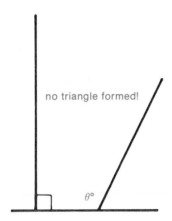

no triangle formed!

$\theta°$

Examples:
Find the values of sin 130°, cos 190° and tan 260° using a calculator.
sin 130°....130 [sin] → 0·766 044 44 [inv] [sin] → 50
cos 190°....190 [cos] → − 0·984 807 7
tan 260°....260 [tan] → 5·671 281 82
Using tables in reverse, or [inv] on the calculator, we find that sin 130° = sin 50°.

Exercise 18·3

Use a scientific calculator

1 (a) Find the values of (i) sin 95° (ii) sin 140° (iii) sin 179° (iv) sin 132·5°
   (b) Find angles between 0° and 90° which have the same sines as (i) 95° (ii) 140°
      (iii) 179° (iv) 132·5°

2 (a) Find the values of (i) cos 98° (ii) cos 160° (iii) cos 135° (iv) cos 200° (v) cos 225°
      (vi) cos 300°
   (b) You will notice that cos is sometimes positive and sometimes negative. Try to find a
      simple rule which will tell you what values of θ produce a negative value of cos θ.

3 (a) Find the values of (i) tan 127° (ii) tan 190° (iii) tan 145° (iv) tan 200°
      (v) tan 250° (vi) tan 312° (vii) tan 325°
   (b) Find angles between 0 and 90° which have the same numerical value as (i) tan 127°
      (ii) tan 200° (iii) tan 312°
   (c) Find a simple rule which will tell you when tan θ will have a negative value.

4 Copy and complete the table below using your calculator. Check that the rules that you have found in questions 2 and 3 agree with this table of results. Look out for patterns!

θ	$\sin\theta$	$\cos\theta$	$\tan\theta$	θ	$\sin\theta$	$\cos\theta$	$\tan\theta$
10°	0·174	0·985	0·176	190°	− 0.174		
20°	0·342			200°	− 0·342		
30°	0·5			210°	− 0·5		
40°	0·643			220°	− 0·643		
50°	0·766			230°	− 0·766		
60°	0·866			240°	− 0·866		
70°	0·940			250°	− 0·940		
80°	0·985			260°	− 0·985		
90°	1·000			270°	− 1		
100°	0·985			280°	− 0·985		
110°	0·940			290°	− 0·940		
120°	0·866			300°	− 0·866		
130°	0·766			310°	− 0·766		
140°	0·643			320°	− 0·643		
150°	0·5			330°	− 0·5		
160°	0·342			340°	− 0·342		
170°	0·174			350°	− 0·174		
180°	0			360°	0		

18·4   Graphs of sin and cos functions

The tables which have been constructed for Question 4 above can be used to draw the graph of the function $y = \sin x$. This beautiful shape is known as the sine curve. All waves are based on this shape.

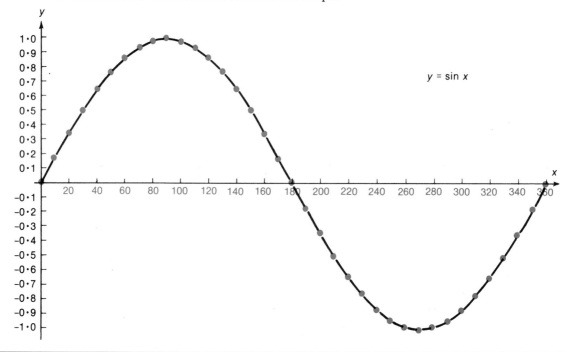

$y = \sin x$

Exercise 18·4

1 Use the graph to *estimate* the value of:
(a) sin 24° (b) sin 56° (c) sin 102° (d) sin 160°
(e) sin 188° (f) sin 232° (g) sin 288° (h) sin 304°
Check by calculator.

2 Use the graph to estimate two possible values of θ for which:
(a) sin θ = 0·3 (b) sin θ = 0·6 (c) sin θ = 0·9
(d) sin θ = − 0·2 (e) sin θ = − 0·4 (f) sin θ = − 0·8
Note: only one value can be found from the calculator using inv sin

3 Draw an accurate graph of cos θ on 1 mm² graph paper from the values of cos θ found in Question 4 of Exercise 18·3.
What is the connection between this graph and the graph of sin θ?

4 Use your graph of cos θ to estimate
(a) cos 24° (b) cos 56° (c) cos 102° (d) cos 160°
(e) cos 188° (f) cos 232° (g) cos 288° (h) cos 304°
Check by calculator.

5 Use the graph of cos θ to estimate two possible values of θ if
(a) cos θ = 0·4 (b) cos θ = 0·6 (c) cos θ = 0·9
(d) cos θ = − 0·15 (e) cos θ = − 0·35 (f) cos θ = − 0·75

6 Which of the following statements are true:
(a) sin θ lies between − 1 and + 1 whatever the value of θ
(b) cos θ lies between − 1 and + 1 whatever the value of θ
(c) cos θ = 0 ⟹ θ = 90° or 270° (d) sin θ = 1 ⟹ θ = 90° or 270°
(e) sin θ = cos θ ⟹ θ = 45° or 135°

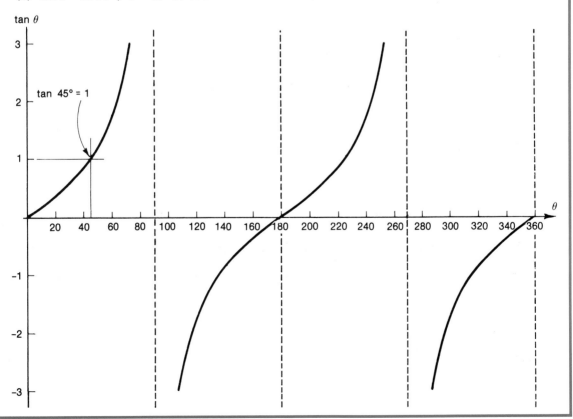

7 Investigate values of tan θ: (a) for $0 < \theta < 90°$ (b) for $90° < \theta < 180°$
Why would it be impossible to draw a complete graph for tan θ from 0 to 360°?

8 The graph of tan θ is given above. Use the graph to estimate values of θ for which
(a) $\tan \theta = 0.8$ (b) $\tan \theta = 1.6$ (c) $\tan \theta = -2$ (d) $\tan \theta = -3.5$

18·5 The unit circle

Sin, cos and tan ratios can be measured on a unit circle.

P is a point on a circle of unit radius.
The vector **OP** makes an angle θ with Ox, the x-axis.
$\sin \theta = $ PM
$\cos \theta = $ OM
$\tan \theta = $ RT

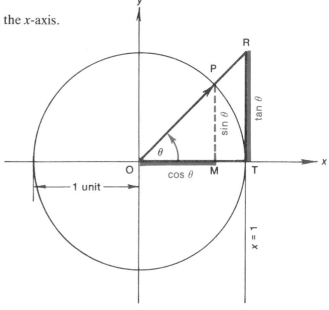

As **OP** moves round the circle we can see the changes taking place in
$\sin \theta$, $\cos \theta$ and $\tan \theta$.

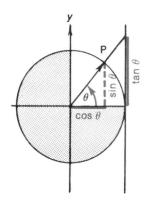 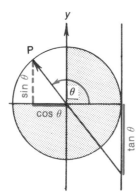 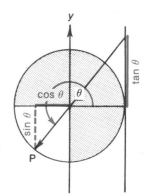 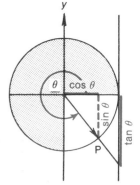

1st quadrant	**2nd quadrant**	**3rd quadrant**	**4th quadrant**
$0 < \theta < 90°$	$90° < \theta < 180°$	$180° < \theta < 270°$	$270° < \theta < 360°$
$0 < \sin \theta < 1$	$0 < \sin \theta < 1$	$-1 < \sin \theta < 0$	$-1 < \sin \theta < 0$
$0 < \cos \theta < 1$	$-1 < \cos \theta < 0$	$-1 < \cos \theta < 0$	$0 < \cos \theta < 1$
$\tan \theta > 0$	$\tan \theta < 0$	$\tan \theta > 0$	$\tan \theta < 0$

Exercise 18·5

1 (a) Draw a circle of radius 5 cm on 1 mm² paper and make a copy of the diagram at the beginning of this section.

Since the unit is 5 cm, the values of sin, cos and tan must be found by measuring in cm and then dividing by 5.

(b) Show that your diagram gives a good estimate of sin θ, cos θ and tan θ for (i) $\theta = 30°$
(ii) $\theta = 45°$ (iii) $\theta = 60°$

2 Use the four quadrant diagrams above to decide on the sign (+/−) of the following ratios. Then check with a calculator.

(a) (i) sin 36°   (ii) sin 96°   (iii) sin 125°   (iv) sin 206°
    (v) sin 310°   (vi) sin 282°   (vii) sin 195°   (viii) sin 325°

(b) (i) cos 80°   (ii) cos 100°   (iii) cos 200°   (iv) cos 325°
    (v) cos 166°   (vi) cos 290°   (vii) cos 306°   (viii) cos 265°

(c) (i) tan 118°   (ii) tan 98°   (iii) tan 140°   (iv) tan 340°
    (v) tan 276°   (vi) tan 196°   (vii) tan 300°   (viii) tan 249°

3 Use the quadrant diagrams to write down the values of
(a) sin 0°, sin 90°, sin 180°, sin 270°, sin 360°
(b) cos 0°, cos 90°, cos 180°, cos 270°, cos 360°
(c) tan 0°, tan 90°, tan 180°, tan 270°, tan 360°
Check using your calculator.

4 Which of the following statements are true?
(a) $0 \leqslant \sin \theta \leqslant 1$ for all values of θ from 0° to 360°.
(b) $-1 \leqslant \sin \theta \leqslant 1$ for all values of θ from 0° to 360°.
(c) $-1 \leqslant \cos \theta \leqslant 1$ for all values of θ from 0° to 360°.
(d) $-1 \leqslant \tan \theta \leqslant 1$ for all values of θ from 0° to 360°.
(e) $\sin \theta > \cos \theta$ for all values of θ from 90° to 180°.
(f) $\tan \theta > \sin \theta$ for all values of θ from 0° to 180°.
(g) $\tan \theta \geqslant \sin \theta$ for all values of θ from 0° to 90°.
(h) $\dfrac{\sin \theta}{\cos \theta} = \tan \theta$ for all values of θ.

5 This diagram *summarises* the +/− sign of sin, cos, tan of angles between 0° and 360°. Use this diagram to decide on the sign (+/−) of the following:
(a) sin 208° (b) cos 176° (c) tan 266°
(d) sin 185° (e) cos 311° (f) tan 112°
(g) sin 115° (h) cos 280°

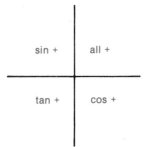

6 *Investigation 1*
It is clear from the graph of sin θ that the equation sin $\theta = 0·5$ has two solutions: $\theta = 30°$ and $\theta = 150°$.
This can be shown on the calculator by the sequence*
150 [sin] [inv] [sin]
150 0·5 0·5 30
Investigate the results of the following sequences:
(a) 200 [sin] [inv] [sin]   (b) 305 [sin] [inv] [sin]   (c) 140 [cos] [inv] [cos]
(d) 320 [cos] [inv] [cos]   (e) 150 [tan] [inv] [tan]   (f) 285 [tan] [inv] [tan]

*On your calculator the sequence may be slightly different.

7 *Investigation 2*

The diagram shows the four triangles associated with the angle θ. Use the diagram to investigate the following:

(a) $\sin \theta = \sin (180° - \theta)$

(b) $\cos \theta = \cos (360° - \theta)$

(c) $\sin \theta = - \sin (180° + \theta)$

(d) $\cos \theta = - \cos (180° + \theta)$

(e) $\sin (360° - \theta) = - \sin \theta$

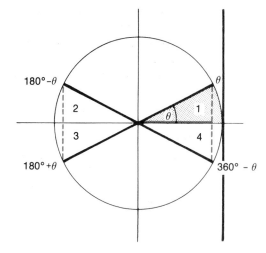

8 *Investigation 3*

The relationships $\dfrac{\sin \theta}{\cos \theta} = \tan \theta$ and $\sin^2 \theta + \cos^2 \theta = 1$

are easy to demonstrate on a right-angled triangle.

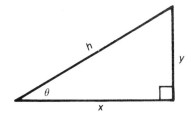

(a) Prove $\dfrac{\sin \theta}{\cos \theta} = \tan \theta$

and $\sin^2 \theta + \cos^2 \theta = 1$

for the triangle given.

(b) Investigate the relationships $\dfrac{\sin \theta}{\cos \theta} = \tan \theta$ and

$\sin^2 \theta + \cos^2 \theta = 1$ for angles between 90° and 360°.

Don't forget the four special cases when $\theta = 90°, 180°, 270°$ and 360°.

9 *Investigation 4*

(a) Investigate the diagram below. What does it show?

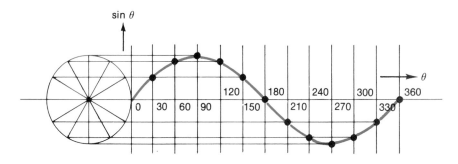

(b) Construct a similar drawing for $\cos \theta$.

(c) What difficulties would you expect if you tried to make a similar drawing for $\tan \theta$?

10 *Investigation 5*

Investigate $\sin \theta$, $\cos \theta$ and $\tan \theta$ for angles greater than 360°.

Unit 19 Functions and inverses

19·1 Function as a 'magic box'

Functions in mathematics are like verbs in English; without them
nothing happens.
A function can be shown as a 'magic box': numbers are fed into it,
processed, and other numbers come out.

Example:

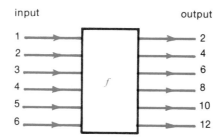

This function is doubling numbers so it is written

$$f: x \rightarrow 2x$$

This f warns you
that a function
is being used

This tells you that this function will change any number into its
double

Exercise 49·1

A Complete the output numbers and write the function as $f: x \rightarrow \ldots$

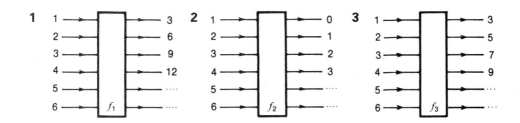

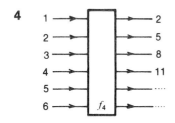

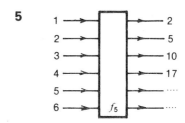

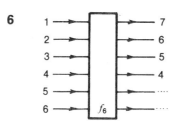

B Write down the outputs of the functions for the given inputs.
1 $f: x \rightarrow 4x$ Input: 0, 1, 2, 3, 4
2 $f: x \rightarrow x^2$ Input: 0, 2, 4, 6, 8
3 $f: x \rightarrow 3x - 2$ Input: 0, 1, 2, 3, 4
4 $f: x \rightarrow x^2 - 1$ Input: 1, 2, 3, 4, 5
5 $f: x \rightarrow -x$ Input: 0, 1, 2, -1, -2
6 $f: x \rightarrow 2x^2 + 1$ Input: 0, 1, 2, -1, -2
7 $f: x \rightarrow 3(x + 1)$ Input: -3, -2, -1, 0, 1, 2
8 $f: x \rightarrow (x + 1)(x + 2)$ Input: 0, 1, 2, -1, -2

C Find out what the inputs must have been for the following outputs:
1 $f: x \rightarrow 4x$ Output: 28, 36
2 $f: x \rightarrow x^2$ Output: 144, 196
3 $f: x \rightarrow 3x - 2$ Output: 28, 148
4 $f: x \rightarrow x^2 - 1$ Output: 48, 99
5 $f: x \rightarrow -x$ Output: -20, 35
6 $f: x \rightarrow 2x^2 + 1$ Output: 51, 99
7 $f: x \rightarrow 3(x + 1)$ Output: 33, 90
8 $f: x \rightarrow (x + 1)(x + 2)$ Output: 20, 72

19·2 Functions on the calculator

Most calculators have some function buttons. These behave like a
function box. The input number is put on to the calculator display. Then
the function button is pressed and the output number appears on
display.

Example:
961 $\boxed{\sqrt{\ }}$ The input is 961
Display $\rightarrow$ 961 $\rightarrow$ 31   The output is 31
                     The function is $f: x \rightarrow \sqrt{x}$
So the button behaves exactly like a function.

A scientific calculator will usually have the following
functions on buttons:

$\boxed{x^2}$ $f: x \rightarrow x^2$ $\boxed{+/-}$ $f: x \rightarrow -x$
$\boxed{1/x}$ $f: x \rightarrow 1/x$ $\boxed{\log}$ $f: x \rightarrow \log x$
$\boxed{\sqrt{}}$ $f: x \rightarrow \sqrt{x}$ $\boxed{\ln}$ $f: x \rightarrow \ln x$
$\boxed{\sin}$ $f: x \rightarrow \sin x$ $\boxed{x!}$ $f: x \rightarrow x!$
$\boxed{\cos}$ $f: x \rightarrow \cos x$ and possibly some
$\boxed{\tan}$ $f: x \rightarrow \tan x$ others as well.

Exercise 19·2

Use a scientific calculator

A For each of the function buttons listed above, write down the output for the following inputs.

1	0	**2**	1	**3**	10	**4**	90	**5**	0·5
6	0·05	**7**	− 1	**8**	− 10	**9**	− 90	**10**	− 0·5

Enter your results into a copy of the table below. Work to 3 or 4 decimal places.

Input→ Function	0	1	10	90	0·5	0·05	− 1	− 10	− 90	− 0·5
$x \rightarrow x^2$	0	1	100	8100	0·25	0·0025	1	100	8100	0·25
$x \rightarrow 1/x$										
$x \rightarrow \sqrt{x}$										
$x \rightarrow \sin x$										
$x \rightarrow \cos x$										
$x \rightarrow \tan x$										
$x \rightarrow -x$										
$x \rightarrow \log x$										
$x \rightarrow \ln x$										
$x \rightarrow x!$										

Note: the calculator will give E or error for some of these. Why?

B In each of the following, input and output are given. Find which function button was pressed.

1	5→0·2	**2**	25→5	**3**	0·3→0·09	**4**	4→24	**5**	90→1
6	100→2	**7**	4·5→ − 4·5	**8**	60→0·5	**9**	− 3→E (or error)	**10**	135→ − 1

C For the following functions, output only is given. What was the input?
   1 $f: x \rightarrow x^2$ Output: 144   **2** $f: x \rightarrow 1/x$ Output: Error
   3 $f: x \rightarrow \sqrt{x}$ Output: 1·5   **4** $f: x \rightarrow \sin x$ Output: 0·4226
   5 $f: x \rightarrow \cos x$ Output: 0·7071   **6** $f: x \rightarrow \tan x$ Output: 1
   7 $f: x \rightarrow -x$ Output: 0·8   **8** $f: x \rightarrow \log x$ Output: 1·5
   9 $f: x \rightarrow \log x$ Output: E   **10** $f: x \rightarrow \sqrt{x}$ Output: 0·7071

19·3 Functions as mappings

A function can be shown as a mapping from one set into another, using
arrows.
This diagram shows a function in which the five elements of X are
mapped onto the four elements of Y

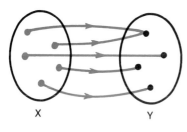

X could be a set of five girls.
Y could be the set of their mothers.
Two of the girls would then be sisters!

$f : X \rightarrow Y$

The second set is often a set of numbers.
This function might give position in class after an examination.
The girls are mapped onto the set of numbers and are therefore placed
in order.

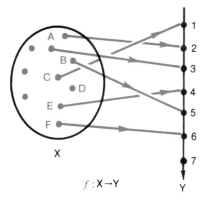

$f : X \rightarrow Y$

Note: **1.** Always mark a function f: and then name the sets.
      2. Every point of X must have just one image point in Y to avoid
        confusion. (You will see why later)

Very often both sets are sets of numbers. The function can then be expressed in algebra.

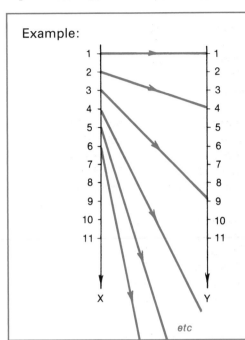

Example:

Each number is mapped onto its square.

$$f: x \rightarrow x^2$$

shows that a function is in action

shows that any number is mapped onto its square

Exercise 19·3

A Identify the sets and the function in each diagram.

1

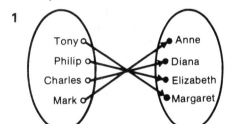

2

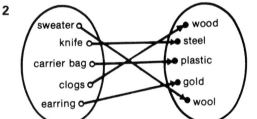

3

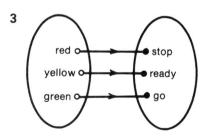

4

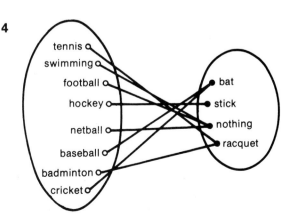

5 Suggest two more pairs of sets which are related by a function.

B The following sets are mapped on to the set of numbers. What do you think is the connection in each case? (Name each set and each function)

1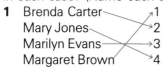
Brenda Carter → 1
Mary Jones → 2
Marilyn Evans → 3
Margaret Brown → 4

2
David ⟶ 72
Chris ⟶ 69
Mike ⟶ 68
Don ⟶ 66
Kevin

3
New York ⟶ 3441
Paris ⟶ 215
Rome ⟶ 908
Tokyo ⟶ 5959
Buenos Aires ⟶ 6919

4
Jones E. ⟶ 263 8412
Jones F. ⟶ 861 4923
Jones F. G. ⟶ 759 9174
Jones G. ⟶ 518 6254
Jones Geraint. ⟶ 365 7195

5
Biggleswade ⟶ 0767
Caerleon ⟶ 0633
Leicester ⟶ 0533
Sheffield ⟶ 0742
Glasgow ⟶ 041

6
William I ⟶ 13
Charles I ⟶ 19
George I ⟶ 05
Elizabeth I ⟶ 08
Henry I ⟶ 25
Edward I ⟶ 04

C Write these functions in algebraic form (with x's).

1
$1 \rightarrow 2$
$2 \rightarrow 4$
$3 \rightarrow 6$
$4 \rightarrow 8$
$5 \rightarrow 10$
$6 \rightarrow 12$

2
$1 \rightarrow 0$
$2 \rightarrow 1$
$3 \rightarrow 2$
$4 \rightarrow 3$
$5 \rightarrow 4$
$6 \rightarrow 5$

3
$1 \rightarrow 3$
$2 \rightarrow 5$
$3 \rightarrow 7$
$4 \rightarrow 9$
$5 \rightarrow 11$
$6 \rightarrow 13$

4
$1 \rightarrow 2$
$2 \rightarrow 5$
$3 \rightarrow 8$
$4 \rightarrow 11$
$5 \rightarrow 14$
$6 \rightarrow 17$

5
$1 \rightarrow 2$
$2 \rightarrow 5$
$3 \rightarrow 10$
$4 \rightarrow 17$
$5 \rightarrow 26$
$6 \rightarrow 37$

6
$1 \rightarrow -1$
$2 \rightarrow 6$
$3 \rightarrow 25$
$4 \rightarrow 62$
$5 \rightarrow 123$
$6 \rightarrow 214$

7
$1 \rightarrow 0.0174$
$2 \rightarrow 0.0349$
$3 \rightarrow 0.0523$
$4 \rightarrow 0.0697$
$5 \rightarrow 0.0871$
$6 \rightarrow 0.1045$

8
$1 \rightarrow 1.0$
$2 \rightarrow 0.5$
$3 \rightarrow 0.333$
$4 \rightarrow 0.25$
$5 \rightarrow 0.2$
$6 \rightarrow 0.1666$

9
$1 \rightarrow 1.0$
$2 \rightarrow 1.414$
$3 \rightarrow 1.732$
$4 \rightarrow 2.000$
$5 \rightarrow 2.236$
$6 \rightarrow 2.449$

19·4 Inverse functions

We have seen that a function takes an input number and changes it to an output number.

Input $\xrightarrow{\quad f \quad}$ Output

The output number itself could be changed by another function (e.g. by pressing another function button on the calculator), producing a third number.

Input $\xrightarrow{\quad f_1 \quad}$ First output $\xrightarrow{\quad f_2 \quad}$ Second output

---

Example:

$5 \xrightarrow{\quad f_1 : x \to 1/x \quad} 0{\cdot}2 \xrightarrow{\quad f_2 : x \to x^2 \quad} 0{\cdot}04$ (5 $\boxed{1/x}$ $\boxed{x^2}$ on your calculator)

If the second output is the same as the first input, **for all inputs the second function is the** inverse **of the first function. It is written** f^{-1}.

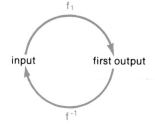

Example:

$1{\cdot}46 \xrightarrow{\quad f : x \to x^2 \quad} 2{\cdot}1316 \xrightarrow{\quad f^{-1} : x \to \sqrt{x} \quad}$ (1·46 $\boxed{x^2}$ $\boxed{\sqrt{x}}$ on your calculator)

$x \to \sqrt{x}$ is the inverse function of $x \to x^2$

Exercise 19·4

You will need a scientific calculator for this exercise.

A f_1 and f_2 are two functions. $f_1 : x \to x^2$ and $f_2 : x \to 1/x$

   1   Find the first and second outputs for inputs of:
   (a) 10   (b) 0·5   (c) 3·5   (d) 0   (e) −3

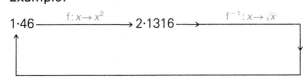

   2   Find the outputs below.

   $\boxed{5} \xrightarrow{f_1} \boxed{?} \xrightarrow{f_1} \boxed{?} \xrightarrow{f_1} \boxed{?} \xrightarrow{f_1} \boxed{?}$

   3   Find the outputs from repeated use of f_2:

   $\boxed{8} \xrightarrow{f_2} \boxed{?} \xrightarrow{f_2} \boxed{?} \xrightarrow{f_2} \boxed{?} \xrightarrow{f_2} \boxed{?}$

   What do you notice?

4 How many times can f_1 be repeated before the calculator shows Error
(a) for an input of 100   (b) for an input of 9999?

5 How many times can f_2 be repeated without getting E?

6 Investigate the combined functions f_2f_1 and f_1f_2 for different inputs.

Is the second output the same for f_1f_2 as for f_2f_1, whatever number you start with?

7 Find the output for each combination of functions shown below, for the given input. Note the short form of writing the function, to correspond with a calculator button:
$$\sqrt{} \ldots x \to \sqrt{x}$$
$$x^2 \ldots x \to x^2$$
$$+/- \ldots x \to -x$$

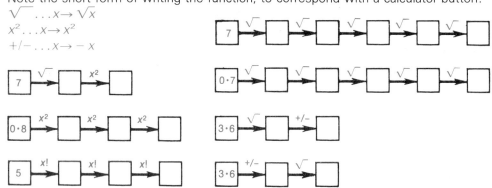

8 Use your calculator function buttons to check that the following statements are correct:
(a) $[1 + (3\cdot4)^2]^2 = 157\cdot7536$ 　　　(b) $\sqrt{(4\cdot65)^2} = 4\cdot65$
(c) $(\sqrt{82\cdot9})^2 = 82\cdot9$ 　　　　　　　(d) $\sqrt{\sin 30°} = 0\cdot7071 = \sin 45°$
(e) $(\cos 42°)^2 + (\sin 42°)^2 = 1$ 　　　(f) $2(\cos 35°)^2 - 1 = \cos 70°$

B **1** Find the inverse (f^{-1}) of each of the following functions:
(a) $f: x \to 2x$ 　　　　(b) $f: x \to x + 3$ 　　　　(c) $f: x \to x - 3$
(d) $f: x \to 2x + 3$ 　　(e) $f: x \to 3(x - 2)$ 　　(f) $f: x \to (x + 1)^2$

Show that $\boxed{4\cdot5} \xrightarrow{f} \boxed{} \xrightarrow{f^{-1}} \boxed{4\cdot5}$ in each case.

2 Show that f is the inverse of f^{-1} for the six functions above.

3 Show that the functions $f: x \to 1/x$ and $f: x \to -x$ are their own inverses. Can you find any other functions with this property?

19·5 Inverse trig functions

Sometimes, in a problem, we know the sine of an angle and want to find the angle itself. This requires the inverse of the sine function, $\sin^{-1}x$.
Your calculator will have a way of finding the inverse, probably like this:

$$\sin x \xrightarrow{\boxed{\text{inv}}\,\boxed{\text{sin}}} x$$

(Inversing $\sin x$ is the same as using tables in reverse, i.e. finding the value of $\sin x$ in the tables and reading off the angle.)
The calculator will inverse $\cos x$ and $\tan x$ by the same method.

Example:

Find x if (a) $\sin x = 0{\cdot}74$

(b) $\cos x = 0{\cdot}285$

(c) $\tan x = 1{\cdot}43$

$0{\cdot}74 \xrightarrow{\boxed{\text{inv}}\boxed{\text{sin}}} 47{\cdot}7°$

$0{\cdot}285 \xrightarrow{\boxed{\text{inv}}\boxed{\text{cos}}} 73{\cdot}4°$

$1{\cdot}43 \xrightarrow{\boxed{\text{inv}}\boxed{\text{tan}}} 55°$

Exercise 19·5

1 Find out the way your calculator gives inverse trig functions.

2 Use your calculator to find the values of

(a) $\sin^{-1} 0{\cdot}66$ (b) $\sin^{-1} 0{\cdot}08$ (c) $\sin^{-1} 0{\cdot}36$ (d) $\sin^{-1} 0{\cdot}47$

(e) $\cos^{-1} 0{\cdot}26$ (f) $\cos^{-1} 0{\cdot}49$ (g) $\cos^{-1} 0{\cdot}98$ (h) $\cos^{-1} 0{\cdot}02$

(i) $\tan^{-1} 0{\cdot}55$ (j) $\tan^{-1} 0{\cdot}78$ (k) $\tan^{-1} 1{\cdot}32$ (l) $\tan^{-1} 4{\cdot}58$

3 Use inverse functions to calculate the angle θ in the triangles below (not drawn to scale).

(a)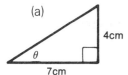

(b)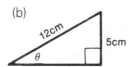

(c)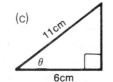

(d)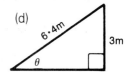

(e)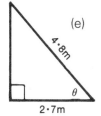

(f)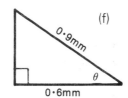

(g)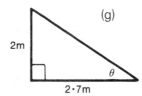

(h)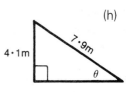

4 You will find that the inverse sine function gives E for values of x greater than 1 or less than -1 (see Unit 8).

Thus $1{\cdot}4 \xrightarrow{\boxed{\text{inv}}\boxed{\text{sin}}} \mathsf{E}$

This is because $\sin x$ is always between -1 and $+1$.

Investigate the numbers that your calculator will accept as inputs for $\sin^{-1}$, $\cos^{-1}$, and $\tan^{-1}$.

5 Investigate these calculator sequences for different inputs.

(a) $\boxed{\text{sin}}\ \boxed{x^2}\ \boxed{+/-}\ \boxed{+}\ 1\ \boxed{=}\ \boxed{\sqrt{\ }}\ \boxed{\text{inv}}\ \boxed{\text{cos}}$

    (i) restrict input to $0 < x < 90°$

    (ii) try inputs $90° < x < 180°$

    (iii) try inputs $180 < x < 270°$

(b) $\boxed{\text{cos}}\ \boxed{x^2}\ \boxed{+/-}\ \boxed{+}\ 1\ \boxed{=}\ \boxed{\sqrt{\ }}\ \boxed{\text{inv}}\ \boxed{\text{sin}}$

(c) $\boxed{\text{cos}}\ \boxed{x^2}\ \boxed{\times}\ 2\ \boxed{=}\ \boxed{-}\ 1\ \boxed{\text{inv}}\ \boxed{\text{cos}}$

(d) $\boxed{\text{sin}}\ \boxed{x^2}\ \boxed{\times}\ 2\ \boxed{=}\ \boxed{+/-}\ \boxed{+}\ 1\ \boxed{=}\ \boxed{\text{inv}}\ \boxed{\text{cos}}$

6 *Calculator game: 'Function chain' A game for two players*
In the first game 2 is entered on the display. The players then take it in turns to press function buttons only until one wins or loses.
To win, press a function button that produces a positive number < 0.01 on the display.
To lose, press a function button that produces E or $\emptyset$ on the display. The next game starts with 3, the next with 4, etc. The overall winner is the first player to win 6 games.

19·6 Powers

Most scientific calculators will have an $\boxed{x^y}$ button. This enables you to calculate powers: x is the number on the display, y is the index of the power.

Example:
Calculate $(1.25)^6$

Sequence: $1.25 \boxed{x^y} 6 \boxed{=} 3.814\,697\,266$
  x y

Notes: **1** The exact answer will end in 5, but that will be in the 12th decimal place!
  2 Alternative methods of calculation could be:
   (i) $1.25 \boxed{\times} 1.25 \boxed{\times} 1.25 \boxed{\times} 1.25 \boxed{\times} 1.25 \boxed{\times} 1.25$ slow and liable to error
   (ii) $1.25 \boxed{\times} 1.25 \boxed{\times} 1.25 \boxed{=} \boxed{x^2}$ better
   (iii) $1.25 \boxed{\times} \boxed{\times} \boxed{=} \boxed{=} \boxed{=} \boxed{=}$ using constant multiplier function

---

Exercise 19·6

A Calculate the values of the following powers. Check each calculation by an alternative method.
  1 3^6 **2** $(1.5)^{15}$ **3** 12^7 **4** $(1.08)^{20}$
  5 31^4 **6** $(0.8)^{10}$ **7** $(0.075)^5$ **8** $(10.95)^{11}$

B Check the truth of the inequalities below.
  1 $2^{10} > 10^6$ **2** $3^6 > 6^3$ **3** $8^9 < 9^8$
  4 $(1.04)^{50} > 100$ **5** $36^{25} > 25^{36}$ **6** $(1.015)^{20} > (1.15)^{10}$

C The x^y button will give values even where y is *not* a positive whole number. Investigate.

Unit 20 Using money

20·1 Earning

Most people get paid for the work they do. The pay is generally
calculated by the hour, the week or the year, but some people get a sum
of money for each job completed (called 'piece-work'). The main forms
of pay are summarised below.

Weekly wage: An agreed sum of money is paid for
the week's work. Sometimes the hours are specified,
e.g. a 30-hour week or a 35-hour week. Overtime is
added in some jobs. For many jobs there is a standard
weekly rate of pay agreed by the unions and
management, e.g. £85 p.w. for 32 hours.

Hourly rate: An agreed sum of
money is paid for each hour
worked, e.g. £3·60 per hour. This is
the typical way of paying part-time
workers. If evening, weekend or
night work is done then extra
money may be paid at a higher rate.
This is called overtime.

Yearly salary: An agreed sum of money is paid for a year's work, e.g.
£4800 p.a. A salary is usually divided into 12 parts, each part being paid
at the end of a month. The money is usually paid into the employee's
bank account by the employer.

Exercise 20·1

A **1** Calculate the total amount earned at the rate shown for each of the following:
  (a) 14 hours at £2·75 an hour.
  (b) 42 hours at £3·60 per hour.
  (c) 28 hours at £2·50 an hour, plus 12 hours at £3·75 an hour.
  (d) 35 hours at £3·00 an hour, plus 8 hours at £3·80 an hour.
  (e) 13 days from 9 a.m. to 5 p.m. at £4·20 per hour.
  (f) 18 days from 6 p.m. to 2 a.m. at £5·20 per hour.

2 Calculate the hourly rate of pay for these jobs:
  (a) A nurse receiving £72 for a 50-hour week.
  (b) An electrician receiving £140 for a 42-hour week.
  (c) A bus driver being paid £185 for a 48-hour week.
  (d) A computer programmer earning £210 for a 34-hour week.

3 Calculate the monthly payment you would expect on a salary of:
  (a) £4200 p.a.   (b) £4900 p.a.   (c) £5400 p.a.

4 A job pays £132 a week. What annual salary would give about the same money?

5 A job pays £6500 p.a. Is this more or less than £125 per week?

6 The basic rate for a job is £120 for a 36-hour week, with time-and-a-half for overtime. What would the pay be for a person who worked a 44-hour week?

B **1** A job pays £160 per week with 4 weeks' paid holiday (including Christmas and Easter). Find the hourly rate of pay if the working week is
  (a) 36 hours
  (b) 30 hours
  (*Hint:* Calculate the total amount earned and the total hours worked in a year first.)

2 A girl is offered two jobs. One job pays £4·60 an hour, of which the agency takes 10%. She can expect to work (on average) 24 hours a week. The other job pays £75 per week. Which job pays her more?

3 A boy is apprenticed for 4 years before becoming a craftsman. As an apprentice he is paid £72 per week, but on qualifying this goes up to £140 per week. How much is he likely to earn in his first five years (ignoring pay rises)?

4 Compare the following jobs for pay:
  (a) A designer earning £2000 for a piece of work that takes him 3 months (working about 40 hours a week).
  (b) A carpet fitter who charges £6 per hour and works an average of 22 hours per week.
  (c) A bricklayer who is paid £12 for every 1000 bricks laid (it takes him about 15 seconds to lay a brick).

5 (a) A man earning £180 per week negotiates a 12% wage rise. What is his new wage?
  (b) A firm offers all its workers an 8% rise in wages. What would be the new wage of people now earning: (i) £150 per week   (ii) £210 per week   (iii) £6·50 per hour
    (iv) £5600 per year   (v) £10 200 per year

6 A company pays a Christmas bonus to all its workers: each person receives $\frac{1}{12}$ of their earnings over the last year. How much do the following people get for their bonus?
  (a) Mrs Parsons (secretary) earning £84 per week.
  (b) Mr Jenks (stoker) earning £4·20 per hour on a 36-hour week.
  (c) Ms Elks (sales manager) earning £12 400 p.a.

C Investigations
  1 List the jobs advertised in your local newspaper. Sort them into jobs which are:
  (a) under £5000 p.a.   (b) £5001–£8000   (c) £8001–£11 000
  (d) £11 001 –£14 000   (e) over £14 000 p.a.

2   Find out the wages per week for the following jobs. Which job pays the best rate per hour?
    Nurse; bricklayer; bus driver; secretary; primary-school teacher; shop assistant; factory
    production-line worker.

3   Ask some older people what they earned in their first full-time job. You might ask
    members of your family, grandparents, old-age pensioners and neighbours. (Explain that
    you are making a survey or they will think that you are just being nosey!)

20·2   Spending

When you have money to spend, it is helpful to keep a simple account.
In this way you can make up your mind to save, know where your
money goes, and learn to manage money. The simplest method is to use
a simple in/out system, shown below. The balance can be worked out
once a month, or whenever you like.

Date	IN	£	p	Date	OUT	£	p
	Balance	40	75	3/1	Present for Ma	8	50
7/1	Wages	65	25	8/1	Food	12	90
				10/1	Rent	32	00
				13/1	Cash for haircut etc	5	00
14/1	Wages	65	25	15/1	Cinema (2)	6	00
				18/1	Rent	32	00
				20/1	Electricity	46	00
	Total	171	25			142	40
21/1	Balance	28	85				
21/1	Wages	65	25	21/1	Food	23	60

In this example, the account was checked on 20.1.85 and the new
balance found to be £171·25 − £142·40 = £28·85. After the balance is
made up, the account continues as before.

Exercise 20·2

1   Draw up a careful account from the information below. Calculate a balance at the end of each
    month from January to March.
    Tom and Jerry are sharing a flat. Each month they pay £178 rent and £42 rates. They have
    quarterly bills for electricity, gas and telephone:
    Gas: £49 paid 17 January
    Electricity: £52·50 paid 28 January
    Telephone: £27·50 paid 9 February

Tom is a plumber earning £182 per week, with £61 deducted for tax, etc. So he brings home £121 each week. Jerry brings home £95. They each take £25 a week for personal spending-money and put the rest towards running the home. Together, they spend £35 a week on food and £12 a week on drink. They share a car, which they are buying on hire purchase: they pay £95 on the 12th of each month. A TV and video are hired for £4·50 a week (paid on Mondays) and they spend about £6 a week hiring extra video films. Whoever uses the car pays for the petrol out of their own spending money, but the garage bills are taken from the shared money. The bills for January–March 1984 are:

Jan 12: New tyre £38·50
Feb 10: Service £37·60
Feb 18: Repair £26
Mar 10: Car tax £42
Mar 16: Car insurance (1 year) £125

Tom and Jerry start the new year with £240 in hand. What is their position at the end of March? Compare your results with other people's in the class.

2 Keep an account of your own spending for a full month. Explain how such an account can help you to manage your money.

20·3 Profit and loss

When you buy something in a shop, the price you pay is very much higher than the cost of manufacture. The diagram below shows where your money goes for a pair of shoes that you buy for £28.

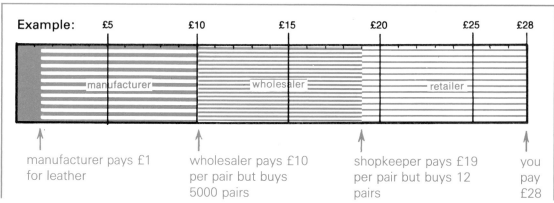

Example:

| £5 | £10 | £15 | £20 | £25 | £28 |

manufacturer — wholesaler — retailer

manufacturer pays £1 for leather

wholesaler pays £10 per pair but buys 5000 pairs

shopkeeper pays £19 per pair but buys 12 pairs

you pay £28

212

It is easy to calculate the raw profit for each business, as follows:

	buys at	sells at	raw profit	profit %
Retailer	£19	£28	£9	$\frac{9}{19} \times 100 = 47 \cdot 37\%$
Wholesaler	£10	£19	£9	$\frac{9}{10} \times 100 = 90\%$
Manufacturer	£1	£10	£9	$\frac{9}{1} \times 100 = 900\%$

Profit % is (Raw profit) ÷ (Money invested) × 100

Exercise 20·3

A These questions refer to the example above.

1 It looks as though the manufacturer made 900% profit, but this impression is very misleading: there are many things that have to be paid for out of the money. Make a list of the costs you would expect the manufacturer to incur (e.g. workers' wages, etc.).

2 Make a list of the costs that the wholesaler and shopkeeper would have to meet out of raw profits (remember that the wholesaler might buy 5000 pairs of shoes and sell them to 1000 different shops).

3 A lot of goods are sold in markets. Why do you think this makes the goods cheaper?

4 A carpet made in Kidderminster sells to a wholesaler in Manchester for £40. The wholesaler sells it to a shop for £65. The shop sells the carpet to a customer for £108. Calculate the percentage profit made by the wholesaler and retailer.

B Calculate the percentage profit on the following transactions.

1 A car is sold for £3500 to a dealer and then sold again for £4500 to a customer.

2 A VTR is bought wholesale for £285 and sold to a customer for £395.

3 A home computer is bought for £140 from the manufacturer. It is then sold to a shop for £195. The shop sells the computer to a school for £285.

4 A market trader buys 100 shirts for £75. He sells them all at £1·25 each.

5 Another trader buys a roll of cloth 50 metres long for £120. She sells 40 metres of the cloth for £3·25 a metre and gets £30 for the remaining 10 metres.

6 A shopkeeper buys 20 beds for £1400. He tries to sell them at £120 each but cannot find customers. He then puts them in a 25% discount sale (25% off the marked price*), and sells them all. Show that his profit is £400. What is his percentage profit?

7 Find the percentage profit a shop makes on each of these sales:

	cost to shop	full price	discount
a clock-radio	£28	£42·50	£5
a scientific calculator	£12	£16·50	10%
a pair of ice-skates	£36	£52	25%
a coat	£25	£45	20%

8 A manufacturer makes wine-glasses from materials which cost £45 for each 1000 glasses made. He sells 5000 glasses for £800 to a wholesaler, who sells them to shops in batches of 100. Each batch costs £27. A shop buys 4 batches and sells the glasses at £2·40 for a set of six.
Calculate the percentage profit for the manufacturer, the wholesaler and the shop, if:
(a) All the glasses are sold at the set price.
(b) The shop sells only 300 glasses at £2·40 for six, the rest being sold off at half price.
(c) The wholesaler sells only 30 batches to shops: the remaining glasses are sold to a market trader for £100 the lot.

*To calculate sale price, use ☒ 0·75 to allow for 25% discount.

9 Sometimes a trader will make a loss. Calculate the raw loss and the percentage loss on these transactions.

(a) A girl buys a bike for £72 and sells it again for £55.
(b) A boy buys a scuba-diving set for £120. He sells it for £75 to buy a better one.
(c) A trader buys a batch of 60 sheepskin coats for £2100. He sells 20 for £75 each, but the remainder all have faults so that he can only get £15 each. He manages to sell 25 at this price, but the final coats he 'gives away' at £5 a time.
(d) A family buys a boat for £1250. They find it needs £700 worth of repairs, which they have done. After one summer they decide to sell the boat but get only £1250 for it.

10 Suggest some situations that you know where profits and losses are made.

20·4 Saving and borrowing

The most important idea to understand here is interest.
Money earns interest when it is saved in a bank, Post Office account or building society.
You pay interest when you borrow money.
Interest is usually stated as a percentage rate. For example, interest of 8% p.a. means that £100 earns £8 each year. It is often best to think of the interest earned by a single pound. In this case, £1 earns 8p in one year, so £1 grows to £1·08 after 1 year at 8% interest.

Examples:

1 A man saves £300 for 1 year at 6% interest. What is his money worth at the end of 1 year?
At 6% p.a. each £1 becomes £1·06, so
£300 → 300 × 1·06 = £318
The extra £18 is the interest. The £300 he started with is called the capital or the principal sum.

2 A woman saves £200 in her Post Office account for 3 years at $7\frac{1}{2}$% compound interest; i.e. the interest is added to the account at the end of each year and attracts further interest.
1st year: £200 ———→ 200 × 1·075   £215
2nd year: £215 ———→ 215 × 1·075   £231·125
3rd year: £231·125 → 231·125 × 1·075 = £248·46
The principal of £200 produces interest, after 3 years, of £48·46

Note: This could have been calculated using the sequence
1·075 ☒ ☒ ☰ ☰ ☒ 200 ☰ 248·459 375
　　　‿‿‿
　　　constant
　　　multiplier
This can be used as a check.

Exercise 20·4

A Find the interest on one year's saving of:
  1 £50 at 8% interest
  2 £185 at 11% interest
  3 £220 at 9% interest
  4 £240 at $11\frac{1}{2}$% interest
  5 £360 at 14% interest
  6 £1500 at $12\frac{1}{2}$% interest

B Find the final balance in a building society account if:
  1 £100 is saved for 1 year at 7% interest.
  2 £450 is saved for 1 year at $9\frac{1}{2}$% interest.
  3 £60 is saved for 2 years at 8% interest.
  4 £320 is saved for 2 years at 12% interest.
  5 £680 is saved for 3 years at 10% interest.
  6 £3900 is saved for 3 years at 9% interest.

C **1** A boy is given £50 for his 16th birthday present. He deposits it in a building society until his 21st birthday. The rate of interest is 11%. How much can he take out on his 21st birthday?
  2 A couple are saving to get married. They put £500 on deposit at the post office, earning $8\frac{1}{2}$% interest. What is their money worth after four years?
  3 A couple are saving for a deposit on a house. They put £500 on deposit at 8% on 1st January 1984. What is this money worth six years later?
  4 A woman borrows £4500 from a bank to buy a new car. The interest rate is 13%. She pays nothing for two years; what is her debt to the bank then?
  5 A family in a council house has the chance of buying the house for £18 000. They borrow the money at 12% interest and each year they pay the annual interest on the amount outstanding, plus £900. What is their total payment
  (a) in the first year?
  (b) in the second year?
  (c) in the third year?

20·5   An investigation into borrowing

People borrow money in many different ways, some of which are much more expensive than others. Choice of credit facilities can make a big difference to the way your money works for you.

Example:
In January 1984 the following annual interest charges were in force:
Mortgage (for buying a house) . . . . 8% (this is low because of income-tax allowances)

Bank overdraft 12%
Bank loan 15%
Finance house (for buying cars, goods in stores, etc. on hire purchase) 22%
Visa or Access card 24%
Pawnbrokers 30%

Exercise 20·5

Use the interest rates given above.

1 A family decides to borrow the money to buy a new caravan for £2400. Find the interest charges per year if they borrow the money:
  (a) on overdraft
  (b) as a bank loan
  (c) from a finance house (HP)
  (d) on Visa (Barclaycard)
What is the difference in the annual repayment between the dearest and the cheapest loan if they repay the £2400 over three years?

2 Mrs Jones buys a videotape recorder for £450 on Barclaycard. How much does she pay altogether for the recorder (including interest) if
  (a) she pays off the loan after 1 year.
  (b) she pays off the loan after 2 years.

3 Find out all you can (by visiting banks, stores, etc.) about the interest rates that are charged for different sorts of loans at present. Also compare Barclays Bank, Lloyds Bank, Midland, Nat. West., Bank of Scotland, Yorkshire Bank, Trustee Savings Bank, etc.

4 Some big stores effectively lend people money to buy goods, through a 'budget account'. Find out all you can about this in a local store or from local newspapers. How do the rates of interest compare with those on bank loans?

5 Bert has £1000 cash and wants to save at the best possible rate of interest. Find out where he can get the best return on his money (compare building societies, Post Office savings accounts, bank deposit accounts, etc.).

6 Compare the interest rates charged on credit schemes for new cars by different dealers and for different makes of car (visit some car showrooms or look in the local paper). Can you find the best deal available in your district? Why do you think the interest rates are so different?

Unit 21 Three-dimensional space

21·1 3-D coordinates

A point in space can be given an 'address' by using three numbers as
coordinates. The numbers usually taken are the distances from an
origin, measured parallel to three perpendicular axes (an x- and y-axis,
both horizontal, and a z-axis which is vertical).

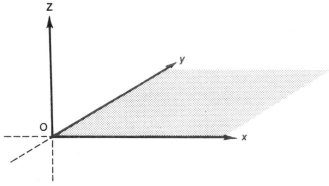

It will help to think of O, the origin, as the corner of a room. The x and
y-axes are then the lines where the walls meet the floor, and the z-axis is
a vertical line where two walls meet.

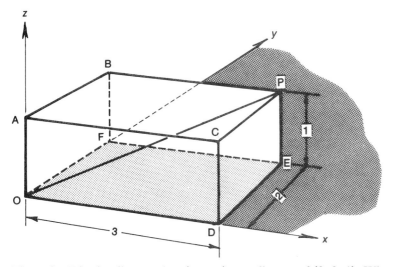

The point P in the diagram has (x, y, z) coordinates of $(3, 2, 1)$. What
this means is that to get from O to P you have to go 3 units in the x
direction, 2 units in the y direction and 1 unit in the z direction.

The coordinates of P define a cuboid which fits into a corner at O (like a box in the corner of a room).

A direct line from O to P (a diagonal of the cuboid) is called the position vector of P.

Note: It takes practice to understand a 3-dimensional diagram, because we are trying to show three dimensions on a flat surface which really has only two dimensions. Holding an exercise book horizontal to represent the (x, y) plane, with a pencil vertical at one corner to represent the z-axis, will give you a real model of axes in three dimensions.

Exercise 21·1

1 Describe where the following would be found in the above diagram. As an example, (0, 0, 1) is just 1 unit up the z-axis from 0, i.e. it is at A.
   (a) (0, 2, 0)   (b) (0, 2, 1)   (c) (0, 0, $\frac{1}{2}$)   (d) (3, 0, 0,)   (e) (3, 0, 1)
   (f) (3, 1, 0)   (g) (3, 2, 0)   (h) (1$\frac{1}{2}$, 1, 0)   (i) (1$\frac{1}{2}$, 1, $\frac{1}{2}$)   (j) (1$\frac{1}{2}$, 2, 1)

2 (a) The points (2, 3, 0), (3, 4, 0), (1, 1, 0) and (5, 4, 0) can all be found in a special part of the diagram. Which part?
   (b) Where would you look for (0, 0, 1), (0, 0, 2), (0, 0, 3), etc.?
   (c) Where would you look for (0, 1, 0), (0, 2, 0), (0, 3, 0), etc.?

3 A 'rectangular' room is 8 metres long, 6 metres wide and 4 metres high. The door is in one of the long walls, just by the corner. This corner, at floor-level, is taken as (0, 0, 0).
   (a) Where are the points (8, 6, 4), (4, 3, 4)?
   (b) Give the coordinates of the eight corners of the room.
   (c) Give the coordinates of
       (i)   The four centre-points of the walls.
       (ii) The centre of the floor.
       (iii) The four points halfway up the vertical lines at the corners of the room.

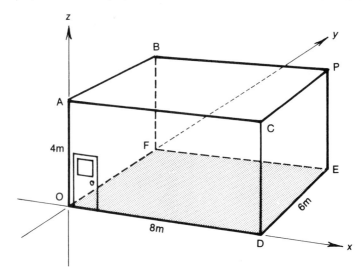

4 Suggest how coordinates could be used to describe:
   (a) The exact position of an aircraft in the sky.
   (b) The point where an oil rig drill cuts into the sea-bed.
   (c) The location of a hospital bed where your friend is recovering from an operation.

21·2   Distances between points

Distances between points can be found using Pythagoras's theorem. For example:

The coordinates of G are (3, 0, 0)
The coordinates of F are (3, 2, 0)

$$OF^2 = 3^2 + 2^2 = 13 \ (\triangle FGO)$$
so $OF = \sqrt{13}$
$$OC^2 = OF^2 + CF^2 \ (\triangle CFO)$$
$$= 13 + 1 = 14$$
so $OC = \sqrt{14} = 3{\cdot}74 \text{ cm}$

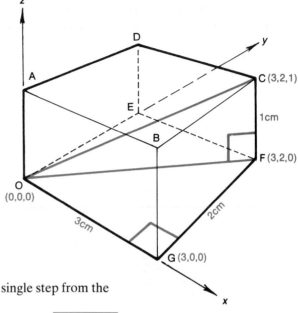

The length of OC can in fact be calculated in a single step from the coordinates of C.

If C is the point (3, 2, 1), its distance from (0, 0, 0) $= \sqrt{3^2 + 2^2 + 1^2}$
$= \sqrt{9 + 4 + 1} = \sqrt{14} = 3{\cdot}74 \text{ cm}$ (to 2 decimal places)

The distance of any point (x, y, z) from (0, 0, 0,) is $\sqrt{x^2 + y^2 + z^2}$

Example:

Find the length of a diagonal of a cube of side 5 cm.

If one vertex of the cube is taken as (0, 0, 0), the opposite vertex will be (5, 5, 5).
Length of diagonal $= \sqrt{5^2 + 5^2 + 5^2} = \sqrt{75} = 8{\cdot}66 \text{ cm}$

Exercise 21·2

1   These questions refer to the cuboid ABCDEFGO shown above.
   (a) Write down the coordinates of A, B, C, D, E, F and G.
   (b) Calculate the distance from O, by using $\sqrt{x^2 + y^2 + z^2}$, for all seven points A, B, C, D, E, F and G.

2   We know that $OB = \sqrt{3^2 + 1^2} = \sqrt{10}$. Since ABGO is a rectangle, AG is also $\sqrt{10} \text{ cm}$ long. What is the connection between the length of AG and the coordinates of A and G?

3   Calculate the length of GC. What is the connection between this length and the coordinates of G and C?

4   The last two questions indicate a way of calculating the distance between any two points in space from their coordinates.* Use it to show that the four long diagonals of the cuboid ABCDEFGO are the same length.

---

* The distance between two points (x_1, y_1, z_1) and (x_2, y_2, z_2) is
$\sqrt{(x_1 - x_2)^2 + (y_1 - y_2)^2 + (z_1 - z_2)^2}$

5 (a) Calculate the distance from a corner of the floor to a diagonally opposite corner of the ceiling in a rectangular room 8 metres × 6 metres × 5 metres.

(b) Estimate the length of the longest diagonal of your classroom, and find a way of checking it by measurement and calculation.

6 An aircraft is over a point 20 km east and 30 km north of a landing strip. The height of the aircraft is 5 km. Calculate its distance from the airstrip.

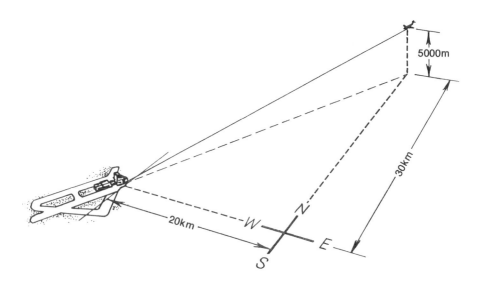

7 Calculate the distance from A to B, given that A is (4, 0, 3) and B is (1, 1, 5).

8 Two aircraft in flight are at points with coordinates (21, 13, 6) and (14, 19, 7) in relation to a control at (0, 0, 0).

(a) Which of the two is nearer the control tower?

(b) How far are the aircraft from each other?

21·3   Lines in space

In this section, the word 'line' is taken to mean a straight line.

Lines become much more interesting when you think of them in three dimensions. The simplest lines to consider are vertical lines, like those running from top to bottom of the corners of a room. We usually show a vertical line as running from top to bottom of a page, but of course this is only a picture.

Any line at right angles to a vertical line is horizontal (like the horizon). Horizontal lines can intersect (meet) other horizontal lines, but two vertical lines cannot meet, because they are parallel.

Lines that are neither horizontal nor vertical are oblique.

Lines which do not meet are either parallel (like opposite lanes of a straight road) or skew (like a straight road crossing a motorway).

Skew lines cannot be drawn properly on paper, so they are sometimes shown as below. The continuous line is supposed to be nearer to you than the broken one.

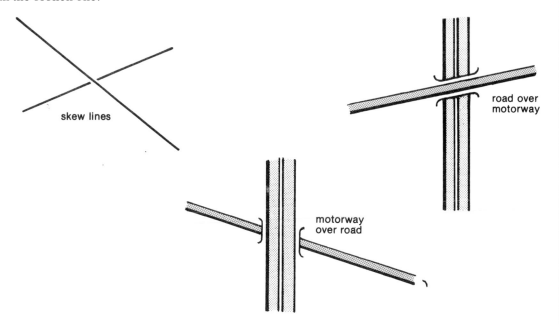

skew lines

road over motorway

motorway over road

If two aircraft are flying along skew lines there will be a moment when they are as near as they will ever be.
At that moment they will be at the ends of the common perpendicular of the two lines.

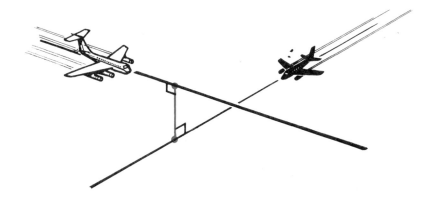

Exercise 21·3

A **1** Name four different vertical lines in your classroom.

    2 Is it true that all vertical lines are parallel? Give reasons for your answer.

    3 Is it true that all horizontal lines are parallel?

    4 (a) Give four examples of a horizontal line intersecting a vertical one.

       (b) Give four examples in which a horizontal line and a vertical one do not intersect.

    5 List four pairs of skew lines in your classroom. Can you find pairs of oblique skew lines in the classroom?

    6 Experiment with two rulers and a rubber band to check that every pair of skew lines has one and only one common perpendicular. What are the common perpendiculars for the pairs of lines you listed in question 5?

B Investigate these statements about three lines L_1, L_2 and L_3 which exist in three dimensions. Use rulers or wires as models of the lines.

    $\perp$ means 'perpendicular to' $\parallel$ means 'parallel to'

    1 $(L_1 \parallel L_2$ and $L_2 \parallel L_3) \Rightarrow L_1 \parallel L_3$

    2 $(L_1 \perp L_2$ and $L_2 \perp L_3) \Rightarrow L_1 \perp L_3$

    3 $(L_1$ skew to L_2 and L_2 skew to $L_3) \Rightarrow L_1$ skew to L_3

    4 $(L_1 \perp L_2$ and L_1 horizontal$) \Rightarrow L_2$ is vertical

    5 $(L_1 \perp L_2$ and L_1 vertical$) \Rightarrow L_2$ is horizontal

    6 $(L_1 \perp L_2$ and $L_1 \perp L_3) \Rightarrow L_2 \parallel L_3$

C Write down all the pairs of parallel lines, perpendicular lines and skew lines that you can find in these diagrams. Indicate, if possible, the common perpendicular for every pair of skew lines.

1

Cuboid

3

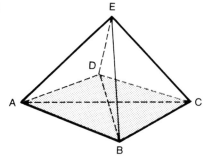

Pyramid on a square base

2

Regular tetrahedron

4

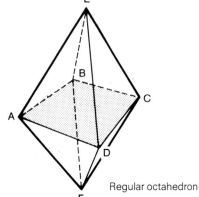

Regular octahedron

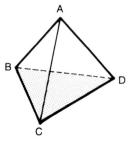

222

D Describe some situations in which it is important whether lines are skew or not. (*Hint:* Think of sport, or architecture, or warfare, or engineering.)

21·4   Geometric planes

A plane is a flat surface like a wall or a floor. There are horizontal planes, vertical planes and oblique planes. Three important planes in the (x, y, z) coordinate system are shown below.

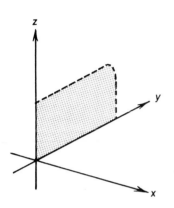

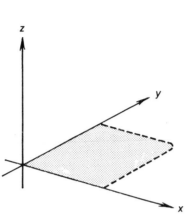

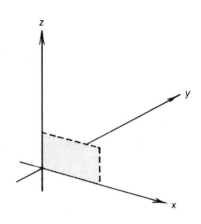

Part of the (y, z) plane, a vertical plane containing the y-axis and the z-axis, and perpendicular to the x-axis. $x = 0$ everywhere on this plane, so all its points have coordinates like $(0, 3, 4)$, $(0, 1, 1)$, etc.

Part of the (x, y) plane, a horizontal plane containing the x-axis and the y-axis. $z = 0$ everywhere on this plane so all its points have coordinates like $(4, 5, 0)$, $(1, 1, 0)$, etc.

Part of the (x, z) plane, a vertical plane containing the x-axis and the z-axis. $y = 0$ everywhere on this plane so all its points have coordinates like $(2, 0, 3)$, $(5, 0, 9)$, etc.

Planes can be thought of as families of lines, even though it is hard to see how a set of lines can contain *every* point in a plane. You would think that however closely the lines were packed, there would always be spaces between them.

Exercise 21·4

A   Which plane contains the following sets of points:
   1 $\{(5, 0, 3); (7, 0, -5); (-6, 0, -7); (-2, 0, -7)\}$
   2 $\{(2, 3, 0); (4, 5, 0); (-2, 1, 0); (-2, 5, 0)\}$
   3 $\{(0, 4, 7); (0, 6, 2); (0, 5, 5); (0, +1, +2)\}$
   4 $\{(2, 3, 4); (2, 5, 6); (2, -7, -9); (2, -1, 0)\}$
   5 $\{(3, 1, 6); (-1, 1, 0); (4, 1, 2); (0, 1, 0)\}$
   6 $\{(7, 5, -3); (0, 1, -3); (2, 4, -3); (3, 4, -1)\}$

B   Investigate the truth of the following statements:
   1   Only one straight line can be drawn through two given points.
   2   Given three points there is only one plane that passes through all of them.
   3   Any plane that contains two points of a line contains the whole line.
   4   Two planes are bound to meet in a straight line unless they are parallel.
   5   It is not possible for a line and a plane to have only one point in common.
   6   (a) Two intersecting lines define a plane.
         (b) Two parallel lines define a plane.
   7   Describe two planes in your classroom that do not meet and would not meet however far they were extended.
   8   Describe two planes in your classroom that meet in a line.

C   Investigate whether the following situations are possible. (Use two pieces of flat card to help your thinking.)
   1   A vertical line contained in a horizontal plane.
   2   A horizontal line contained in a vertical plane.
   3   Two horizontal planes meeting in a horizontal line.
   4   Two vertical planes meeting in a vertical line.
   5   A vertical plane and a horizontal plane meeting in a vertical line.
   6   A vertical plane and a horizontal plane meeting in a horizontal line.
   7   An oblique plane meeting a horizontal plane in a horizontal line.
   8   An oblique plane meeting a vertical plane in a vertical line.

D   What planes are involved in the making of:
   (a) tools   (b) houses   (c) furniture   (d) sailing boats

21·5   The sphere: volume and surface area

A sphere is a perfectly symmetrical shape. It has a centre, and all points on the surface are the same distance (the radius) from the centre.
A great circle of the sphere is a circle drawn on the surface, whose centre is the centre of the sphere. It therefore has the same radius as the sphere itself.
If a circle is rotated about a diameter a sphere is formed.

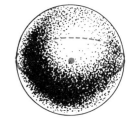

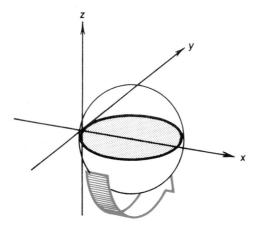

The volume and surface areas of spheres can be calculated from the formulae:

Volume $= \frac{4}{3}\pi r^3$ Surface area $= 4\pi r^2$

It is interesting to note that the surface area of a sphere is the same as that of a cylinder that would fit around the sphere.

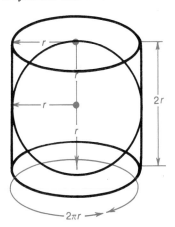

Surface area of sphere $4\pi r^2$
Curved surface area of cylinder $2\pi r \times 2r = 4\pi r^2$

If the sphere is sliced, the above relationship still holds. (This result was known to Archimedes)

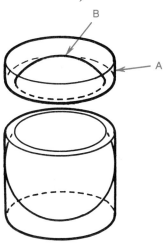

The surface area of zone A of the cylinder is the same as the surface area of zone B, the corresponding zone of the sphere.

Exercise 21·5

A **1** Calculate the volumes of spheres with radius
   (a) 4 cm   (b) 10 cm   (c) 2·5 m   (d) 0·06 mm

2 Calculate the surface areas of spheres with radius
   (a) 4 cm   (b) 10 cm   (c) 2·5 m   (d) 0·06 mm

3 Calculate the volumes of hemispheres with radius
   (a) 3 cm   (b) 5·5 m   (c) 1·6 km   (d) 0·05 mm

4 Calculate the surface areas of hemispheres with radius
   (a) 12 cm   (b) 4·8 m   (c) 0·39 m   (d) 0·08 mm
   Don't forget to add the area of the circle.

B **1** A sphere has a radius of 4 cm.
    (a) What is its volume and surface area?
    (b) What is the surface area (including the ends) of the smallest cylinder that could contain the sphere?

    2 (a) What radius sphere would be large enough to enclose 300 cm³ of air?
    (b) What would be the surface area of such a sphere?

    3 (a) What would be the dimensions of a cylinder, of radius 3 cm, with an internal volume of 300 cm³?
    (b) What would be the surface area of such a cylinder (including the ends)?

    4 A cylindrical tin is made to contain 300 cm³ of soup. Investigate the smallest area of metal that could be used in making such a tin.

    5 It is suggested that the surface area : volume ratio of the sphere is the smallest of any shape. Do you agree? Make-up some examples of different shapes containing the same volume and calculate the (surface area : volume) ratio for each.

    6 Find some examples from nature in which the ratio of surface area to volume is important.

C **1** A hollow sphere is made from material 1 cm thick.
    (a) Calculate the internal and external surface areas if its internal radius is 4 cm.
    (b) Calculate the internal and external volumes of the hollow sphere.
    (c) Deduce the volume of the material from which the sphere is made.

    2 How much water could be held in a hemispherical bowl 4 cm thick and of external radius 2 metres?

    3 A lorry carries liquid nitrogen in a sphere whose external diameter is 2·4 metres. Regulations demand that the material of the container must be 30 cm thick. What is the maximum volume of liquid that can be carried?

    4 A spherical diving bell has an internal diameter of 3 metres. It is made of metal 15 cm thick which has a density of 3·2 g/cm³.
    (a) Calculate the volume of the interior of the diving bell.
    (b) Calculate the mass of the material of the diving bell.
    (c) Calculate the mass of the air inside the diving bell (1·35 g per 1000 cm³).
    (d) The upthrust on the bell will be equal to the mass of water displaced. What mass could be added inside the bell to make it sink?

21·6 Latitude and longitude

When a sphere is sliced by a plane, a circular surface is exposed. The radius of this circle is related to the angle θ in the diagram, which is the angle between a radius of the sphere (drawn from O to a point on the circle) and the axis of symmetry of the sphere perpendicular to the plane.

Radius of exposed circle $= r \sin \theta$

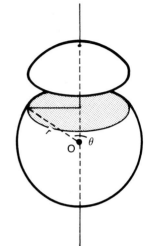

The chief application of the geometry of a sphere is in navigation. We divide the Earth's surface into zones by imaginary planes parallel to the equator. The zones are bounded by circles of latitude, marked on the diagram in degrees.

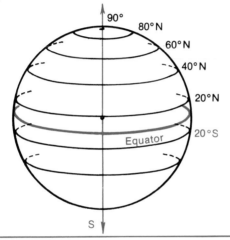

Example:

London is on the 52°N circle of latitude.
The radius of the 52° circle through London is $R \cos 52°$, where R is the radius of the earth (6378 km).
A journey round the world at latitude 52°N would therefore cover a distance of $2\pi \times 6378 \times \cos 52°$
$= 24\,672$ km

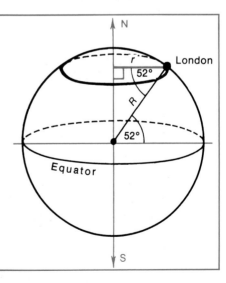

The surface of the earth can also be divided up by a series of 360 great circles which pass through the North and South Poles. These circles are called *meridians* and are counted from 0° to 180° West and from 0° to 180° East. The 0° meridian is defined as the great circle which passes through Greenwich, the North Pole and the South Pole. Any position on the globe can thus be identified by a circle of latitude and a circle of longitude (a meridian); for example, Boston, Mass., is to be found at latitude 42°N, longitude 70°W.

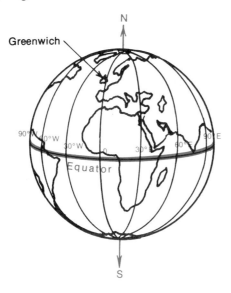

In fact, the Earth is not a perfect sphere: it is slightly flattened at the North and South poles. For rough calculations it can be treated as a sphere with radius 6366 km and great-circle circumference of 40 000 km, but more exact measurements are:

    equatorial semi-diameter   6378 km
    meridional semi-diameter 6357 km

A nautical mile is 1 minute of longitude at the equator, a minute of longitude being $\frac{1}{60}$ of a degree.

A knot is a speed of 1 nautical mile per hour. The knot is used as a unit of speed by ships and aircraft because it matches the Earth's geography.

Exercise 21·6

Use an atlas for this exercise

1 Find the cities with the following latitudes and longitudes:
    (a) 56°N, 3°W   (b) 51°30′N, 3°20′W   (c) 1°N, 104°E
    (d) 36°N, 140°E   (e) 37°30′S, 145°E   (f) 35°S, 59°W

2 (a) Make a table of the radii and circumferences of circles of latitude 0°, 10°, 20° ... 80°, 90°. (Find the radius first.)
     (b) Make a table which gives the distance equivalent to 1° of longitude on each of the circles of latitude from 0° to 80°.

3 Calculate the distance along a meridian from a point with latitude 30°N to another at 60°S.

4 Two aircraft travel from 50°N 20°W to 50°N 160°E. One flies along the 50° circle of latitude while the other flies over the North Pole. Find the distance travelled by each aircraft.

5 Show that the great circle distance between two points on a sphere will always be less than the distance along any other path between the two points.

Further information about navigation around the globe can be obtained from the geography department!

Unit 22 Volumes

22·1 Solids with regular cross-section

The volume of any solid with a regular cross-section is found in two steps:
1∅ Calculate the area of the cross-section.
2∅ Multiply the area by the length of the solid.

Example:
Calculate the volume of the solid shown. It is 6 metres long and has a regular cross-section which is an isosceles trapezium.
1∅ Area of cross-section $= \frac{1}{2}(2 + 4) \times 3 = 9\,\text{m}^2$
2∅ Volume of solid $= 9 \times 6 = 54\,\text{m}^3$

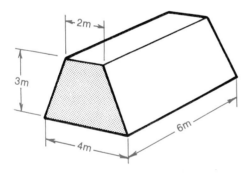

Exercise 22·1

A Calculate the volumes of the following objects.

1. A plank, 7 inches wide, $1\frac{1}{4}$ inches thick and 27 inches long.
2. A solid wire, of length 45 cm, whose cross-section is a circle of radius 2 mm.
3. The drain-pipe whose cross-section is shown in the diagram, and whose length is 10 metres.

4 A box pipe. The cross-section consists of a hollow square of external perimeter 48 cm and internal perimeter 40 cm. The length of the pipe is 12 metres.

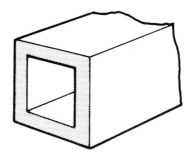

5 A concrete box-girder with square section. Internal perimeter 120 cm, thickness of material 12 cm. Length of girder 2·8 metres.

6 A rope whose cross-section consists of seven circles, each of radius 1·5 cm. Length 25 metres.

B Remember that mass = volume × density.

1 A solid square concrete beam is 14 cm × 14 cm in cross-section and 2·8 metres long. Calculate the volume of the beam (in cm³) and then the mass in kg (the density of concrete = 2·4 g/cm³)
Could one man lift the beam on his own?

2 Another concrete beam for a block of flats has a hollow square cross-section. The sides of the square measure 30 cm on the outside and 20 cm inside. Calculate the volume of a 5-metre beam of this shape. What is its mass?

3 A steel girder used for making a bridge has the cross-section shown – a rectangle with two semicircles removed. Calculate the mass of 25 metres of this girder in metric tonnes. (1 metric tonne = 1000 kg; the density of steel is 7·5 g/cm³ = 7500 kg/m³ = 7·5 tonnes/m³.)
Do the calculation in cm, then again in metres to check your work.
Take plenty of time with this question.

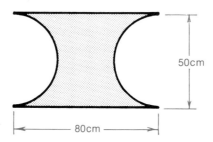

50cm

80cm

4 Bricks are usually 21 cm × 10 cm × 6 cm.
  (a) Calculate the volume of a single brick.
  (b) Calculate the mass of a single brick (density 2 g/cm³).
  (c) Estimate the number of bricks used to build a wall 3 metres high, 5 metres wide and 20 cm thick.
  (d) Estimate the mass of such a wall.

5 The shape of a jet aircraft is roughly that of a cylinder 40 metres long, with a radius of 3 metres. Calculate the approximate volume of air in the aircraft when it is sealed. If there are 178 people aboard when the oxygen supply fails with the aircraft at 10 000 metres, how long will the air sealed into the cabin last them? (Assume that one person can live for one hour on 1 m³ of air.)

C 1 Some timber is sold by the cubic metre. Calculate the cost of 12 5-metre lengths of timber, each with a cross-section 7 cm square. The price of the timber is £42 per cubic metre.

2 A five-litre can of paint is sufficient to cover 12 m² of flat surface. Calculate the average thickness of the paint. If the paint costs £8·50 per 5 litres, how much would it cost to paint the four walls of a room 5 m long, 4 m wide and 3 m high (excluding the door, which has an area of 2 m²)?

3 A tonne of copper costs £120. What is the cost of the copper used to make 100 metres of copper pipe of external diameter 22 mm and thickness 2 mm? A shop sells the copper pipe at £1·20 per metre: what rate per tonne is this? (The density of copper is 8·9 g/cm³.)

4 A large box of soap powder has dimensions 30 cm × 10 cm × 50 cm and costs £4·25. A small box of the same powder has dimensions 6 cm × 16 cm × 22 cm.
  What would you expect the small box to cost?

5 A cylindrical container of washing-up liquid is 25 cm high, with diameter 7·5 cm. Would you expect the container to hold 1 litre of liquid?

6 A 'double-size' bottle contains 2 litres of washing-up liquid and stands 30 cm high. What is its diameter?

22·2 Packing

The packing of materials for transport is a very important part of the cost. For some substances, packaging plus transport costs more than the substance itself. The best-shaped package for transport is the cuboid, but even awkward shapes like bottles are usually organised into some rectangular shape (e.g. a box). Cylindrical tin cans are economical, however, in the amount of material needed to contain a given volume.

Example:

Find the area of metal used to make:

(a) A carton 16 cm high, of square cross-section, which contains exactly 800 cm³ of milk.

(b) A cylindrical tin of height 16 cm which contains 800 cm³ of milk.

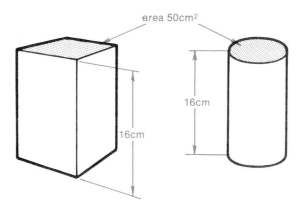

area 50cm²

16cm

16cm

Cuboid

Volume of cuboid = 800 cm³

1∅ Volume = area of base × height

2∅ 800 cm³ = area of base × 16 cm

3∅ Area of base = 50 cm²

4∅ Side of square = $\sqrt{50}$ = 7·071 cm

5∅ Total surface area =
50 + 50 + (4 × $\sqrt{50}$ × 16) = 552·5 cm²

Cylinder

Volume of cylinder = 800 cm³

1∅ Volume = area of base × height

2∅ 800 cm³ = area of base × 16 cm

3∅ Area of base = 50 cm² = πr^2

4∅ Radius of base = $\sqrt{50/\pi}$ = 3·99 cm

5∅ Total surface area =
50 + 50 + (2 × π × r × 16) = 501·1 cm²

↓   ↓

perimeter of base   height

This represents a 10% saving in material

Exercise 22·2

A 1 Six circles of diameter 1·3 cm are cut from a flat piece of metal 5 cm long and 3·5 cm wide. Calculate the area of metal wasted.

2 A rectangular box is made to contain 12 cylindrical tins. Each tin is 110 mm high with a base diameter of 75 mm. Calculate

(a) The volume of the box.

(b) The combined volume of the tins.

(c) The area of the cardboard used in making the box (ignore overlapping).

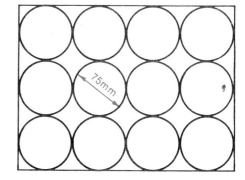

75mm

3 Tree trunks with uniform cross-section are sawn into planks as shown in the diagrams. Compare the fraction of wood wasted by each of the two methods for a tree trunk of diameter 50 cm. (The dimensions shown on the diagram are the widths of the planks, which are all 5 cm thick.)

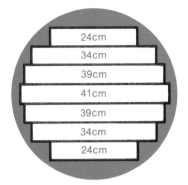
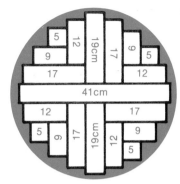

4 (a) Find the area of metal used to make a cylindrical tin 120 cm high with diameter 60 cm, with closed ends.

(b) The thickness of the metal is about 2 mm. Calculate the volume of metal in the tin.

(c) The density of the metal is 7 g/cm³. Calculate the mass of the tin.

B Investigate the volumes and surface areas of a number of food containers. Keep a record of your work. How many different basic shapes of food containers can you find?

C *Mixed problems*

1 A container is 2 metres wide, 4 metres high and 10 metres long.

(a) Calculate the volume of the space inside the container.

(b) Estimate how many boxes 30 cm × 40 cm × 60 cm would fit into the container.

(c) Investigate different ways of packing the container. How could you pack the boxes so that the least space would be wasted?

(d) Each box is packed with butter in 40 mm × 75 mm × 100 mm packets which weigh 500 g. What is the weight of each box?

(e) What would the container's load weigh if the container were filled up with butter?

2 Wine is transported in bulk in cylindrical containers whose length is 8 metres and diameter 6 metres. Estimate the volume of wine the container would hold when half full.

3 A jet uses 26 litres of fuel per kilometre of flight.

(a) Estimate the amount of fuel used on a flight across the Atlantic Ocean (about 5400 km).

(b) What does this fuel weigh? (Density 0·85 g/cm³)

(c) The amount of fuel used depends on both altitude and wind velocity. Why do you think this is so?

(d) The fuel tanks are carried in the wings. Estimate the minimum length of the tanks for a transatlantic crossing if they are rectangular, 3 metres wide and 50 cm deep.

4 Oil tankers bring crude oil from Saudi Arabia to South Wales.

(a) A tanker can carry 200 000 tonnes of oil of density 0·8 g/cm³. What volume does the oil occupy?

(b) The Welsh authorities plan to send back the tankers filled with pure water (which is valuable in Saudi Arabia). How many cubic metres of water can be transported? What is this shipload of water worth, at a price of:

(i) 0·5 pence per litre   (ii) 1·5 pence per litre   (iii) 3·5 pence per litre

(*Note:* 1 m³ = 1000 litres; 0·8 g/cm³ = 0·8 tonnes/m³.)

5 A drop of oil (volume 12 mm³) will spread out over water to cover 1100 cm². What is the average thickness of the oil when it has spread?

6 In an oil-pollution disaster, 60 000 tonnes of crude oil escaped from a tanker. The density of the oil was just less than that of sea water, so the oil formed a thin slick. Calculate the area of sea polluted if the oil spread until it was:
(a) 5 cm thick   (b) 1 mm thick
(1 tonne of crude oil occupies approximately 1 m³)

22·3 Pyramids

A cube can be sliced into six equal pyramids. Each pyramid will have a square base which is one face of the cube. The height of the pyramid will be half the height of the cube.

Exercise 22·3

A *Investigation*

Make six model pyramids using the net drawn below.

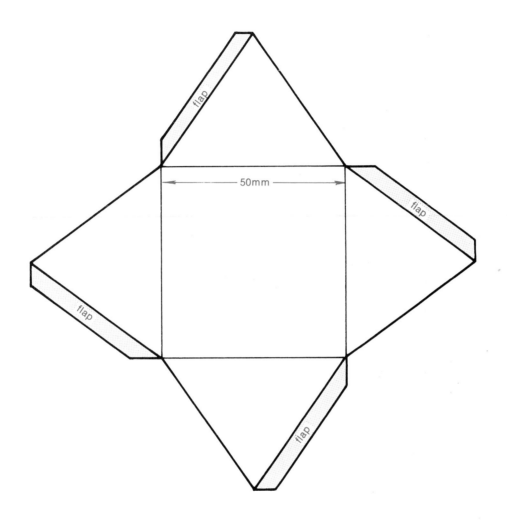

The sides of the squares should be 50 mm long.

The shorter sides of the triangles should be 43 mm long.

A larger model can be made by multiplying the lengths by any suitable factor.

Construct a hollow cube so that the six pyramids fit exactly inside it.

1 Measure the height of your pyramids and the shortest distance from the vertex to the edge of the base.

2 Explain the connection between the diagonals of the cube and the sloping edges of your pyramids.

3 Show that the lengths of the sloping edges of the pyramids are all the same, and equal to $\frac{1}{2} \times \sqrt{3} \times 50$ mm.

4 Calculate the volume of each pyramid.
   (*Hint:* Six of them make up a cube.)

B *Investigation*

1 Make five tetrahedra and a cube from the nets below. The dimensions should be copied exactly, or all enlarged by a factor of 2.

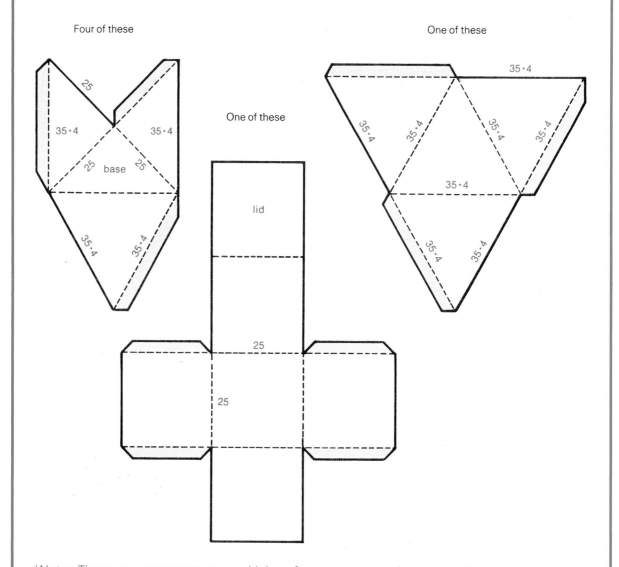

Four of these

One of these

One of these

(*Note:* These measurements are multiples of square roots and so cannot be convenient whole numbers. If the side of the cube (in mm) is a whole number n, the diagonals will be $\sqrt{2}n$ and $2\sqrt{3}n$, i.e. $1.414n$ and $3.464n$.)

2 Measure the heights and calculate the base areas of the five tetrahedra.

3 Show that the five tetrahedra can be packed into the cube (it will be a tight fit).

4 Investigate the suggestion that each small tetrahedron has $\frac{1}{6}$ of the volume of the cube and that the large tetrahedron has $\frac{1}{3}$ of the volume of the cube.

You probably enjoyed making the models in this investigation. If so, and if you have time, make a very accurate set of models, with the sides shaded in different colours. These models should be kept, as they illustrate many ideas in the geometry of three dimensions.

22·4 Volume of a pyramid

The first investigation of Exercise 22·3 showed that the volume of each pyramid is $\frac{1}{3} \times$ area of base $\times$ height. This formula can be proved to be true for every type of pyramid, including cones.

$$\text{Vol}_{\text{pyramid}} = \tfrac{1}{3} \times \text{area of base} \times \text{height}$$

Examples:

1 Find the volume of a pyramid 6 cm high on a square base of side 4 cm.

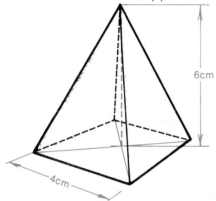

Volume $= \frac{1}{3} \times$ area of base $\times$ height
$= \frac{1}{3} \times 16 \times 6$
$= 32 \text{ cm}^3$

2 Find the volume of a cone with base radius 5 cm and height 9 cm.

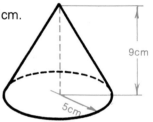

Area of base $= \pi r^2 = 78 \cdot 54 \text{ cm}^2$
Volume $= \frac{1}{3} \times 78 \cdot 54 \times 9 = 235 \cdot 6 \text{ cm}^3$

Exercise 22·4

A Calculate the volume of each of the following solids.

1 A pyramid 8 cm high on a base 6 cm square.

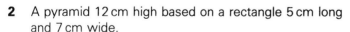

2 A pyramid 12 cm high based on a rectangle 5 cm long and 7 cm wide.

3 A pyramid 14 cm high based on a right-angled triangle whose sides are 3 cm, 4 cm and 5 cm long.

4 A tetrahedron based on an equilateral triangle with sides 5 cm long. The height of the tetrahedron is 8 cm.

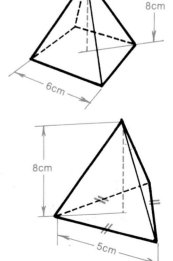

5 A cone of base radius 18 cm and height 9 cm.

6 A cone with base radius 3 metres and height 4·8 metres.

B *Problems*

1 A village has a conical water tower. The diameter of the top of the tower is 8 metres and the depth of water when the cone is full is 5 metres at the centre.
Calculate:

(a) The volume of water stored when the tank is full.

(b) The mass of the water. (1 m³ of water weighs 1 tonne.)

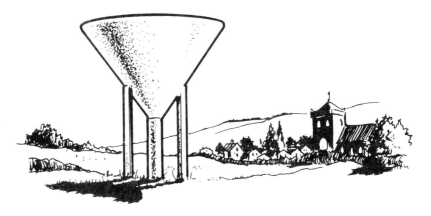

2 The information below refers to the great pyramids of Ancient Egypt.

Place	King	Date of construction	Side of base	Height
Medum	Sneferu	4750 B.C.	144·3 m	91·9 m
Gizeh	Khufu	4700 B.C.	230·3 m	146·7 m
Gizeh	Khafra	4600 B.C.	215·3 m	143·7 m
Gizeh	Menkaura	4550 B.C.	105·5 m	64·5 m
Dahshur	?	?	189·4 m	105 m

(a) Calculate the volume of each pyramid. Estimate the mass of each, assuming an average density of 2·8 g/cm³ (2·8 tonnes/m³).

(b) Which pyramids weigh more than 6 million tonnes?

3 A new coal mine is allocated a space on which waste is to be dumped. The area is 50 000 m². In two years about 6 million tonnes of waste are dumped, to form a conical tip. The density of the waste is 2 tonnes/m³. Find the height of the cone of waste.
(*Hint:* Calculate the volume of the waste first.)

4 A modern church steeple is in the form of a hollow concrete cone 84 metres high. The external diameter of the steeple at its base is 9 metres and the internal diameter is 8 metres.
(a) Calculate the volume of the exterior of the cone.
(b) Calculate the volume of the interior of the cone. (Allow 0·5 m less for the internal height, to allow for thickness of concrete.)
(c) Deduce the volume of the concrete forming the cone.
(d) Calculate the mass of the steeple (the density of concrete is 2·1 tonnes per cubic metre).

22·5 Spheres

The volume of a sphere is given by the formula
$V = \frac{4}{3}\pi r^3$
where r is the length of the radius.
The surface area of a sphere is $4\pi r^2$
(*Note:* this is the same as the curved surface area of the cylinder surrounding the sphere.)

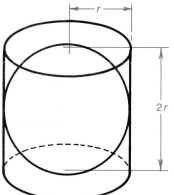

Examples:

1 Find the volume and surface area of a sphere with radius 12 cm.
Vol = $\frac{4}{3}\pi r^3$ = (4 × π × 12³) ÷ 3 = 7238 cm³
4 ⊠ π ⊠ 12 ⊠ 12 ⊠ 12 ÷ 3 = 7238
Surface area = $4\pi r^2$ = 4 × π × 12² = 1809·5 cm²

2 A sphere has a surface area of 1480 cm². What is its diameter?
Surface area = $4\pi r^2$
1480 = 4 × π × r^2
$\Rightarrow r^2 = \dfrac{1480}{4\pi} = 117\cdot77$
$\Rightarrow r = 10\cdot85$ cm   1480 ÷ 4 ÷ π = √ 10·85
$\Rightarrow$ diameter = 21·7 cm

3 A spherical drop of water weighs 0·8 g. What is the radius of the drop?
The volume of the drop is 0·8 cm³   (the density of water is 1 g/cm³)
$\frac{4}{3}\pi r^3 = 0\cdot8$

$\Rightarrow r^3 = \dfrac{0\cdot8 \times 3}{4 \times \pi}$

$\Rightarrow r = \sqrt[3]{\dfrac{0\cdot8 \times 3}{4 \times \pi}} = 0\cdot576$ cm
0·8 ⊠ 3 ÷ 4 ÷ π = x^y 0·33333 = 0·576

Exercise 22·5

A 1 Calculate the volumes and curved surface areas of spheres with radius 5 cm, 10 cm, 20 cm and 1·5 metres.

2 Calculate the volume and surface area of these international standard tennis, cricket and soccer balls.

Tennis: diameter 6·5 cm

Cricket: circumference 22·6 cm

Soccer: circumference 27 inches

3 The radius of the earth is roughly 4000 miles. Calculate the approximate area of the surface.

4 71% of the earth's surface is water and the rest is land. Using the result of Question 2, calculate the area of the land.

5 The equatorial circumference of the Earth is 24 902 miles.
The meridional circumference of the Earth is 24 860 miles.
(a) Calculate the volume and surface areas of spheres with circumference:
    (i)   Equal to the equatorial circumference of the Earth.
    (ii) Equal to the meridional circumference of the Earth.
    (iii) Equal to the average of the equatorial and meridional
        circumferences of the Earth..
    (Calculate *r* first)
(b) An atlas gives the following data about the Earth:
    Volume: 2·6 × 10¹¹ cubic miles
    Surface: Land: 57 510 000 square miles
              Sea: 139 440 000 square miles
    Which of the three spheres in part (a) gives data closest
    to that of the atlas?

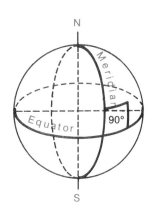

6 A church has a hemispherical dome with internal radius 18 metres and external radius 20 metres. Calculate:
  (a) The internal and external surface areas of the dome.
  (b) The volume of the space in the dome.
  (c) The volume of the material in the dome.
  (d) The mass of the dome, if its average density is 2·2 tonnes/m³.

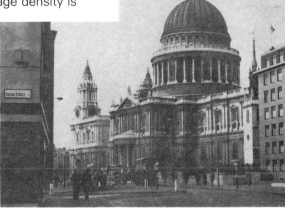

B 1 The volume of a sphere is 450 cm³. Calculate its radius and surface area.

2 The volume of a hemisphere is 21 m³. Calculate the surface area, including the area of the base.

3 The surface area of a balloon is 450 m³.
(*Hint:* the balloon is almost spherical.)
What is the radius of the balloon? What volume of gas does it hold? (Why do balloons stay up?)

4 A theatre is built in the form of a hemispherical bowl with internal surface area 4000 m³. Calculate the radius of the bowl.

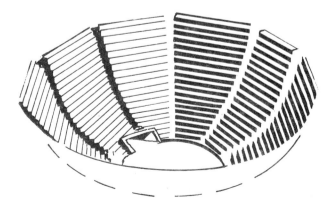

5 A balloon will burst if its surface area is increased beyond 1400 m³. What is its maximum possible radius?

C **1** Calculate the volume of a regular octahedron whose edges are all 7 cm long.

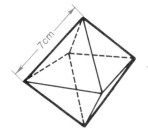

2 An ice-cream cone is 40 mm in diameter with a depth of 100 mm. A hemispherical ball of ice-cream is put on top of the cone.
The cone and ice-cream are left in the sun and the ice-cream melts and runs down into the cone. Will the cone hold all the melted ice-cream? If so, what will be the distance of the ice-cream surface below the top of the inverted cone?

3 A vessel is in the shape of an inverted cone. Liquid is poured into the cone to a depth of 40 cm. The radius of the surface of the liquid is then found to be 8 cm. Calculate the volume of liquid in the vessel.

4 In a chemical process in a laboratory, acid is passed from a funnel to a flask at 4 cm³ per minute.
At a certain moment the surface of the acid in the funnel is a circle of radius 3 cm and its depth at the centre is 5 cm. Calculate the depth and radius one minute later.

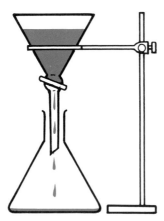

5 A sphere has a surface area of $4\pi r^2$. Show from this that the volume must be $\frac{4}{3}\pi r^3$.
Hint: Treat the sphere as a solid made up of cones with vertices at the centre of the sphere.

6 Part of an axle consists of a cylinder with two cones removed, as shown in the diagram. Calculate the volume of the object, given that:
(i) the radius of the cylinder is 12 mm.
(ii) the length of the cylinder is 50 mm.
(iii) the height of each cone is 18 mm.

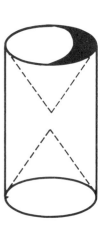

D *Investigations*

1 What is the largest possible cylinder, in terms of volume, that can be made from 100 cm² of sheet metal. Compare your findings for the ratio $\dfrac{\text{height}}{\text{diameter}}$ with various food cans.

2 The surface of a cone is a sector of a circle.

  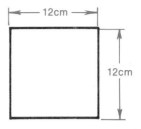

What is the largest capacity* of cone that can be made from a square of metal? Start off with a 12 cm square. Extend the investigation to rectangular sheets of metal.

*The volume of liquid that the cone can contain.

Unit 23 Statistics

23·1 Dispersion

The mean (average) is a single number which can represent a set of
data. This, on its own, is not enough to give a full picture: another
measure is needed to show the spread (dispersion) of the data around
the mean.

Example:

In one particular week, a bus journey, timetabled as 120 minutes, took:

118 minutes on Monday
125 minutes on Tuesday
119 minutes on Wednesday
128 minutes on Thursday
122 minutes on Friday
114 minutes on Saturday

Mean for the week = $(118 + 125 + 119 + 128 + 122 + 114) \div 6$

$\qquad\qquad\qquad = 121$ minutes

From the mean alone it might seem that the bus time was always close to 120 minutes.
However, the spread of times was from 114 minutes to 128 minutes. This spread from
smallest to largest is called the range.

The range is the simplest measure of spread but is not really satisfactory,
because the end-values of a set of data can be 'freaks'. The interquartile
range gives a more reliable spread. It is found by the following steps:

1∅   Arrange the data in order of size, smallest first (i.e. rank the
     data).

2∅   Find the values which divide the frequency into four equal
     parts. These values are (in order) the lower quartile, the median
     and the upper quartile.

3∅   Calculate the difference between the lower and the upper
     quartiles. This is the interquartile range.

Example:

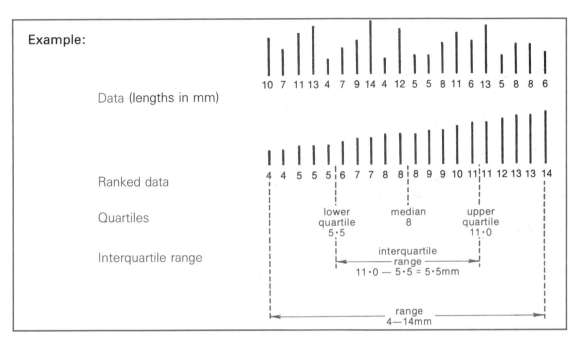

Data (lengths in mm)

10 7 11 13 4 7 9 14 4 12 5 5 8 11 6 13 5 8 8 6

Ranked data

4 4 5 5 5 6 7 7 8 8 8 9 9 10 11 11 12 13 13 14

Quartiles

lower quartile 5·5 median 8 upper quartile 11·0

Interquartile range

interquartile range
11·0 — 5·5 = 5·5mm

range
4—14mm

Half the values lie between the two quartiles; the other half lie below the lower quartile or above the upper quartile. 'Freak' values at the extremes of the range do not affect the interquartile range.

Exercise 23·1

A Find the mean, range and interquartile range of each of the following sets of data.

   1 Costs of a collection of second-hand cars.

2 Age of the same collection of cars.

3 Weights of a sample of eggs.

36 g 40 g 41 g 35 g 40 g 42 g 40 g 38 g 42 g 45 g 48 g 52 g 44 g
28 g 30 g 30 g 36 g 40 g 48 g 44 g

4 Prices of bargain Spring Holidays:
(a) 1-week holidays
(b) 2-week holidays
(c) Flights only

5 Marks in a French examination (30 students)

42 18 46 54 20 22 54 56 70 64 68 44 70 30 36 19 27 36
62 43 45 52 38 68 71 77 22 29 40 58

B Find the mean, range and interquartile range for each set of data below. Use these to compare the two sets of data in each question, and write brief notes about the differences between them.

1 Heights at age 14 (in cm) of a sample of boys and girls:

Boys: 179 178 181 175 170 166 164 180 173 176 160 184 183
169 172

Girls: 160 174 157 170 180 164 163 176 175 153 181 182 167
169 162

2 Average maximum January and June temperatures (°C) for the UK, 1976–1985:

	1976	1977	1978	1979	1980	1981	1982	1983	1984	1985
Jan	4·3	6·0	4·2	2·6	4·7	4·4	5·1	1·0	4·0	4·2
June	13·5	15·4	14·0	15·3	16·0	15·0	13·9	14·9	14·2	14·6

3 Average number of hours of sunshine per day, month-by-month, over the thirty years 1941–70:

	Jan	Feb	Mar	Apr	May	Jun	Jul	Aug	Sep	Oct	Nov	Dec
Scotland	1·40	2·53	3·36	4·99	5·74	5·79	4·81	4·48	3·71	2·70	1·73	1·14
Wales	1·52	2·39	3·70	5·25	6·07	6·45	5·42	5·17	3·98	2·88	1·74	1·31

4 Weights at birth (to the nearest 500 g) of 300 girls and 300 boys:

Weight at birth (kg)	2·0	2·5	3·0	3·5	4·0	4·5	5·0	5·5	6·0
Girls	34	97	48	35	62	17	5	2	0
Boys	24	80	76	29	54	34	0	3	0

5 The oil in a car engine is kept clean by passing it through a filter. The filter collects the dirt, and after a time becomes clogged. From then on it is useless and unable to clean the oil. The table below gives the number of miles before clogging for a sample of oil filters.

Miles	Number of filters
7500	12
8000	18
8500	39
9000	53
9500	60
10 000	102
10 500	140
11 000	85
11 500	17
12 000	2
12 500	5
13 000	1
13 500	0
14 000	0
14 500	3
15 000	1
Total	538

Find the median, range and interquartile range of this data. When would be the best time to change the oil filter, in view of this information? (You would not want to waste money by throwing away a good filter. On the other hand, you would not want to run the car with oil that was not being cleaned.)

23·2   Experiment and observation

When data is collected in science, social science, etc., the spread or
dispersion may be as important as the values themselves.

Example:

A doctor is called to see a boy who seems ill. He takes the boy's pulse and finds it to be 98
(beats to the minute). Is this serious?

The doctor has the following information about normal pulse rate:
Median pulse rate for 14-year-old boys: 72 per minute
Range: 60 per minute
Interquartile range: 10 per minute

The doctor might think as follows:
(a) The boy's pulse rate is 26 beats per minute above average.
(b) 50% of boys have a pulse rate between 67 and 77 (calculating from the interquartile
     range).
(c) The extremes of fast and slow are 42 and 102 beats to the minute (calculating from the
     range).
(d) The boy's pulse rate is 98 beats per minute, so he is more likely to be ill than for this high
     rate to be normal

Exercise 23·2

A   Comment on the dispersion you find after collecting data in the following investigations:
   1   Distance from school to home (for members of your class)
   2   Height (of members of your class).
   3   Weight (of members of your class).
   4   Average pocket-money and earnings per week (for members of your class)
   5   Number of hours spent each week in watching TV.
   6   Pulse rate.

B *Experiments*

The ideas of probability were first explored through experiment. Often the experiments were very simple – tossing coins, drawing cards from packs and so on. Nowadays, computers may be used to simulate (i.e. provide models of) these experiments.

Investigate the following situations. Pay particular attention to the spread of the values, i.e. the dispersion of the data.

1   Test reaction time by dropping a ruler between another person's thumb and first finger.

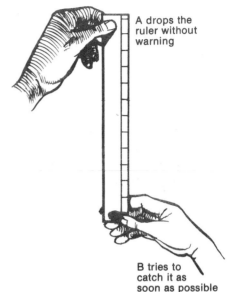

A drops the ruler without warning

B tries to catch it as soon as possible

The reaction times can be found by using the following table:

Distance fallen by ruler (cm)	1	2	3	4	5	6	7	8	9	10	11	12
Reaction time (secs)	0·05	0·06	0·08	0·09	0·10	0·11	0·12	0·13	0·14	0·14	0·15	0·16
Distance fallen by ruler (cm)	13	14	15	16	17	18	19	20	21	22	23	24
Reaction time (secs)	0·16	0·17	0·17	0·18	0·19	0·19	0·20	0·20	0·21	0·21	0·22	0·22

2   *Memory test (letters)*

Write out 20 letters on a piece of paper. They can be all different or some can be the same. Allow a friend to look at the letters for 10 seconds, then take the piece of paper away. Two minutes later ask the friend to write down as many of the letters as he or she can remember. Score 1 mark for each correct letter.

Carry out the test on a number of different people and investigate the dispersion of the results.

You could vary this experiment, for example by keeping your list of letters in alphabetical order.

3   *Memory test (words):*

Repeat the previous experiment using a list of 20 words instead of 20 letters.

Do the results of your experiment suggest that words are easier to remember than single letters?

4 Investigate the number below, which is π calculated to 200 decimal places. Suggest ways in which this number could be used to find the winner of a raffle with 100 tickets.

3·1415926535 → 8979323846 → 2643383279 → 5028841971 → 6939937510 →
5820974944 → 5923078164 → 0628620899 → 8628034825 → 3421170679 →
8214808651 → 3282306647 → 0938446095 → 5058223172 → 5359408128 →
4811174502 → 8410270193 → 8521105559 → 6446229489 → 5493038196

(a) How often does each of the digits 0, 1, 2, ... etc. appear in the number?
(b) How many 'pair' repeats are there, e.g. 77 or 99?
(c) How many 'triple' repeats are there, e.g. 111 or 333?

5 If you press $\sqrt{}$ after a number which is not a perfect square, a long decimal is produced. Do some digits occur more often than others in these tails? Investigate.

6 Consider only the first three digits from a $\sqrt{}$ decimal tail. Find out how frequently a triangle can be formed which uses these three digits as the lengths of the sides.

Examples:

23 $\sqrt{}$ 4·795 831 5
It is possible to draw a triangle with sides 7 cm, 9 cm and 5 cm.

7 $\sqrt{}$ 2·449 489 743
It is not possible to draw a (4, 4, 9) triangle!

---

7 Investigate other function buttons (e.g. $\boxed{\text{sin}}$, $\boxed{\text{log}}$) in the same way as in questions 5 and 6 above.

23·3 Sampling

The purpose of statistics is to give clear information, but this is not always possible. Collection of data is difficult and expensive. Usually a small part of the whole population is measured and, on the basis of those measurements, a guess is made about the whole population. This process is called sampling.

Examples:
1 A cook tastes the soup by taking a sample spoonful.
2 An opinion poll is taken to find out if the people of a city support the idea of capital punishment. One hundred people are chosen at random from the telephone directory. They are phoned and asked for their opinion.
This method of taking a sample, although often used, does not give a reliable opinion, because poorer people often do not have a telephone in their house. The sample is thus biassed towards middle-class opinion.

The results of a random sample can be used to estimate values for the whole population. The larger the sample, the more reliable the estimate will be.

Example:
In one class, 12 children liked the head teacher and 18 did not. If this sample is typical of the 1200 children in the school, how many did not like the head teacher?

Sample proportions: $\frac{12}{30}$ liked, $\frac{18}{30}$ did not like.

Assuming the same proportion for the whole school,

$12 \times \frac{18}{30} = 720$ did not like the head teacher.

(*Note:* This answer depends on an assumption. If the assumption is not true, the calculation does not give a correct result!)

Exercise 23·3

A Explain the sampling that takes place in the following situations:
  1 A couple of girls go out to buy clothes.
  2 You are set an exercise for homework.
  3 A pair of dice are thrown 50 times and the results recorded.
  4 Drinking water is tested for purity.
  5 You have a blood test.
  6 A local paper asks its readers for opinions about a new motorway.
  State the population that is being sampled in each case.

B **1** Suggest some situations that you have experienced where sampling takes place.
  2 How could you use your calculator to help pick an unbiassed sample?

C In the following questions, state the assumptions that you make in finding an answer to the question.
  1 The figures below give viewing figures taken from *The Listener*, 15 March 1984.

BBC1	million	BBC2	million
1. That's Life	12·15	1. Alias Smith and Jones	5·60
2. Dallas	10·70	2. Your Life in Their Hands	4·15
3. Holiday	10·40	3. Mouse on the Moon	3·95
4. A Question of Sport	10·15	4. Gardeners' World	3·90
5. The Superstars	9·75	M*A*S*H	3·90
6. Diana	9·60	6. Call My Bluff	3·75
7. Top of the Pops	9·35	7. Leo	3·60
8. Some Mothers do 'Ave 'Em	9·25	8. Geoffrey Smith's World of Flowers	3·50
9. The Living Planet	9·20	9. Tucker's Luck	3·00
10. Mastermind	9·10	10. Pot Black 84	2·90
ITV	million	C4	million
1. Coronation Street (Mon)	14·85	1. Treasure Hunt	3·40
2. Coronation Street (Wed)	14·50	2. Cheers	3·15
3. 3–2–1	14·10	3. Brookside (Wed)	2·95
4. Duty Free	14·05	4. The Boy in the Bush	2·65
5. Minder	13·95	5. The Lady is a Tramp	2·60
6. Wish You Were Here . . . ?	13·40	6. Brookside (Tues)	2·20
7. Child's Play	12·85	7. Athletics: European Indoor Championships	2·10
8. Crossroads (Tues)	12·50	8. The World at War	1·85
9. Crossroads (Thurs)	12·45	9. Ace Eli and Rodger of the Skies	1·70
10. This is Your Life	12·10	10. The Heart of the Dragon	1·65
		Bewitched	1·65

Breakfast Time (BBC1) 1·6 million; Good Morning Britain (TV-am) 1·2 million (Mon–Fri average)

  (a) How do you think such figures are obtained?
  (b) How many times has your own family been asked about the programmes they watch?
  (c) Which of the programmes are still being shown (as far as you know)?
  (d) In 1984 the BBC had 45% of the audience and the commercial channels 55%. Is the split still the same?

2 In 1984, the viewing figures for the four TV channels (BBC1, BBC2, ITV and Channel 4) were analysed day-by-day for one week, and summarised in this table:

	Mon	Tue	Wed	Th	Fri	Sat	Sun
BBC1	30	41	27	41	30	39	41
ITV	52	40	59	41	52	51	44
BBC2	12	11	11	11	11	5	10
C4	6	8	3	7	7	5	5

(a) What do you think the figures stand for?
(b) Do these figures correspond to a division of the audience into 55% watching commercial TV and 45% watching BBC?
(c) Calculate median, range and interquartile range for each of the 4 channels (rough only).

3 A die is thrown 1200 times. How many sixes would you expect?

4 In an opinion poll, 100 workers were asked if they would support a strike. 60 said 'Yes', 30 said 'No', and 10 did not know. What would you expect the Yes, No and Don't know figures to be for 600 000 workers?

5 A batch of light-bulbs consists of 240 000 bulbs. A sample of 240 from the batch is tested and two are found to be faulty. How many faulty bulbs are there likely to be in the whole batch?

6 *Investigation*
The sequence 20 $\boxed{\sin}$ gives on the display the decimal number 0·342020 143. The first three figures after the decimal point are 342. Investigate the first three digits of the sequence n $\boxed{\sin}$ for different values of n, to see whether these three-figure numbers can be used as a set of random numbers.
If the numbers are random, then:
(a) They should be even about half of the time.
(b) They should be multiples of 3 about a third of the time.
(c) They should be multiples of 5 about 20% of the time.
Your calculator may have a special method of generating random numbers. All computers have this property, as it is used in computer games.
If you enjoyed this investigation, try out other function buttons as a means of generating random numbers.

23·4 Mean deviation

A more accurate measure of dispersion than interquartile range is needed in some applications of statistics. We therefore define the mean deviation as the average of all the differences between the data values and the arithmetic mean.

Example:
The heights of a sample of 12 children are given. Calculate the mean deviation of the sample.
Heights (cm): 160   161   163   164   166   168   168   170   171   172   174   176

1⃝   The mean is calculated: $\bar{x} = \dfrac{1}{n}\sum x_i = 167\cdot75$

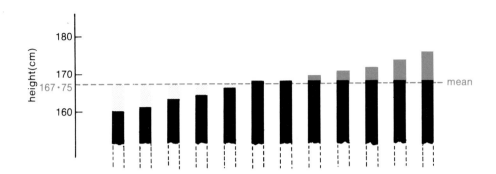

2⃝   The deviation (difference) from the mean is calculated for each item in the data, as shown in the table. Note that a straight bracket is used for 'difference', which is always positive: $|6-4| = 2 = |4-6|$.

These differences are shown as coloured distances in the diagram

Data values x_i	Mean $\bar{x}$	Deviations $\lvert x_i - \bar{x} \rvert$	
160		7·75	
161		6·75	
163		4·75	below the mean
164		3·75	
166		1·75	
	167·75	....	
168		0·25	
168		0·25	
170		2·25	
171		3·25	above the mean
172		4·25	
174		6·25	
176		8·25	
		49·25	

3⃝   The sum of the deviations is found – in this case it is 49·25.

4⃝   The mean deviation is found by dividing the sum by n. In this case, $49\cdot25 \div 12 = 4\cdot104$

The above example, which is very important, shows how to calculate a mean deviation. It also shows that, in the given example, the deviation is small compared with the mean: this suggests that the heights are all fairly close to the average.

Mean deviation does not have the instability of range.
In the example, the interquartile range can be taken as the difference
between the 3rd and the 9th values of the ranked data ($171 - 163 = 8$).
This is about double the mean deviation.

Exercise 23·4

1 Check through the example on mean deviation. Make sure you understand the steps in the calculation and that you agree with the values for $\bar{x}$, for $\sum |x_i - \bar{x}|$, and for the mean deviation.

2 All the children whose heights are given in the above example are at least 160 cm tall. We could thus subtract 160 from each value, to give us the set of data (0, 1, 3, 4, 6, 8, 8, 10, 11, 12, 14, 16).

Check that the same value for the mean deviation is obtained using (0, 1, 2, ... etc.) as values for x_i as when using (160, 161, 162, ... etc.). This method is called changing the origin.

3 Find the mean deviation of the following sets of data:

(a) Heights of sixteen 4-year-old children (cm): 104, 106, 107, 107, 109, 110, 111, 111, 113, 114, 114, 115, 118, 120, 121, 122.

(b) Weights of twelve fish caught in a fishing competition (kg): 1·7, 1·8, 1·8, 1·9, 1·9, 2·0, 2·2, 2·3, 2·5, 2·5, 2·7, 2·9.

(c) Number of worms per square metre in a study of soil under different conditions: 10, 14, 22, 19, 13, 28, 40, 48, 14, 32, 66, 41.

(d) Number of planes shot down each day during the final two weeks of the Battle of Britain: 24, 45, 61, 32, 58, 48, 10, 23, 35, 19, 45, 57, 92, 137.

(e) Number of peas per pod in a sample of 100 pods:

x_i	f_i
7	4
8	14
9	22
10	39
11	15
12	6
	$N = 100$

In this case $\bar{x} = \dfrac{1}{N} \sum x_i f_i$

and mean deviation $= \dfrac{1}{N} \sum |x_i - \bar{x}| f_i$

4 Find the interquartile range of each of the sets of data in Question 3. Is it true that the mean deviation is approximately half the interquartile range in these examples?

5 Investigate ways in which the calculation of mean deviation could be shortened.

Hint: It may help to separate those values which are greater than $\bar{x}$ from those which are less than $\bar{x}$.

Try out your shortened methods on a set of data of your own choosing, and compare your results with those produced by the long method.

Unit 24   Numbers and ratios

24·1   Factors, multiples and primes

5 is a factor of 20 because there is an exact number of fives in 20. This means that there is no remainder when 20 is divided by 5.

20 is a multiple of 5. Other multiples of 5 are 5 itself, 10, 15, 25, 30, 55 etc.

5 is a prime number because it has no factors other than 1 and 5.

5 is a factor of $20 \Leftrightarrow 20$ is a multiple of 5

Every whole number is either a prime number or the product of a set of prime factors

---

Example:

Show that 107 is a prime number.

We show that 107 is prime by testing for possible prime factors.

2 is not a factor because 107 is odd

3 is not a factor because the digits add to 8, which is not a multiple of 3

5 is not a factor because 107 does not end in 5 or 0

7 is not a factor because (a) 105 is a multiple of 7, so 107 cannot be an exact multiple of 7
(b) $107 \div 7 = 15 \cdot 287\,714\,29 \ldots$ so 7 is not a factor of 107

11 is not a factor because 110 is a multiple of 11 so 107 cannot be a multiple of 11
So 107 has no factors other than 1 and 107

Notes: 1   We do not bother to check divisibility by 4, because $4 = 2^2$, so any number divisible by 4 is also divisible by 2, and we have checked that already. Similarly we do not check divisibility by 8 or 9, because we have already checked for 2 and 3. We check only for divisibility by prime numbers.

2   *There is no need to go beyond 11 because $11^2 = 121$, which is greater than 107. (If there were a prime factor greater than 11, there would also be a smaller one and we would already have found it.)*

3   It is very convenient to use Basic Mathematical Tables to test whether a number is prime.

Exercise 24·1

A **1**   Write down all the factors of each of these numbers: (a) 24   (b) 40   (c) 96   (d) 144   (e) 243

  2   Find the smallest number which is a multiple of 2, 3, 4 and 5.

  3   Find the smallest number which is a multiple of 3, 7, 9 and 12.

  4   Which number is a factor of 15, 24 and 36?

  5   Find a number which is a multiple of 8 and a factor of 200.

6 Complete these sentences.
(a) *a* is a factor of *b* ⇒ *b* is a .... of *a*.
(b) if *n* is a multiple of *p* then *kn* is a .... of *p* (if *k* is a whole number).

B **1** Write down the first 20 prime numbers.
2 Find the prime numbers in this set: (45, 57, 83, 95, 101)
3 The first five prime numbers are 2, 3, 5, 7 and 11. We notice that (2 × 3) + 1 is also prime and (2 × 5) + 1 is also prime.
(a) Is it generally true that if *p* and *q* are prime then (*p* × *q*) + 1 is prime?
(b) Is it true that (2 × 3) + 1, (2 × 3 × 5) + 1, (2 × 3 × 5 × 7) + 1, ... etc. are all prime?
4 Find all the factors of: (a) 2537   (b) 111   (c) 1001   (d) 10 001
5 Write each of the following numbers as a product of prime factors: (a) 63   (b) 120
(c) 32   (d) 81   (e) 28   (f) 24   (g) 91   (h) 243   (i) 777   (j) 96   (k) 270   (l) 1000
6 One of the following large numbers is prime. Which is it?
37 259   77 777   54 321   83 521   131 071

C *Investigations with prime numbers*
1 Find a prime number which is more than 1000.
2 It has been suggested that every square number is the sum of two primes. Do you agree?
3 A number *p* is a factor of two other numbers, *q* and *r*.
What can you say about these numbers:
(a) *q* + *r*   (b) *q* × *r*   (c) *q* ÷ *r*   (d) 2*q* + 3*r*
Illustrate each of your answers with an example.
4 The 'triangular' numbers {1, 3, 6, 10 ...} can be shown as dot triangles:

Find the next six 'triangular' numbers. Are there any primes among them? Do you think that there are any numbers which are both triangular and prime?
5 The number 6 is called 'perfect' because it is the sum of its factors: the factors of 6 are 1, 2, 3 and   6 = 1 + 2 + 3
Can you find another perfect number? If you manage to find it you may want to look for a third one!

24·2   Extending the number system

The set of whole numbers {1, 2, 3, 4, ...} is not sufficient for all the uses that are made of numbers. Over thousands of years the system has been extended so that it now includes positive and negative integers, zero, rational numbers, irrational numbers, imaginary numbers, infinite numbers ...

(a) 1, 2, 3, 4, ...   The positive integers

(b) 0   The number zero is very special

(c) $\frac{1}{2}, \frac{2}{3}, \frac{3}{4}, \ldots$ The rational numbers, so called because each one is a ratio of a pair of integers

(d) $-1, -2, -3, -4, \ldots$ The negative integers. They are the solutions of equations like x + 5 = 0 and x + 9 = 0

(e) $\sqrt{2}, \sqrt{3}, \sqrt{5}, \sqrt[3]{6}, \ldots$ The irrational numbers. These numbers are solutions of equations like $x^2 = 2$
$$x^2 = 3$$
$$x^2 = 5$$
$$x^3 = 6$$
They cannot be written as rational numbers

Exercise 24·2

A Give four different examples to show that each of the following rules works for both positive and negative integers.

1 $a + b = b + a$ **2** $a \times b = b \times a$ **3** $a + 0 = a$

4 $a + b = 0 \Rightarrow b = -a$ **5** $a - (-b) = a + b$ **6** $a \times (-b) = -(a \times b)$

7 $a \times (b + c) = (a \times b) + (a \times c)$ **8** $a \times 0 = 0$

B Give four different examples to show that the following statements are *not necessarily true* for all positive and negative integers.

1 $a - b = b - a$ **2** $a \div b = b \div a$ **3** $(-a) \times (-b) = -(a \times b)$

4 $a \times b = 0 \Rightarrow a = -b$ **5** $a + (b \times c) = (a + b) \times (a + c)$ **6** $a \div 0 = a$

C **1** Rational numbers have a decimal form, obtained by dividing the top number (numerator) by the bottom number (denominator).

(a) Find the decimal forms of the following rational numbers:

(i) $\frac{2}{3}$ (ii) $\frac{4}{9}$ (iii) $\frac{7}{8}$ (iv) $\frac{9}{100}$ (v) $\frac{105}{160}$

(b) Show that the decimal form of any rational number either ends after so many decimal places or forms a regular repeating pattern. Can you give a reason for this?

2 Irrational numbers, such as $\sqrt{5}$, have decimal forms, e.g. $\sqrt{5} = 2 \cdot 236\,067\,977\,49\ldots$ Can you find an irrational number which has a regular pattern in its decimal form? Use your calculator.

3 Investigate these suggested rules for irrational numbers:

(a) $\sqrt{a} + \sqrt{b} \neq \sqrt{a+b}$ (b) $\sqrt{a} \times \sqrt{b} = \sqrt{a \times b}$ (c) $(\sqrt{a} - \sqrt{b})^2 = a + b - 2\sqrt{ab}$

(d) $(\sqrt{a} + \sqrt{b})^2 = a + b + 2\sqrt{ab}$ (e) $\frac{\sqrt{a}}{\sqrt{b}} = \sqrt{\frac{a}{b}}$ (f) $\sqrt{a} > \sqrt{b} \Rightarrow a > b$

Try the rules with integers for *a* and *b*, then investigate the rules when *a* and *b* are rational numbers.

24·3 Ratios and their applications

Sometimes it is convenient to compare two measurements. This is done by using a ratio, consisting of two or more numbers separated by :

Example 1:

In a vote about capital punishment the ratio of votes was 5 : 3 against. If 208 people voted altogether, how many voted against capital punishment?

The ratio 5:3 tells you that the total vote can be divided into 8 equal lots: five against capital punishment and three for it.
208 votes can be split into 8 equal lots of 26 votes each.
$$5 \text{ lots} = 5 \times 26 = 130 \text{ votes}$$
So 130 people voted against capital punishment

Example 2:

In making blackcurrant jam the weights of the fruit, sugar and water used should be in the ratio 4:6:3
(a) How much sugar and water are needed with 15 pounds of fruit?
(b) If in a jam factory all the ingredients in a batch weigh 650 kg, what weight of fruit does this include?

(a) There should be 6 lb of sugar and 3 lb of water to every 4 lb of fruit
     Multiply all three numbers by $\frac{15}{4}$ to obtain the correct quantities for 15 lb of fruit.

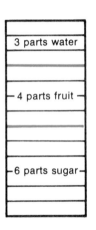

(b) The ratio 4:6:3 means the total can be divided into 13 equal parts
     4 parts will be fruit
     6 parts will be sugar
     3 parts will be water
     650 kg of ingredients → 13 parts of 50 kg each.
     Weight of fruit will be 4 × 50 kg = 200 kg.

Exercise 24·3

A **1** Divide 30 km² in the ratio 5:1. What is the area of the larger part?
  2 A forest has an area of 400 km². The ratio of softwood to hardwood is 3:2. What area is planted with hardwood?
  3 The ratio (air-fare:hotel costs) for a holiday in Majorca is 7:5. The complete holiday costs £480, including the flight. How much does the hotel cost?
  4 A recipe for pastry uses flour, fat and water in the ratio 6:3:1. How many grammes of fat are needed if the mixture is to weigh 3 kg?
  5 Concrete is made from sand and cement in the ratio 4:1. (10% water is then added to the mixture.) Calculate the cement needed to make 30 tonnes of concrete.

6 Carbon dioxide contains carbon and oxygen, their ratio by weight being 3:8. How much oxygen is contained in 5 kg of liquid carbon dioxide?

B 1 The ratio of male:female newborn babies in 1984 in Britain was 35:33. Altogether there were 650 000 babies born. How many were girls?

2 It is expected that by 2001 AD there will be 3 250 000 men and 4 900 000 women over 65 years old in the UK. What ratio is this, expressed in its simplest form?

3

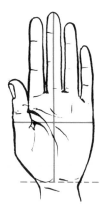

Measure the ratio of length to width for your left hand.
Compare it with the ratio of others in the class.

4 The literacy ratios for adults (number who can read:number who cannot) are listed below for various countries. Calculate the number of adults in each country who cannot read.

Country	Ratio	Adult population (millions)
Great Britain	99:1	44
South Africa	81:19	17
Argentina	93:7	17
India (men)	51:49	200
India (women)	28:72	198

These figures were taken from the United Nations 'Statistical Pocketbook, 1981'.

5 The table below summarises the manpower of the National Health Service in England over the four years 1979–1982.

NHS MANPOWER IN ENGLAND				
	1979	1980	1981	1982
Doctors and dentists	37 061	38 219	39 000	39 400
Nurses and midwives	358 447	370 080	391 800	397 100
Professional & technical	60 137	61 893	65 200	67 200
Ancillary staff	171 896	171 967	172 200	170 500
Ambulance staff	17 129	17 768	18 200	18 300
Works staff	5 606	5 931	6 200	6 100
Maintenance staff	20 112	20 572	21 000	21 000
Administrative & clerical	102 962	105 430	108 800	108 800
Totals	773 350	791 860	822 400	828 500

Source: DHSS.

Calculate the following ratios in the form (1 : *n*) for each of the four years.
(a) Doctors : nurses
(b) Doctors : administrative and clerical staff
(c) Ambulance : maintenance staff
(d) Nurses : ancillary staff
Which ratios have changed over the four years?
It is claimed that the National Health Service is increasing its professional service while cutting administrative costs. Is this consistent with the figures you have?

6 Foods are made up mainly of protein, fat, carbohydrate and water. The ratios in which these occur in various foods are given below.

	Protein		Fat		Carbohydrate		Water
Biscuits	10	:	21	:	66	:	9
Bread	8	:	1	:	53	:	38
Cheese	25	:	35	:	0	:	40
Fried egg	14	:	20	:	0	:	66
Sausage	12	:	25	:	13	:	50
Apple	0	:	0	:	10	:	90
Peanuts	28	:	49	:	9	:	14

(a) Which foods have the highest (fat : protein) ratios?
(b) Which foods have a low (carbohydrate : protein) ratio?
(c) Which foods should an overweight person avoid?

24·4   Constant ratio

Many ratios in mathematics and science are found to be constant: this means that although such a ratio may be measured in many situations, it will always be the same.

Example:
Show that for a square the ratio diagonal : side is constant.
The problem may be approached through drawing and measurement. First, squares with sides 3 cm and 2 cm are drawn. Their diagonals are then measured. Next, a less 'special' square is drawn and its diagonal measured.

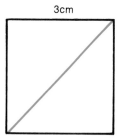

3cm

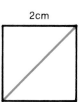

2cm

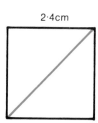

2·4cm

The results are tabulated, and the ratio (diagonal : side) calculated for each drawing, in the form $n:1$

Side (s cm)	Diagonal (d cm)	$s:d$
3	4·25	1·42 : 1
2	2·9	1·45 : 1
2·4	3·4	1·42 : 1

These results suggest that the ratio is constant. This conclusion can be proved by using Pythagoras's Theorem.

1∅ Data Square, side s cm, diagonal d cm

2∅ Deduction $d^2 = s^2 + s^2 = 2s^2$ Pythagoras

3∅ Deduction $d = \sqrt{2}s$ from 2∅

4∅ Deduction $d : s = \sqrt{2}s : s$
$\qquad\qquad\qquad \sqrt{2} : 1$ from 3∅

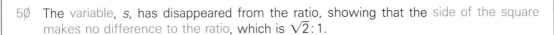

5∅ The variable, s, has disappeared from the ratio, showing that the side of the square makes no difference to the ratio, which is $\sqrt{2} : 1$.

Exercise 24·4

A 1 Show that the ratio (diameter : circumference) is constant for all circles.
  2 Show that the (perimeter : height) ratio for an equilateral triangle is constant.
  3 What constant ratios can you find in a right-angled triangle with one angle of 40°?
  4 Show that the (diagonal : perimeter) ratio is not constant for rectangles.
  5 What constant ratios can you find in a regular pentagon? (Investigate the lengths on an accurately drawn figure.)

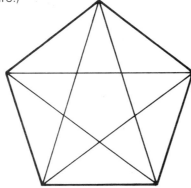

  6 Find other geometrical figures with constant ratios.
  7 The (diagonal : side) ratio for a cube is constant. What is it?
  8 Investigate the ratio (volume : surface area) for cubes of different sizes.

B You will meet constant ratios in science (for example, in connection with light, chemical compounds and density). Collect as many examples as you can of constant ratios and write brief notes about each one.

C 1   Follow the example below which shows how to divide a line in a given ratio.

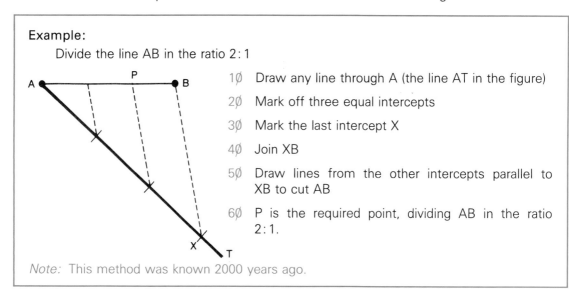

Example:
    Divide the line AB in the ratio 2 : 1

1∅ Draw any line through A (the line AT in the figure)

2∅ Mark off three equal intercepts

3∅ Mark the last intercept X

4∅ Join XB

5∅ Draw lines from the other intercepts parallel to XB to cut AB

6∅ P is the required point, dividing AB in the ratio 2 : 1.

Note: This method was known 2000 years ago.

2   Draw a line 10 cm long. Divide it into two parts in the ratio 2 : 5. Check by measurement.

3   ABCD is a parallelogram. E is the midpoint of DC. Investigate the point X, where AE meets BD.

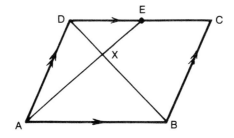

4   A, B and C are three points on one line; D, E and F are three points on another.

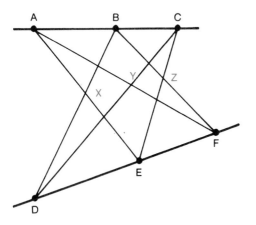

A is joined to E and F.
B is joined to D and F.
C is joined to D and E.
Investigate the points X, Y and Z.

5

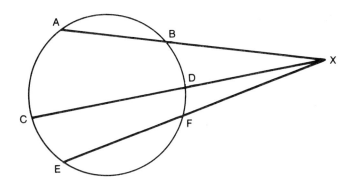

X is any point outside any circle.
Investigate the lengths XA, XB, XC, XD, XE and XF.
Can you find any constant ratios?

6   Investigate the situation in which the point X is inside the circle.

D   We have two bottles of wine, one red and one white. A teaspoonful of the red wine is taken from the red-wine bottle and put into the white-wine bottle, which is then shaken up. A teaspoonful of wine is then taken from the white-wine bottle and poured into the red-wine bottle. Is there more red wine in the white-wine bottle or more white wine in the red-wine bottle?

Unit 25 Approximation and error

25·1 Assessing error

When you make an estimate, you expect it to be slightly inaccurate. The difference between the exact value and your estimate is called the error of the estimate.

The error can be shown as a quantity known as the absolute error, or as a proportion of the exact value, i.e. as relative error. Relative error is usually expressed as a percentage.

Example 1:

_____ This line is exactly 81 mm long.

An estimate of length of 80 mm would have an absolute error of 1 mm, corresponding to a relative error of $\frac{1}{81} = 0·012$ or 1·2%

Example 2:

Compare the errors when $(123)^2$ is estimated as
(a) 100×150 (b) 120×120

The exact answer is 15 129.
(a) $100 \times 150 = 15\,000$
    The absolute error is 129
    The relative error is $\frac{129}{15129} = 0·0085 = 0·85\%$
(b) $120 \times 120 = 14\,400$
    The absolute error is 729
    The relative error is $\frac{729}{15129} = 0·048 = 4·8\%$

Remember, an error is not just a mistake, it is a feature of a measurement or an approximation.

Exercise 25·1

A 1 Each of the calculations below was estimated as shown. Calculate the error and percentage error in each case.
(a) $4·2 \times 3·8$ Estimate: $4 \times 4 = 16$
(b) $140 \div 27$ Estimate: $140 \div 28 = 5$
(c) $275 \div 17$ Estimate: $300 \div 20 = 15$
(d) $(39·8)^2$ Estimate: $40^2 = 1600$

2 Estimate the following before using your calculator. Then calculate the percentage error of your estimates. Which was your best estimate?

(a) 4.05×16.3 (b) $2.08 \div 41$ (c) $37 \times (1.08 + 3.26)$
(d) $\frac{270 \times 65.8}{132}$ (e) $(42)^2$ (f) $62 \times 48 \times 12.3$

Suggested steps:
1∅ Make an estimate
2∅ Write down estimate
3∅ Calculate exact value (calculator)
4∅ Calculate difference between 2∅ and 3∅ (calculator)
5∅ Divide 4∅ by 3∅ (calculator)
6∅ Convert 5∅ to percentage
7∅ END

3 *Challenge (A game to play with a friend)*

1∅ **A** has a calculator, **B** does not. **A** sets **B** a calculating problem to estimate. **B** makes an estimate and writes it down.

2∅ **A** uses his calculator to find the exact value and to calculate **B**'s percentage error of estimate.

3∅ **A** and **B** reverse roles.

4∅ The player with the lower percentage error wins the round.

Repeat for as many rounds as you like (include $\sqrt{}$ and powers).

4 Suggest ways of estimating answers to the following calculations which are quick but give an error less than 10%.
(a) $1428 + 3761$ (b) $5097 - 2112$ (c) $50.12 \div 36$ (d) 19.4×0.75
(e) $(21.6 + 30.2) \times 15.3$ (f) $(47 \times 23 \times 6.1) \div 3.2$
(g) $(42 \times 17) - (41 \times 36) + 25^2$ (h) $\sqrt{(14.2)^2 + (7.8)^2}$

B Calculate the percentage error in the following cases.

1 A circle has an exact radius of $2.45\,\text{cm}$. Its circumference is roughly estimated as $6 \times 2.5\,\text{cm}$.

2 A circle has exact radius 3.09 metres. Its area is estimated as $3 \times 3^2 = 27\,\text{m}^2$.

3 A rectangular swimming pool is $31\,\text{m}$ long $\times 11\,\text{m}$ wide. Its average depth is 2.8 metres. The volume is estimated as $30 \times 10 \times 3$ cubic metres.

4 A cube whose precise dimensions are $4.8\,\text{cm} \times 4.8\,\text{cm} \times 4.8\,\text{cm}$ is taken to be a $5\,\text{cm}$ cube: this gives an estimated surface area of $150\,\text{cm}^2$ and an estimated volume of $125\,\text{cm}^3$.

5 Wood sold as $7''$ by $2''$ is actually $170\,\text{mm}$ by $50\,\text{mm}$. Find the percentage error involved. $(1'' \times 25.4\,\text{mm})$

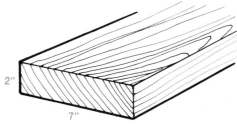

C Use the idea of percentage error to decide which of the two given estimates is closer in questions 1, 2 and 3.

1 (a) 1348×396 is estimated as $1250 \times 400 = 500\,000$
(b) $793 \div 482$ is estimated as $800 \div 400 = 2$

2   (a)   A car of length 4·2 metres is estimated at 4 metres

      (b)   An oil-tanker of length 420 metres is estimated as 440 metres long

3   (a)   A journey by air from Edinburgh to Paris is estimated to take 1 hour 10 minutes, but in fact takes 77 minutes

      (b)   A journey by air from London to New York is estimated to take 5 hours 50 minutes but actually takes 6 hours 10 minutes.

4   Which of these scientists is working more accurately?

      (a)   A scientist who measures the distance from the Earth to the Sun (150 000 000 km) to the nearest 10 000 km

      (b)   A scientist who measures the length of a molecule (0·000 000 6 m) to the nearest 0·000 005 cm

5   Estimate (without using a calculator) the volumes of the solids shown in the diagram.

      (a)   Calculate the exact volumes using your calculator (take $\pi = 3·1416$)

      (b)   Do the estimates give the same order as the exact volumes?

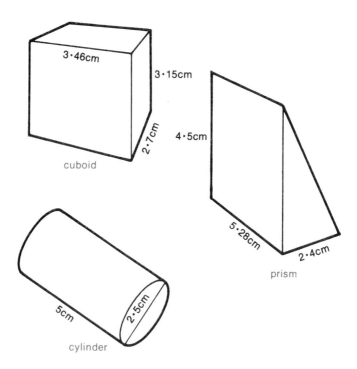

6   The speedometer on a car underestimates the speed by 10%. Calculate the true speed when the speedometer shows   (a) 30 mph   (b) 70 mph

25·2   Degree of accuracy

The calculator can give far more places of decimals than you generally need. There are three methods of reducing a number to a form you can use. These are shown in the example below.

Examples:
A calculator gives 0·422 618 261 as the value of sin 25°. What number should be used?

1 The number can be cut off (truncated) after a certain number of decimal places.
0·422 618 261 → 0·422 ... to three decimal places
→ 0·4226 ... to four decimal places

2 The number can be rounded off to a certain number of decimal places.
0·422 618 261 → 0·42 rounded to two decimal places
→ 0·423 rounded to three decimal places
→ 0·4226 rounded to four decimal places

3 The number can be put in standard form and rounded off to a certain number of significant figures.
0·422 618 261 → 4×10^{-1} ... one significant figure
→ $4·2 \times 10^{-1}$ ... two significant figures
→ $4·23 \times 10^{-1}$... three significant figures

Notes: **1** The choice is yours: the methods are all correct. If you cut off a decimal just before a figure which is larger than 5, the error (known as the truncating error) will be slightly increased.

2 Always present an answer to a sensible degree of accuracy, which takes into account the accuracy of the other measurements in the problem.

Exercise 25·2

A **1** Write out the following numbers, cutting them off before the fourth decimal place.
(a) 3·141 592 (b) 1·414 213 5 (c) 1·709 975 942
(d) 65·383 838 (e) 5·501 258 211 (f) 0·087 488 663

2 Write the numbers in question 1:
(a) rounded to 2 decimal places
(b) rounded to 3 decimal places
(c) in standard form, to 3 significant figures
(d) in standard form, to 4 significant figures

B The number of decimal places used indicates the degree of accuracy of a given measurement.

Example:
Explain the difference between a measurement of 1·4 metres and a measurement of 1·40 metres.
'1·4 metres' suggests that the measurement is accurate to the nearest tenth of a metre, i.e. the exact length is between 1·35 metres and 1·45 metres. Anything less than 1·35 m would be written as 1·3 m, while anything more than 1·45 m would be written as 1·5 m.
'1·40 metres' suggests that the measurement is accurate to the nearest centimetre, i.e. the length is between 1·395 and 1·404 metres.

1 A line is measured and found to be 1·27 metres long. What are its greatest and least possible lengths, to the nearest millimetre?

2 A race is won in 14·3 seconds. What are the longest and shortest possible times, to the nearest $\frac{1}{100}$th of a second, that this figure could represent?

3 Which of the following would be an incorrect approximation for the diameter of the earth (7926 miles):

(a) $7·9 \times 10^3$ miles   (b) $7·92 \times 10^3$ miles   (c) $7·926 \times 10^3$ miles

4 A rectangle is measured as 54 cm long and 35 cm wide, correct to the nearest centimetre. What are the largest and smallest possible values of the area of the rectangle?

5 A man drives his car at an indicated speed of 60 mph along a motorway. His speedometer is correct to the nearest 5 mph and he can read his watch correct to the nearest minute. What are the greatest and least distances he can travel as his watch moves from 11.10 to 11.30?

6 A cube is supposed to be made with 45 mm edges and must fit into a cube-shaped space with a volume of 92 150 mm³. The edges are measured to the nearest millimetre. Is it possible that the cube will be too big for its space?

C The accuracy of measurements must make sense in the real world. For example, it would not normally be possible to measure the weight of a lorry to the nearest gram; any machine that was strong enough to weigh a lorry would not be sensitive enough to show differences of 100 g, let alone 1 g.

1 Measure as accurately as you can:

(a) the volume of a 2p piece

(b) the volume of a match

(c) the volume of a sheet of paper

Suggest the largest and smallest possible values in each case, i.e. give your answer as 'The volume of a 2p piece is between .... and ....'.

2 Draw a line 10 cm long. Divide it into six equal parts using compass and ruler. Measure the length of each part to the nearest millimetre.

3 Discuss the degree of accuracy you might expect in the following measurements:

(a) Vegetables being weighed in a market.

(b) A count of the number of cars per hour leaving London on a bank holiday weekend.

(c) A check on the height of an aircraft in flight.

(d) The amount of money a person has saved in the post office, being checked and written into a Post Office Savings book.

(e) A count of the number of stars in the sky   (i) without a telescope   (ii) with a telescope

(f) The timing of a 500 m race being run   (i) at school   (ii) at an international athletics meeting.

4 Investigate the accuracy of the following:

(a) An ordinary plastic ruler   (b) Your protractor   (c) Your watch

(d) Any other measuring instrument you have used, e.g. thermometer, compass, etc.

5 Discuss the degree of accuracy implied in the following statements. Write each measurement in standard form to a sensible number of significant figures.

(a) The population of France is 53·70 million people, of Italy 57·04 million and of West Germany 61·56 million.

(b) Production of wheat: North America: 86·32 million tonnes

Africa: 8·63 million tonnes

Europe: 98·45 million tonnes

(c) Number of TV's in use (per 1000 population):

UK: 390   USA: 623

USSR: 320   Japan: 272

25·3   Interpolation and difference patterns

Where two values of a function are known, it is possible to estimate values in-between.

Example:
Given $\sqrt{7} = 2\cdot646$ and $\sqrt{8} = 2\cdot828$, estimate $\sqrt{7\cdot4}$

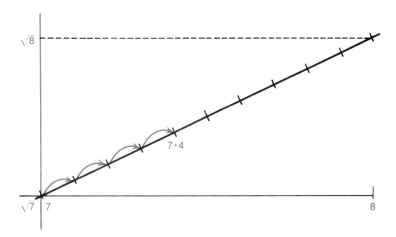

1∅   The difference between $\sqrt{7}$ and $\sqrt{8}$ is $0\cdot182$

2∅   This difference can be divided into ten equal steps of $0\cdot0182$

3∅   Four of the steps will take you from $\sqrt{7}$ to $\sqrt{7\cdot4}$

4∅   An estimate of $\sqrt{7\cdot4}$ is $\sqrt{7} + (4 \times 0\cdot0182) = 2\cdot719$

A calculator gives $\sqrt{7\cdot4} = 2\cdot720$ to 3 decimal places, so this is a good estimate.

The above method assumes that the graph of the function is a straight line. In fact $y = \sqrt{x}$ is not a straight line, but it is quite close to one if you consider only a short section around $x = 7$, so the method gives a good approximation. This technique is called interpolation.

Many sets of numbers have difference patterns which enable you to estimate further values in a sequence.

Example:
Show that the values of the function $y = x^2 + 2x + 3$ have a regular pattern of differences.

The patterns are found by making a difference table.
In calculating the values of $y = x^2 + 2x + 3$ it is quicker to use $x(x + 2) + 3$ rather than $x^2 + 2x + 3$.

x	$x+2$	$x(x+2)$	$x(x+2)+3$	Differences 1st	2nd
0	2	0	3		
1	3	3	6	3	2
2	4	8	11	5	2
3	5	15	18	7	2
4	6	24	27	9	2
5	7	35	38	11	

The differences have the simple pattern 3, 5, 7, 9, 11, ... etc. The differences of the differences are all equal to 2.

Exercise 25·3

A **1** Given that $36^2 = 1296$ and $37^2 = 1369$, estimate without using a calculator (a) $36·2^2$
(b) $36·8^2$
Check by calculator and find the percentage errors of your estimates.

2 Given $\sin 45° = 0·7071$ and $\sin 46° = 0·7193$, estimate (a) $\sin 45·3°$ (b) $\sin 45·7°$
Check by calculator and find the percentage errors of your estimates.

3 Given $\sqrt[3]{5} = 1·710$ and $\sqrt[3]{6} = 1·817$, estimate $\sqrt[3]{5·25}$. Check by cubing your estimate.

4 Given $\sqrt{375} = 19·365$ and $\sqrt{400} = 20$ estimate $\sqrt{380}$ and $\sqrt{395}$.

5 Given $\cos 25° = 0·9063$ and $\cos 26° = 0·8988$, estimate $\cos 25·4°$.

6 Given $\frac{1}{11} = 0·0909$ and $\frac{1}{12} = 0·0833$, estimate the inverse of 11·2. Check by multiplying your estimate by 11·2.

7 A motorbike costing £600 can be bought for 36 monthly payments of £24. A bike costing £900 can be bought for 36 monthly payments of £36 each month. Estimate the monthly payments on (a) a £700 bike (b) an £850 bike.

8 The table below gives conversion rates from Deutschmarks to pounds sterling.

DM	10	20	30	40	50	60	70	80	90	100
£	2·65	5·31	7·96	10·61	13·26	15·92	18·57	21·22	23·87	26·53

Use the table to estimate the values in £ of (a) 25 DM (b) 45 DM (c) 77 DM
(d) 88 DM

B Make difference tables for the following functions using the values shown. State what special patterns can be seen.

1 Function: $y = x^2$ $x = (0, 1, 2, \ldots, 10)$
2 Function: $y = x^2$ $x = (3·1, 3·2, 3·3, \ldots, 4·0)$
3 Function: $y = 2x^2 + 5$ $x = (7, 8, 9, \ldots, 16)$
4 Function: $y = (x+2)(x+3)$ $x = (11, 12, 13, \ldots, 20)$
5 Function: $y = 2^x$ $x = (1, 2, 3, \ldots, 10)$
6 Function: $y = x^3 + x$ $x = (1, 2, 3, \ldots, 10)$

C Investigate the difference patterns in the following sequences. Use the pattern to find the next three numbers of each sequence.

1 1, 4, 8, 13, ...
2 3, 6, 9, 12, ...
3 4, 11, 22, 37, ...
4 1, 3, 7, 13, ...
5 1, 1, 2, 3, 5, ...
6 1, 1·21, 1·44, 1·69, ...

Unit 26 Triangles

26·1 General properties of triangles

The following properties are true for every triangle. You should learn them.

It is usual to use capital letters to mark the vertices and small letters to mark the sides.

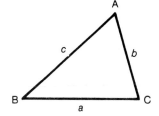

- Any two sides of a triangle must be, together, greater than the third. If the three sides are a, b and c, then $a + b > c$, $a + c > b$ and $b + c > a$.

These three lines would not form a triangle.

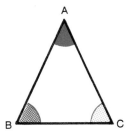

- The angles of a triangle add up to 180°.
  $A + B + C = 180°$.
  This property leads to the useful result that an exterior angle is the sum of the opposite interior angles.

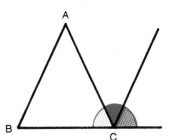

- The larger of two sides is opposite the larger of two angles.

  $\hat{A} > \hat{B} \Rightarrow a > b$ and $a > b \Rightarrow \hat{A} > \hat{B}$.
  The proof of this is given in the exercises.

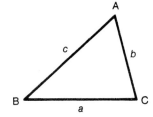

- The area of any triangle is $\frac{1}{2} \times$ base $\times$ height.

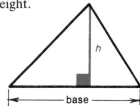

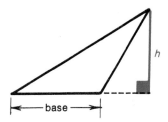

Exercise 26·1

A 1 Decide without drawing which of the following sets of lengths could be the sides of triangles:

    (a) (4 cm, 5 cm, 6 cm)   (b) (7 cm, 7 cm, 9 cm)

    (c) (4·5 cm, 3 cm, 2 cm)   (d) (8 km, 14 km, 5 km)

    (e) (2·8 m, 3·9 m, 8 m)   (f) (14 m, 21 m, 40 m)

  2 What can you say about x if lines x cm, x^2 cm and x^3 cm form a triangle?

  3 A box contains 5 sticks 1 cm, 2 cm, 3 cm, 4 cm and 5 cm in length. Two of the sticks are taken from the box without looking.

    (a) What are the possible lengths of the sticks left in the box?

    (b) How many of these possible sets would form a triangle?

  4 A box contains 10 sticks, their lengths being 1 cm, 2 cm, ..., 10 cm. What is the chance that 3 sticks taken at random from the box will form a triangle? (*Hint:* this is an investigation question.)

    Test your result with an experiment as follows. Write 1 cm, 2 cm, etc. on ten small pieces of paper. Fold up the papers, shake them up in a box (or hat) and ask a friend to choose three pieces of paper. Do you think there is more than a 50% chance that the lengths would form a triangle? Give your reasons.

  5 Investigate the following suggestion: it is always possible to form a quadrilateral from four lengths.

B 1 Calculate the values of the letters which mark the angles in the following triangles.

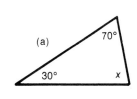
(a)

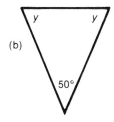
(b)

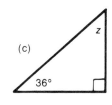
(c)

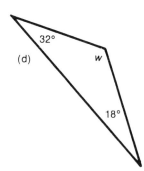
(d)

  2 Calculate the values of the exterior angles in the following triangles:

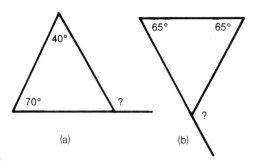
(a)   (b)

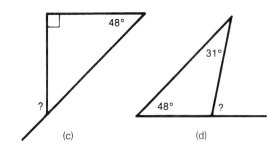
(c)   (d)

3 Calculate all the angles in the diagrams below.

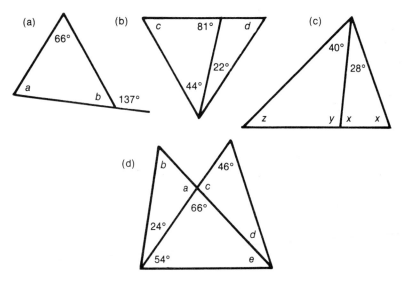

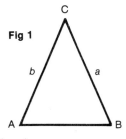

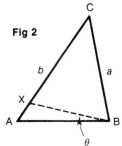

4 Follow the proof below. Make sure you understand each step (work with a friend). We wish to prove that $\hat{A} > \hat{B} \Rightarrow a > b$

Fig 1

Fig 2

10   Data: $\hat{A} > \hat{B}$, A is a larger angle than B.
20   Suppose $a < b$. We 'suppose' the opposite of what we want to prove and see what happens.
30   Deduction a point X can be found so that $CX = CB$ (from 20)
40   Deduction $\triangle CXB$ is isosceles   (from 30)
50   Deduction $C\hat{X}B = C\hat{B}X$ (from 40)
60   Data   (i) $C\hat{X}B = \hat{A} + \theta,$ (ii) $C\hat{B}X = \hat{B} - \theta$
70   Deduction $\hat{A} + \theta = \hat{B} - \theta$ (from 50, 60)
80   Deduction $\hat{A} = \hat{B} - 2\theta$ (from 70)
90   Deduction $\hat{A} < \hat{B}$ (from 80)
100   STOP

An interesting thing has happened. We started with $\hat{A} > \hat{B}$ as data and we have deduced that $\hat{A} < \hat{B}$. Something has gone wrong. The only thing that can be wrong is the 'suppose $a < b$' in line 20. This must be wrong, so we have proved the opposite, $a > b$.

5 (a) Prove that, in a right-angled triangle, the hypotenuse must be the greatest side.
   (b) Show that $\sin \theta < 1$ for all angles less than 90°.
   (c) Explain why $\tan \theta$ can be greater than 1, even though $\sin \theta$ and $\cos \theta$ must be less than 1.

C **1** Use the formula Area $= \frac{1}{2}$(base × height) to find the areas of the triangles drawn below (you may have to change the position of the triangle)

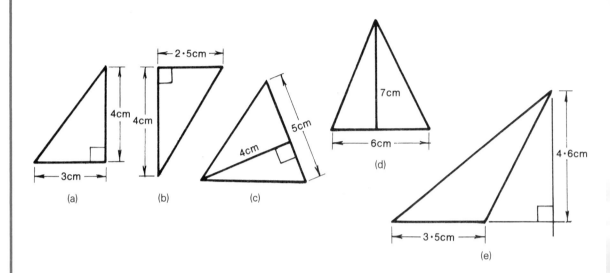

(a)   (b)   (c)

(d)

(e)

2 The sequence of drawings below proves that area $= \frac{1}{2}$(base × height).

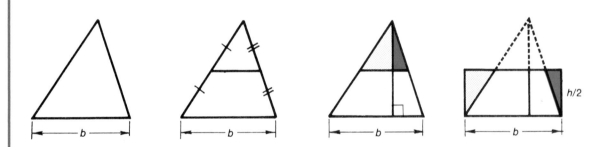

(a) Make sure you understand why these drawings prove $A = \frac{1}{2}(b \times h)$.
(b) Draw sequences of drawings that show $A = \frac{1}{2}$(base × height) for
   (i)   a right-angled triangle,
   (ii)   any triangle of your own choice.
   (iii) an obtuse-angled triangle with a longest side as the base,
   (iv) an obtuse-angled triangle with its shortest side as base.

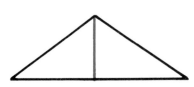
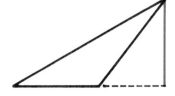

3 Calculate the areas of the shapes below.

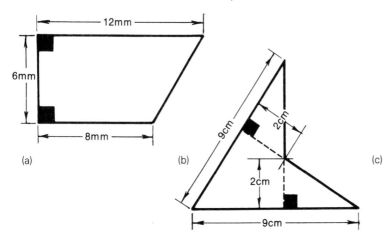

(a)   (b)

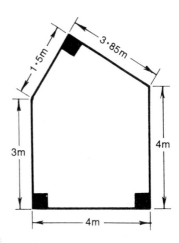

(c)

26·2 Concurrence

The lines joining vertices to midpoints of opposite sides in a triangle are called medians. Note that the three medians all pass through the same point. This point is called the centroid of the triangle.
A set of lines which all pass through a single point are called concurrent

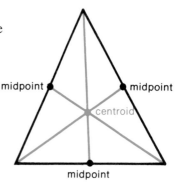

Exercise 26·2

A 1 Draw four large triangles and draw the three medians for each triangle. Do your results agree with the following statement:
The medians of any triangle are concurrent.

2 Show that the median of a triangle divides the triangle into two parts of equal area.

3 Show (by measurement) that the centroid of any triangle is two-thirds of the way along each median.

4 (a) Cut out a paper triangle with sides 8 cm, 10 cm and 11 cm.
    (b) Show by folding that the medians are concurrent, and mark the centroid.
    (c) Show that you can balance the triangle on the point of a pin placed at the centroid of the triangle (a cardboard triangle may give better results).

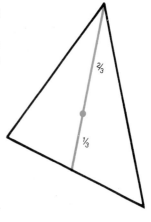

B 1 A line, from the vertex of a triangle, perpendicular to the opposite side is called an altitude of the triangle.
Do you think that the altitudes of any triangle are concurrent?

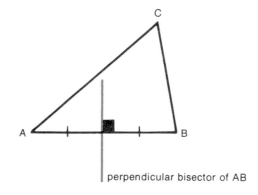

Investigate, using different size and shape of triangles, including right-angled and obtuse-angled triangles.

2 (a) Investigate the perpendicular bisectors of the sides of triangles by drawing or by folding.

(b) Show that the perpendicular bisectors of a right-angled triangle meet on the hypotenuse.

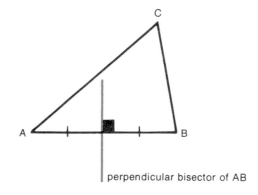

perpendicular bisector of AB

3 Show that the perpendicular bisectors of the sides of a triangle ABC meet at a point which is the same distance from A, B and C

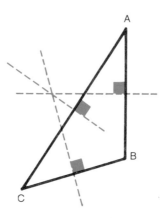

4 Practise bisecting angles with a compass and ruler following the program below.
   1∅ Use a compass to mark equal distances along OX and OY.
   2∅ Using the marks of 1∅ as centres. Draw arcs which intersect.
   3∅ Draw a line through O and intersection 2∅
   4∅ Line 3∅ is the bisector of angle XÔY
   5∅ END

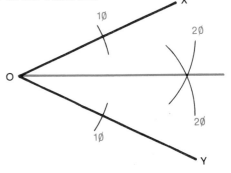

5 (a) Draw a large triangle and bisect the three angles carefully. Note whether the bisectors are concurrent.

   (b) AX is the bisector of angle Â. It cuts BC at D. Show, by careful measurement that
   $$\frac{AB}{AC} = \frac{BD}{DC}.$$

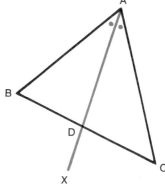

6 (a) In the diagram below, the feet of the altitudes have been joined to form triangle XYZ. The altitudes form a set of concurrent lines for △ XYZ. Which set of concurrent lines are they? Confirm your answer by drawing two more examples.

   (b) Draw triangle ABC of your own choice, but with sides at least 7 cm long. Draw the bisectors of Â, B̂ and Ĉ. Mark the points P, Q and R where the bisectors meet the sides of △ ABC. Draw △ PQR. What is the relationship between △ PQR and the bisectors of Â, B̂ and Ĉ?

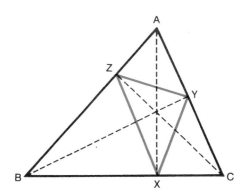

26·3   Circles and triangles

The point of intersection of the perpendicular bisectors of the sides of
ABC is found. This point is the centre of the circle through A, B and C,
the circumcircle of the triangle ABC.

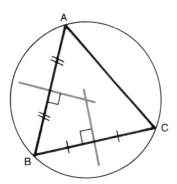

The bisectors of the angles also meet in a point. This point is the centre
of a circle which touches all three sides of the triangle known as the
inscribed circle.

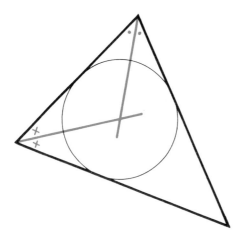

Exercise 26·3

Draw circumcircles and inscribe circles for four triangles of your own choice. One of the triangles
should be right-angled and one should be obtuse-angled. Note that it is very difficult to draw a
perfect inscribed circle.

26·4 Special triangles

Certain triangles are often found in problems and design. It is worth learning their special properties, which are summarised below:

Triangle	Properties
Equilateral 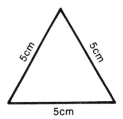 (diagram: equilateral triangle, sides 1, 1, 1, angles 60°, 60°)	All sides and angles equal (60°). Altitudes, medians, bisectors of sides and angles are all the same lines. Length of altitude $= \dfrac{\sqrt{3}}{2}$ units. Area $= \dfrac{\sqrt{3}}{4}$ square units.
Right angled isosceles (half square) (diagram: triangle with sides $\sqrt{2}$, 1, 1, angles 45°, 45°)	Angles 90°, 45°, 45° (half-square). Sides 1, 1 and $\sqrt{2}$ units. Area $= \frac{1}{2}$ square unit. Altitudes meet at the right-angled vertex.
1, 2, $\sqrt{3}$ (half equilateral △) (diagram: triangle with sides 2, $\sqrt{3}$, 1, angles 30°, 60°)	Angles 30°, 60°, 90°. Smallest side is half the hypotenuse. Area $= \dfrac{\sqrt{3}}{2}$ square units. This triangle shows that $\sin 30° = \frac{1}{2}$, $\cos 30° = \dfrac{\sqrt{3}}{2}$, $\sin 60° = \dfrac{\sqrt{3}}{2}$, $\cos 60° = \frac{1}{2}$.
3, 4, 5 Pythagorean (diagram: triangle with sides 5, 3, 4)	The simplest right-angled triangle whose sides are all whole numbers. $3^2 + 4^2 = 5^2$ Angles: 36·87°, 53·13°, 90°. Larger versions of this triangle are (6, 8, 10) and (9, 12, 15).

Exercise 26·4

A Calculate the areas of the triangles drawn below.

1

5cm, 5cm, 5cm

2

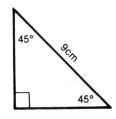

45°, 9cm, 45°

3

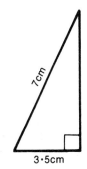

7cm, 3·5cm

4

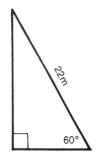

5

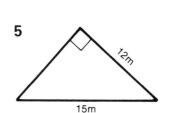

15m

6

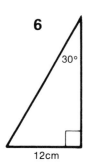

30°

12cm

B Square roots can be estimated from squared paper using Pythagoras's Theorem, by following the program below.

To find $\sqrt{n}$.

1∅ Find a way of expressing n as the sum of squares ... $p^2 + q^2$
2∅ Draw a rectangle with sides p and q
3∅ Measure the diagonal of 2∅

Example:

Find $\sqrt{20}$ $20 = 4 + 16$
                  $= 2^2 + 4^2$

Estimated length of $\sqrt{20}$ is 4·5

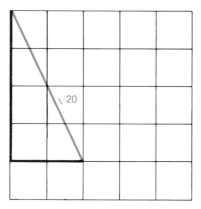

$\sqrt{20}$

(Value using the calculator is 4·472 13 to 5 decimal places)

1 How many square roots of the first 50 numbers could be estimated in this way?
2 Can you find similar ways of estimating (a) $\sqrt{30}$ (b) $\sqrt{120}$ (c) $\sqrt{300}$ (d) $\sqrt{500}$
by using similar drawing methods? Use 1 mm² graph paper.

26·5 More general rules for triangles

Two general rules about triangles are given below together with proofs
and examples of application.

Sine rule $$\frac{a}{\sin A} = \frac{b}{\sin B} = \frac{c}{\sin C}$$

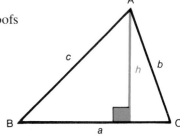

Proof

1∅   Data △ ABC, angles $\hat{A}$, $\hat{B}$ and $\hat{C}$; sides a, b and c as
             shown.

2∅   Deduction $h = c \sin B = b \sin C$ from the figure.

3∅   Deduction $\dfrac{c \sin B}{\sin B . \sin C} = \dfrac{b \sin C}{\sin B . \sin C}$ from 2∅

4∅   Deduction $\dfrac{c}{\sin C} = \dfrac{b}{\sin B}$ from 3∅

5∅   Deduction $\dfrac{c}{\sin C} = \dfrac{a}{\sin A}$ by 2∅, 3∅, 4∅ after
                               drawing the altitude from B to AC

6∅   Deduction $\dfrac{a}{\sin A} = \dfrac{b}{\sin B} = \dfrac{c}{\sin C}$

7∅ END

The sine rule is used to solve a triangle when two angles and one side are known.

Example:

In △ PQR, $\hat{P} = 72°$, $\hat{Q} = 65°$ and PQ $= 12$ cm.
Calculate $\hat{R}$, PR and QR.

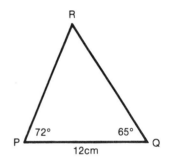

1∅ $\hat{R} = 180 - (72 + 65) = 43°$

2∅ By the sine rule,

    $\dfrac{r}{\sin R} = \dfrac{p}{\sin P} = \dfrac{q}{\sin Q}$

3∅ $\dfrac{12}{\sin 43} = \dfrac{p}{\sin 72} \Rightarrow p = \dfrac{12 \sin 72}{\sin 43} = 16\cdot73$ cm

4∅ $\dfrac{12}{\sin 43} = \dfrac{q}{\sin 65} \Rightarrow q = \dfrac{12 \sin 65}{\sin 43} = 15\cdot95$ cm

5∅ Complete solution of △: $\hat{P} = 72°$ PQ $= 12$ cm
                                   $\hat{Q} = 65°$ QR$= 16\cdot73$ cm
                                   $\hat{R} = 43°$ PR $= 15\cdot95$ cm

6∅ END

Exercise 26·5

A **1** Prove the sine rule for an isosceles triangle XYZ where XY $=$ YZ.

    2 Prove the sine rule for any right angled triangle.

    3 In △ ABC, $\hat{A} = 51°$, $\hat{B} = 60°$, b $= 3$ cm; calculate a.

    4 In △ DEF, $\hat{F} = 42°$, f $= 6\cdot1$ cm, d $= 8\cdot3$ cm; find $\hat{D}$.

    5 In △ UVW, $\hat{U} = 69°$, $\hat{W} = 31°$, v $= 31\cdot7$ m; find u and w.

    6 Investigate the sine rule for triangles in which one angle is greater than 90° (Remember $\sin \theta = \sin (180 - \theta)$)

    7 In △ PQR, $\hat{P} = 102°$, $\hat{Q} = 36°$ and $r = 17$ cm; calculate $\hat{R}$ p and q.

    8 In △ LMN, $\hat{M} = 48°$, MN $= 18$ cm and LN $= 14$ cm. Show that there are two possible values for $\hat{L}$. Find the length of LM where $\hat{L}$ is acute.

Cosine rule

The relation $a^2 = b^2 + c^2$ for a right-angled triangle becomes
$a^2 = b^2 + c^2 - 2bc \cos A$ for an acute angle at A and
$a^2 = b^2 + c^2 + 2bc \cos (180 - A)$ for an obtuse angle at A.

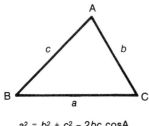

$a^2 = b^2 + c^2 - 2bc \cos A$

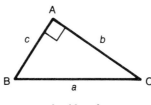

$a^2 = b^2 + c^2$

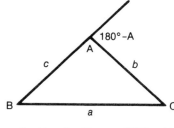

$a^2 = b^2 + c^2 + 2bc \cos(180° - A)$

Since $\cos(180 - A) = -\cos A$ the rule can be written in the single form
$a^2 = b^2 + c^2 - 2bc \cos A$ for all angles at A.
It is easy to see from the diagrams that $a^2 < b^2 + c^2$ for $\hat{A} < 90°$
$$a^2 > b^2 + c^2 \text{ for } \hat{A} > 90°$$

Proof

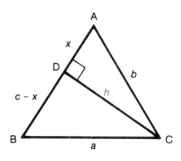

10 Data the figure
20 Deduction $x = b \cos A$ (from 10)
30 Deduction $h^2 = b^2 - x^2$ (from 10)
40 Deduction $h^2 = a^2 - (c - x)^2$ (from 10)
50 Deduction $a^2 - (c - x)^2 = b^2 - x^2$ (from 30, 40)
60 Deduction $a^2 - c^2 + 2cx - x^2 = b^2 - x^2$ (from 50)
70 Deduction $a^2 = b^2 + c^2 - 2cx$ (from 60)
80 Deduction $a^2 = b^2 + c^2 - 2bc \cos A$ (from 20, 70)
90 END

Example:

$\triangle$ ABC has $\hat{A} = 72°$
         AB $= 4{\cdot}5$ cm
         AC $= 3{\cdot}9$ cm
Calculate the length of BC and deduce $\hat{B}$ and $\hat{C}$.

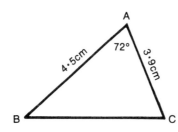

10 Apply the cosine rule: $BC^2 = 4{\cdot}5^2 + 3{\cdot}9^2 - (2 \times 3{\cdot}9 \times 4{\cdot}5) \cos 72$.
                             $BC^2 = 24{\cdot}61 \Rightarrow BC = 4{\cdot}96$ cm*

20 Apply the sine rule: $\dfrac{BC}{\sin 72} = \dfrac{3{\cdot}9}{\sin B} \Rightarrow \sin B = \dfrac{3{\cdot}9 \times \sin 72}{4{\cdot}96}$
                                      $\Rightarrow B = 48{\cdot}4°$

30                    $\hat{A} + \hat{B} + \hat{C} = 180 \Rightarrow C = 59{\cdot}6°$

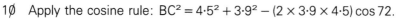

*⌴4⌴·⌴5⌴x^2⌴+⌴3⌴·⌴9⌴x^2⌴−⌴2⌴×⌴3⌴·⌴9⌴×⌴4⌴·⌴5⌴×⌴7⌴2⌴cos⌴=⌴√⌴ on a scientific calculator.

B 1 Study the proof given for the cosine rule. Construct a very similar proof which proves the result for $\hat{A} > 90°$.

2 Show, from the cosine rule, that $\cos A = \dfrac{b^2 + c^2 - a^2}{2bc}$

and write down two similar expressions for $\cos B$ and $\cos C$.

3 In $\triangle DEF$, $\hat{D} = 57°$, $DE = 7\,cm$ and $DF = 9\,cm$. Solve the triangle and calculate its area.

4 In $\triangle LMN$, $\hat{N} = 108°$, LN and NM are both $8.4\,cm$. Calculate the length of MN and the size of $\hat{L}$ by two different methods.

5 A parallelogram ABCD has sides $14\,cm$ and $19\,cm$; $A = 80°$. Calculate the lengths of the diagonals.

6 In $\triangle ABC$, $AB = 4.9\,cm$, $BC = 7.3\,cm$ and $CA = 5.6\,cm$. Calculate the angles $\hat{A}$, $\hat{B}$ and $\hat{C}$ and check by careful drawing.

Problems

The first step in each problem is to make a sketch and put in all the data of the problem. It is not necessary to draw exact angles or lengths but relationships should be clear from the drawing. Then decide on the method you are going to use to solve the problem and work as far as possible without calculations. The calculator should then be used to obtain solutions and also, if possible, to carry out an independent check.

Example:

The angles of elevation of the top of a lighthouse, 300 metres high, from two points X and Y, 400 metres apart, are 31° and 27°. The points X and Y are on the same level as the foot of the lighthouse but not in line with it. Calculate the distances of X and Y from the foot of the lighthouse, Z, and also the angle subtended by XY at Z.

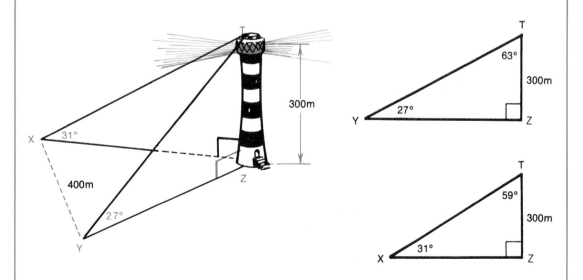

The problem asks you to find XZ, YZ and XẐY. Both $\triangle XTZ$ and $\triangle YTZ$ are right-angled (why?).

Outline of solution

(a) The lengths XZ and YZ will be found by simple trigonometry in $\triangle$'s XTZ and YTZ.

(b) XẐY will be found by using the cosine rule in $\triangle XYZ$.

C **1** Work through the example above and check that you get the same values for XZ, YZ and X$\hat{Z}$Y.

   2 The sides PQ, QR, RS and SP of a quadrilateral are 3 cm, 4 cm, 5 cm and 3·5 cm in length. $\hat{Q} = 60°$. Calculate $\hat{S}$.

   3 Two searchlights at A and B which are 3 km apart pick out an aircraft which is vertically above the line AB. The angles of elevation of the two searchlights are 76° and 46°. Calculate the height of the aircraft. Check by drawing.

   4 A builder marks out a right angle using a rope triangle with sides 15 m, 20 m and 25 m. A workman pegs the ropes in such a way that each side of the triangle is 10 cm too small. Calculate the error in the 'right angle'.

   5 A flat triangle of card AEG just fits as shown in a cuboid whose sides are 9 cm, 12 cm and 17 cm long. Calculate the angles of the triangle AEG.

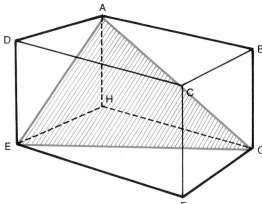

   6 Hero's formula for the area of a triangle is $A = \sqrt{s(s - a)(s - b)(s - c)}$
   where s is the semi-perimeter of the triangle, i.e. $s = \frac{1}{2}(a + b + c)$.
   Show that the formula gives correct results for four triangles of your own choice (include a right-angled and obtuse-angled triangle).

   7 An alternative method for finding the angles of a triangle where the sides are known is given below.
   First step: use Hero's formula to find A.
   Second step: use $A = \frac{1}{2}ab\sin C$ to find sin C and therefore $\hat{C}$.
          Similarly for $\hat{B}$ and $\hat{A}$.
   Compare the above method with using the cosine rule on a triangle of your own choice. Prepare a careful and efficient program for finding all the angles of a triangle, given the three sides. Assume you have a calculator with one memory only.

Unit 27   Algebra

27·1   Equivalence

Most of us use the $=$ sign without thinking very much about its meaning.
When we do investigate it we find that it is a relation between numbers
or things. It has no meaning on its own.
There are three rules of equivalence to be observed. These rules have
special names and are listed below. If any one of the rules is not
observed, the relation is not one of equivalence.

Rule	Meaning	Example	Counter-example
$=$ is reflexive	Every thing is equivalent to itself.	$1·5 = 1·5$ (seems a bit obvious)	$>$ is not an equivalence relation because $3 > 3$ is not true.
$=$ is symmetric	If one thing is equivalent to a second, the second is equivalent to the first.	$0·15 = 15\%$ and $15\% = 0·15$ $a = b \Rightarrow b = a$ (obvious till you think about it)	'is the sister of' is not an equivalence relation because Sue is the sister of Tom, but Tom is the brother of Sue.
$=$ is transitive	If one thing is equivalent to a second and the second is equivalent to a third, then the first is equivalent to the third.	$\frac{1}{2} = 0·5$ and $0·5 = 50\%$ so $\frac{1}{2} = 50\%$	'is a friend of' is not an equivalence relation. Can you see why?

Exercise 27·1

A   Explain the meaning in more detail of $=$ in the following:
1   $3 + 2 = 5$ 2 $7 \times 2 = 14$
3   $0·72 = 72\%$ 4   1 oz of gold $=$ £425
5   $3 \times 4 + 5 = 17$ 6   John $=$ Tom (in weight)
7   Area of rectangle $=$ length $\times$ breadth
8   Volume of a sphere $= \frac{4}{3}\pi r^3$

B   Which of the following relations satisfy all three rules for an equivalence relation (give examples for each rule):
1   'has the same value as'   2   'is less than'
3   'is a friend of'   4   'has the same area as'
5   'is older than'   6   'is the father of'
7   'belongs to the same club as'   8   'is an enlargement of'
9   'is a reflection of'   10   'is a factor of'
11 'is a multiple of'   12 'is the square of'

C In an earlier study of fractions you learned that two fractions were equivalent if they had the same value.

Example 1:

Show that $\frac{2}{5} = \frac{4}{10}$

Value of $\frac{2}{5}$ is $2 \div 5 = 0 \cdot 4$ Value of $\frac{4}{10}$ is $4 \div 10 = 0 \cdot 4$

The fractions are equivalent.

Example 2:

Another definition can be used based on cross multiplication

$\frac{a}{b} = \frac{c}{d}$ if and only if $a \times d = b \times c$

Show that $\frac{2}{5} = \frac{4}{10}$

The cross products 2×10 and 5×4 are equal.

Therefore the fractions are equivalent.

This idea is used a great deal in algebra and trigonometry. It can be expressed as

$\frac{a}{b} = \frac{c}{d} \Leftrightarrow ad = bc$

Note the two headed arrow $\Leftrightarrow$.

Example 3:

Show that $\frac{2}{5} = \frac{4}{10} \Leftrightarrow \frac{5}{2} = \frac{10}{4}$

$\underset{b}{\frac{2}{5}} = \underset{c}{\frac{4}{10}} \Leftrightarrow 2 \times 10 = 4 \times 5 \Leftrightarrow \underset{d}{\frac{5}{2}} = \underset{a}{\frac{10}{4}}$

---

1 24 is 8×3 and 4×6. Use this fact to write down 4 sets of equivalent fractions.

2 Solve the equations   (i) $\dfrac{x}{3} = \dfrac{2}{x}$ and   (ii) $\dfrac{x+1}{5} = \dfrac{3}{x-1}$

3 Use the idea of equivalence to prove that $\dfrac{ka}{kb} = \dfrac{a}{b}$ and explain

how this is used to cancel down fractions like $\frac{200}{300}$.

4 Use the result of question **3** to show
   (a) every fraction is a member of an infinite family of equivalent fractions, and
   (b) every family of equivalent fractions has a simplest member which can represent the whole family.

5 Simplify the following fractions as far as possible.
   (a) $\frac{16}{28}$ (b) $\frac{144}{200}$ (c) $\frac{111}{481}$ (d) $\frac{77}{1001}$

6 Simplify the following algebraic fractions as far as possible.

   (a) $\dfrac{x^2 y}{y^2 x}$ (b) $\dfrac{a(b+c)}{ab+ac}$ (c) $\dfrac{2(x+4)}{x^2+4x}$ (d) $\dfrac{(x-1)(x+3)}{x^2-2x+1}$

27·2   Changing forms

The last exercise showed how the appearance of an expression can be changed without changing its value. This activity is a basic skill in mathematics, similar to cutting and joining in woodwork. The examples which follow show how forms are changed in *factorising*, *equations* and *formulae*.

Example 1:

Factorise $2x^2 + 3x + 1$

Factorising means changing from a collection of terms added together to a collection of terms multiplied together.

$2x^2 + 3x + 1$ to $(2x + 1)(x + 1)$

The two forms will be equivalent for all values of x if the factorisation has been done correctly.

Sample checks:

	$2x^2 + 3x + 1$	$(2x + 1)(x + 1)$
$x = 1$	$2 + 3 + 1$	3×2
$x = 5$	$50 + 15 + 1$	11×6

Example 2:

Solve the equations $2x + y = 4$
$5x - 2y = 1$

There are several ways of solving these equations. The two equivalences must be kept. The method below uses the transitivity of equivalence.

1$\emptyset$	Data	$2x + y = 4, 5x - 2y = 1$	
2$\emptyset$	Deduction	$y = 4 - 2x$	(from 1$\emptyset$)
3$\emptyset$	Deduction	$2y = 8 - 4x$	(from 2$\emptyset$) $a = b \Rightarrow 2a = 2b$
4$\emptyset$	Deduction	$2y = 5x - 1$	(from 1$\emptyset$)
5$\emptyset$	Deduction	$8 - 4x = 5x - 1$	(from 3$\emptyset$, 4$\emptyset$) $a = b$ and $b = c \Rightarrow a = c$
			transitivity
6$\emptyset$	Deduction	$9 = 9x$	(from 5$\emptyset$)
7$\emptyset$	Deduction	$x = 1$	(from 6$\emptyset$)
8$\emptyset$	Deduction	$2 + y = 4$	(from 7$\emptyset$, 1$\emptyset$)
9$\emptyset$	Deduction	$y = 2$	(from 8$\emptyset$)

It is not always necessary to write a solution in such detail, but it is worth doing when you are learning a new technique.

Note: The values $x = 1$ and $y = 2$ are the *only* values of x and y which allow both equations $2x + y = 4$ and $5x - 2y = 1$ to be true.

Example 3:

The formula $V = \frac{1}{3}\pi r^2 h$ gives the volume of a cone. Change the formula so that r can be calculated for values of V and h.

The rules of equivalence are used to obtain a formula of the form $r = ?$

1$\emptyset$	$V = \frac{1}{3}\pi r^2 h$		4$\emptyset$	$r^2 = \dfrac{3V}{\pi h}$	$a = b \Rightarrow b = a$
2$\emptyset$	$3V = \pi r^2 h$	$a = b \Rightarrow ka = kb$	5$\emptyset$	$r = \sqrt{\dfrac{3V}{\pi h}}$	
3$\emptyset$	$\dfrac{3V}{\pi h} = r^2$	$a = b \Rightarrow \dfrac{a}{k} = \dfrac{b}{k}$	6$\emptyset$	END	

This can be checked by choosing values for r and h. Calculate V. Then apply the new formula using V and h. This should give back the r you started with.

$r = 12, h = 5$ $\boxed{1}\,\boxed{2}\,\boxed{x^2}\,\boxed{\times}\,\boxed{5}\,\boxed{\times}\,\boxed{\pi}\,\boxed{\div}\,\boxed{3}\,\boxed{=}$ ←——— V

$\boxed{\times}\,\boxed{3}\,\boxed{\div}\,\boxed{\pi}\,\boxed{\div}\,\boxed{5}\,\boxed{=}\,\boxed{\sqrt{}}$ ←—— $r = 12$

Exercise 27·2

A Factorise the following expressions:

1. (a) $2x + 4$ (b) $3x - 6$ (c) $x - x^2$ (d) $2x^2 + ax$
2. (a) $m^2 + mn$ (b) $ax^2 - bx^3$ (c) $x^2 - 4x$ (d) $2ab + b^2$
3. (a) $x^2 + 6x + 8$ (b) $d^2 - d - 12$ (c) $m^2 + 2m - 8$ (d) $n^2 + n - 20$
4. (a) $1 - 3x - 10x^2$ (b) $1 + 7t - 18t^2$ (c) $3y^2 + 8y - 3$ (d) $12m^2 - 5m - 2$
5. (a) $12b^2 + b - 6$ (b) $3g^2 - 11g + 10$ (c) $2xy + 4x - 3y - 6$ (d) $6x^2 - 11xy + 3y^2$
6. (a) Find a if $x - 3$ is a factor of $x^2 + ax - 3$
   (b) Find b if $x + 5$ is a factor of $x^2 + 8x + b$
   (c) Find c if $2x - 3$ is a factor of $2x^2 + cx - 6$
   (d) Find d if $3x + 2$ is a factor of $12x^2 + dx + 8$
7. Factorise the following differences of squares:
   (a) $x^2 - 4$ (b) $1 - 9h^2$ (c) $4 - 100k^2$ (d) $36x^2 - 25y^2$
8. Show, by choosing random values for a and b, that
   (a) $(a + b)^2 = a^2 + b^2 + 2ab$ (b) $(a - b)^2 = a^2 + b^2 - 2ab$
   (c) $a^3 + b^3 = (a + b)(a^2 - ab + b^2)$ (d) $a^3 - b^3 = (a - b)(a^2 + ab + b^2)$

B Solve the following equations. Indicate clearly where rules of equivalence have been used.

1. (a) $2x + 3 = 17$ (b) $3x - 2 = 10$ (c) $6y - 4 = y + 16$
2. (a) $3 - x = 2 + 2x$ (b) $3m - 2 = 5m + 1$ (c) $4y = 2(3 - y)$
3. (a) $x + y = 5$ (b) $x - 2y = 6$ (c) $3x - 2y = 1$
   $x - y = 1$ $2x + y = 27$ $4x + 3y = 24$
4. (a) $x^2 - 5x + 6 = 0$ (b) $x^2 - 3x = 70$ (c) $y^2 + 9y = 36$
   (d) $x^2 + 2x = 99$ (e) $20x^2 = 7x + 6$ (f) $4x^2 = 6x$
5. (a) $x + 1 = \dfrac{6}{x}$ (b) $3x + 2 = \dfrac{24}{x + 1}$ (c) $9x + \dfrac{4}{x} - 12 = 0$

Note: The solutions of the equations in questions 4 and 5 make use of the rule $ab = 0 \Rightarrow a = 0$ or $b = 0$.

C Change the formulae given into the required forms.

1. $p = \dfrac{Wv^2}{gr} \rightarrow v = ?$

2. $pt = \dfrac{W}{g}(v - u) \rightarrow u = ?$

3. $v = 2\sqrt{gh} \rightarrow g = ?$

4. $\dfrac{1}{u} + \dfrac{1}{v} = \dfrac{1}{f} \rightarrow f = ?$

Check each answer with a calculator sequence (see example).

27·3 Logarithms

You will notice on a scientific calculator that there are two buttons marked $\boxed{\log}$ and $\boxed{\ln}$. The inverse of these functions will probably be marked 10^x and e^x.

The $\boxed{\log}$ function maps any number n into the exponent, where n is written as a power of 10.

Examples:

$\boxed{1}\boxed{0}\boxed{0}\boxed{\text{log}}$ 2

$100 \xrightarrow{\quad\text{log}\quad} 2$

because the number 100 can be written 10^2. We thus have log 100 = 2.

$\boxed{1}\boxed{0}\boxed{0}\boxed{0}\boxed{\text{log}}$ 3

$1000 \xrightarrow{\quad\text{log}\quad} 3$

Similarly log 1000 = 3.

$\boxed{7}\boxed{3}\boxed{\text{log}}$ . . . . 1·8633

because 73 can be written $10^{1\cdot8633}$.

Once a number has been converted to 10^x form, the rules of indices can be applied. This gives convenient methods of
(i)   multiplying by addition
(ii) dividing by subtraction
(iii) finding powers
(iv) finding roots.

Laws of indices for 10^x and logs

1. Multiplication

$$\begin{array}{ccc} m & n & m \times n \\ \downarrow & \downarrow & \uparrow \\ 10^x & 10^y \longrightarrow & 10^{x+y} \end{array} \qquad \text{add logs}$$

2. Division

$$\begin{array}{ccc} m & n & m \div n \\ \downarrow & \downarrow & \uparrow \\ 10^x & 10^x \longrightarrow & 10^{x-y} \end{array} \qquad \text{subtract logs}$$

3. Powers

$$\begin{array}{cc} m & m^3 \\ \downarrow & \uparrow \\ 10^x \longrightarrow & 10^{3x} \end{array} \qquad \text{multiply log by 3 for cube}$$

4. Roots

$$\begin{array}{cc} m & m^{1/2} \\ \downarrow & \uparrow \\ 10^x \longrightarrow & 10^{x/2} \end{array} \qquad \text{divide log by 2 for square root}$$

Examples:

Use the log function to find the values of

(a) $3 \cdot 7 \times 19 \cdot 5$ (b) $473 \div 82$ (c) $(1 \cdot 12)^5$ (d) $\sqrt{14 \cdot 08}$

(a) $\boxed{3}\,\boxed{\cdot}\,\boxed{7}\,\boxed{\log}\,\boxed{+}\,\boxed{1}\,\boxed{9}\,\boxed{\cdot}\,\boxed{5}\,\boxed{\log}\,\boxed{=}\,\boxed{10^x}$ ... $72 \cdot 15$

(b) $\boxed{4}\,\boxed{7}\,\boxed{3}\,\boxed{\log}\,\boxed{-}\,\boxed{8}\,\boxed{2}\,\boxed{\log}\,\boxed{=}\,\boxed{10^x}$ ... $5 \cdot 7683$

(c) $\boxed{1}\,\boxed{\cdot}\,\boxed{1}\,\boxed{2}\,\boxed{\log}\,\boxed{\times}\,\boxed{5}\,\boxed{=}\,\boxed{10^x}$ ... $1 \cdot 7623$

(d) $\boxed{1}\,\boxed{4}\,\boxed{\cdot}\,\boxed{0}\,\boxed{8}\,\boxed{\log}\,\boxed{\div}\,\boxed{2}\,\boxed{=}\,\boxed{10^x}$ ... $3 \cdot 7523$

Exercise 27·3

A 1 Use your calculator to find the log of the following numbers.

    (a) 1, 2, 3, 4, 5   Write your solutions as

    (b) 10, 20, 30, 40, 50   log 1 =

    (c) 100, 200, 300, 400, 500   log 2 =

    (d) 0·1, 0·2, 0·3, 0·4, 0·5   etc.

    What do you notice?

2 Your calculator will give E if you press $\boxed{0}\,\boxed{\log}$, $\boxed{1}\,\boxed{+/-}\,\boxed{\log}$, $\boxed{3}\,\boxed{+/-}\,\boxed{\log}$, etc.

    Find out why the calculator cannot produce the logs of these numbers.

3 Use $\boxed{\log}$ to calculate the following products. (See example above.)

    (a) $47 \times 21 \cdot 3$ (b) $1 \cdot 52 \times 38$ (c) $0 \cdot 154 \times 14$ (d) $2163 \times 5 \cdot 2$

4 Use $\boxed{\log}$ to calculate the following quotients:

    (a) $203 \div 49 \cdot 1$ (b) $0 \cdot 475 \div 15$ (c) $28 \cdot 26 \div 0 \cdot 052$ (d) $38 \div 0 \cdot 452$

5 Use $\boxed{\log}$ to evaluate

    (a) 2^8 (b) 3^5 (c) $(1 \cdot 14)^{10}$ (d) $0 \cdot 65^{16}$

    Check by another method.

6 Use $\boxed{\log}$ to calculate the following roots

    (a) $\sqrt{54 \cdot 7}$ (b) $\sqrt{3082}$ (c) $\sqrt[3]{51 \cdot 5}$ (d) $\sqrt[3]{0 \cdot 45}$

    Check by multiplying up the root to an appropriate power.

B Investigate the effect of the $\boxed{\ln}$ button and its possible use in calculations. Find out all you can about e^x.

    Note: the function e^x can be expressed as the series

$$1 + \frac{x^1}{1!} + \frac{x^2}{2!} + \frac{x^3}{3!} + \ldots + \frac{x^n}{n!} + \ldots \quad \text{where } n! \text{ is } 1 \times 2 \times 3 \times \ldots \times n.$$

Unit 28   Vectors

28·1   Definitions

The arrows in the diagram show the speeds and directions of some of the cars on a section of motorway.
The arrows are called vectors. They represent two separate facts about the movement of the cars.
The length of the vector arrow is called the modulus
Many aspects of the physical world are represented by vectors, for example gravitational force, acceleration and displacement.

North

South

Vectors on a rectangular grid

The vector shown on the grid can be written in the following ways:

$\overrightarrow{OP}$ This gives the tailpoint and headpoint of the vector. These are enough to work out the length and direction of the arrow.

p   A simple letter in bold type. This form is very useful when a vector algebra is being constructed.

$\begin{pmatrix} p_1 \\ p_2 \end{pmatrix}$ This form gives the vector in terms of its components, parallel to the x-axis and parallel to the y-axis, in this case $\begin{pmatrix} 4 \\ 3 \end{pmatrix}$.

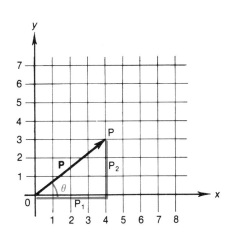

It is clear from the diagram that
(i) the length of $\mathbf{p} = \sqrt{p_1{}^2 + p_2{}^2} = 5$
(ii) $\tan \theta = p_2/p_1 = \frac{3}{4}$
The length of the vector is called the modulus of the vector, written $|\mathbf{p}|$.
The angle θ is called the argument of the vector.

Examples:

Write each of the vectors in the diagram in three different ways. Find the modulus and argument for each one.

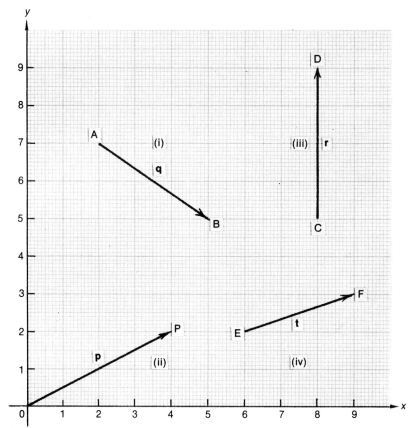

(i) This vector can be written
$\mathbf{q}$ or $\overrightarrow{AB}$ or $\begin{pmatrix} 3 \\ -2 \end{pmatrix}$.

Its modulus is $\sqrt{9+4} = \sqrt{13}$.

Its argument is $\tan^{-1}\dfrac{-2}{3} = -33\cdot69°$.*

(ii) This vector can be written $\mathbf{p}$, $\overrightarrow{OP}$ or $\begin{pmatrix} 4 \\ 2 \end{pmatrix}$;

$|\mathbf{p}| = \sqrt{20}$ argument $\mathbf{p} = \tan^{-1}\dfrac{2}{4} = 26\cdot6°$

*Note: An angle measured 'clockwise' from Ox is negative.

This vector is the position vector of the point P with coordinates (4, 2).

(iii) This vector can be written **r**, $\overrightarrow{CD}$ or $\begin{pmatrix} 0 \\ 4 \end{pmatrix}$; $|\mathbf{r}| = 4$

arg **r** = 90° (90° to Ox)

(iv) This vector can be written **t**, $\overrightarrow{EF}$ or $\begin{pmatrix} 3 \\ 1 \end{pmatrix}$; $|\mathbf{t}| = \sqrt{10}$

arg $\mathbf{t} = \tan^{-1}\dfrac{1}{3} = 18{\cdot}4°$

Note: The angles can be checked with a protractor.

Exercise 28·1

A Draw the following vectors on graph paper. Draw the axes first.

1 The position vector of the point (5, 5).

2 A vector $\begin{pmatrix} 4 \\ 7 \end{pmatrix}$ with its tail at (2, 3).   **3** A vector $\begin{pmatrix} -5 \\ 5 \end{pmatrix}$ with its head at (6, 7).

4 A vector with modulus 5 and argument 60°

5 A vector with modulus 6 and argument 90°.

6 A vector with modulus 3 and argument 180°.

7 A vector from (2, 3) to (7, −1).

8 A vector from (0, 0) with modulus 4.

B Give the names, modulus and argument for all the vectors drawn below.

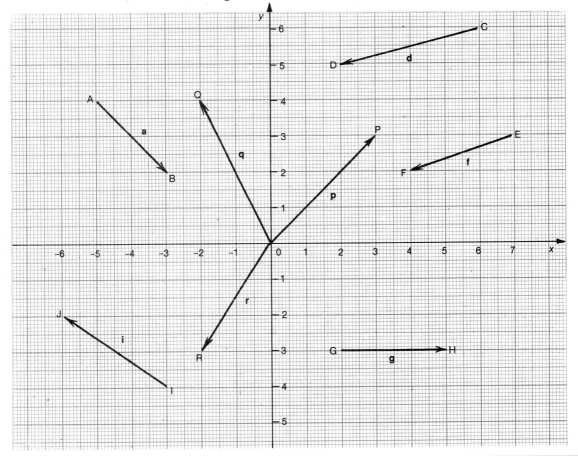

28·2 Equivalence and sum of two vectors

We first decide when two vectors are equivalent.
- Two vectors **p** and **q** are equivalent if $|\mathbf{p}| = |\mathbf{q}|$ and arg **p** = arg **q**.
- Two vectors $\begin{pmatrix} p_1 \\ p_2 \end{pmatrix}$ and $\begin{pmatrix} q_1 \\ q_2 \end{pmatrix}$ are equivalent if $p_1 = q_1$ and $p_2 = q_2$.

Both the above definitions are ways of saying that equivalent vectors must have the same size and direction.

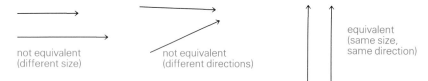

not equivalent
(different size)

not equivalent
(different directions)

equivalent
(same size,
same direction)

Sum

An obvious way to add up two vectors is to make the head of the first and tail of the second join up.

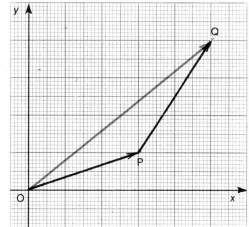

Thus $\overrightarrow{OQ} = \overrightarrow{OP} + \overrightarrow{PQ}$.

Since $\overrightarrow{OP}$ is $\begin{pmatrix} 3 \\ 1 \end{pmatrix}$ and $\overrightarrow{PQ}$ is $\begin{pmatrix} 2 \\ 3 \end{pmatrix}$.

We would expect $\overrightarrow{OQ}$ to be $\begin{pmatrix} 5 \\ 4 \end{pmatrix}$

and this is seen to be the case.

Exercise 28·2

1 Name the vectors in the diagram which are equivalent to

(a) $\begin{pmatrix} 1 \\ 1 \end{pmatrix}$ (b) $\begin{pmatrix} 2 \\ -3 \end{pmatrix}$

(c) $\begin{pmatrix} -3 \\ 0 \end{pmatrix}$ (d) **p**

(e) $\overrightarrow{OR}$ (f) $\overrightarrow{AB}$

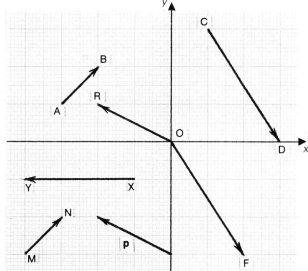

2 $\overrightarrow{OP}$ is the vector $\begin{pmatrix} 2 \\ 3 \end{pmatrix}$, $\overrightarrow{OQ}$ is the vector $\begin{pmatrix} 3 \\ -1 \end{pmatrix}$.

Make a diagram and draw on the same diagram,

(a) $\overrightarrow{OP} + \overrightarrow{OQ}$ (b) $\overrightarrow{OP} + \overrightarrow{OP}$ (c) $\overrightarrow{OQ} + \overrightarrow{OQ}$

3 $\overrightarrow{OP}$ is the vector $\begin{pmatrix} 2 \\ 3 \end{pmatrix}$; write down the component form of vector $\overrightarrow{PO}$.

What is the vector $\overrightarrow{OP} + \overrightarrow{PO}$?

4 $\mathbf{p}$ and $\mathbf{q}$ are two vectors $\begin{pmatrix} p_1 \\ p_2 \end{pmatrix}$ and $\begin{pmatrix} q_1 \\ q_2 \end{pmatrix}$.

(a) Show that $\mathbf{p} + \mathbf{q} = \mathbf{q} + \mathbf{p}$ and illustrate this on a diagram.

(b) $\mathbf{p}$ is the vector $\begin{pmatrix} 3 \\ 4 \end{pmatrix}$ and $\mathbf{q}$ is the vector $\begin{pmatrix} 2 \\ -1 \end{pmatrix}$. Show on the same

diagram the vectors $-\mathbf{p}$, $-\mathbf{q}$, $\mathbf{p} + \mathbf{q}$, $\mathbf{p} + -\mathbf{q}$ and $\mathbf{q} + -\mathbf{p}$.

(c) If we write $\mathbf{p} - \mathbf{q}$ for $\mathbf{p} + -\mathbf{q}$, is it true that $\mathbf{p} - \mathbf{q} = \mathbf{q} - \mathbf{p}$?

5 The vector $\begin{pmatrix} 0 \\ 0 \end{pmatrix}$ is called the zero vector $\mathbf{0}$. Draw diagrams to

show these situations:

(a) $\mathbf{p} + \mathbf{q} = \mathbf{0}$ (b) $\mathbf{p} + \mathbf{q} + \mathbf{r} = \mathbf{0}$

(c) $\mathbf{p} + \mathbf{q} + \mathbf{r} + \mathbf{s} = \mathbf{0}$ (d) $\mathbf{p} - \mathbf{q} = \mathbf{0}$

6 Investigate these statements, giving examples.

(a) $|\mathbf{p} + \mathbf{q}| \leqslant |\mathbf{p}| + |\mathbf{q}|$ $\leqslant$ means less than OR equal to

(b) $|\mathbf{p} + \mathbf{q}| = \sqrt{|\mathbf{p}|^2 + |\mathbf{q}|^2}$

(c) $|\mathbf{p} - \mathbf{q}|^2 = |\mathbf{p} + \mathbf{q}|^2 - 2|\mathbf{p}||\mathbf{q}|$

7 Give the following vectors in terms of $\mathbf{p}$ and $\mathbf{q}$.

(a) $\overrightarrow{AB}$

(b) $\overrightarrow{AE}$ (E is the midpoint of AB)

(c) $\overrightarrow{AC}$ (*Hint:* start with $\mathbf{q} + \overrightarrow{AC} = \mathbf{p}$)

(d) $\overrightarrow{AG}$

(e) $\overrightarrow{DG}$

(f) $\overrightarrow{CE}$

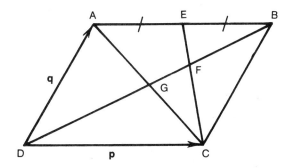

8 Investigate the relationships between vectors given below.

(a) $\mathbf{p}$ and $\mathbf{p} + \mathbf{p}$ (d) $\mathbf{p} - \mathbf{q}$ and $2\mathbf{p} - 2\mathbf{q}$

(b) $\mathbf{q}$ and $\frac{1}{2}\mathbf{q}$ (e) $(\mathbf{p} + \mathbf{q}) + \mathbf{r}$ and $\mathbf{p} + (\mathbf{q} + \mathbf{r})$

(c) $\mathbf{p} + \mathbf{q}$ and $\frac{1}{2}(\mathbf{p} + \mathbf{q})$ (f) $\mathbf{p} - (\mathbf{q} - \mathbf{r})$ and $(\mathbf{p} - \mathbf{q}) - \mathbf{r}$

28·3   Applications in geometry

Many geometrical properties can be expressed very neatly by vectors.

● Two vectors that are equivalent represent a pair of equal and parallel
  lines.

- Vectors such as $2\mathbf{p}$, $3\mathbf{p}$, $\frac{1}{2}\mathbf{p}$ etc are all parallel to $\mathbf{p}$.

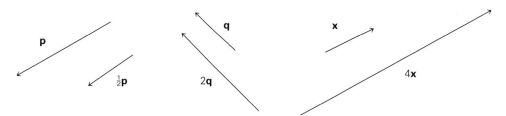

Properties can be proved very easily by vectors, even in three dimensions.

Example:

Prove by vectors that the line joining the midpoints of two sides of a triangle is parallel to the third side and half its length

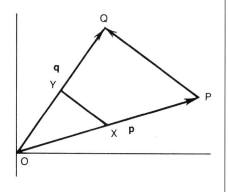

1∅	Data	$\triangle$ OPQ; X, Y are midpoints of OP and OQ.
2∅	Data	$\overrightarrow{OP} = \mathbf{p}$, $\overrightarrow{OQ} = \mathbf{q}$
3∅	Deduction	$\mathbf{p} + \overrightarrow{PQ} = \mathbf{q}$ (from 2∅)
4∅	Deduction	$\overrightarrow{PQ} = \mathbf{q} - \mathbf{p}$
5∅	Deduction	$\overrightarrow{OX} = \frac{1}{2}\mathbf{p}$, $\overrightarrow{OY} = \frac{1}{2}\mathbf{q}$ (from 1∅, 2∅)
6∅	Deduction	$\overrightarrow{XY} = \frac{1}{2}\mathbf{q} - \frac{1}{2}\mathbf{p}$ (from 5∅)
7∅	Deduction	$\overrightarrow{XY} = \frac{1}{2}(\mathbf{q} - \mathbf{p})$ (from 6∅)
8∅	Deduction	$XY = \frac{1}{2}PQ$
9∅	END	

Exercise 28·3

1. Study the above proof of the midpoint theorem and make sure you follow it.
2. ABCD is a parallelogram. Write down all the relationships you can find between the position vectors $\overrightarrow{OA}$, $\overrightarrow{OB}$, $\overrightarrow{OC}$, $\overrightarrow{OD}$, where O is (a) inside, (b) outside ABCD.
3. PR and PQ are divided into 4 equal parts by X_1, X_2, X_3 and Y_1, Y_2, Y_3. Prove that X_3Y_3 is $\frac{3}{4}$ the length of RQ.

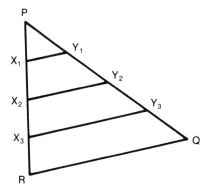

4 Find the position vector of the point R, which is the midpoint of PQ on △ OPQ.

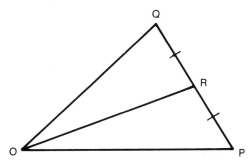

5 ABCD is any quadrilateral. P, Q, R and S are the
four midpoints of the sides. Use vectors to find
out all you can about PQRS.

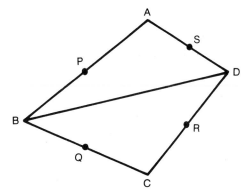

6 PQR is any triangle. The position vectors of P, Q and R are **p, q, r**.
(a) Write down the position vectors of X, Y and Z.
(b) Find the vectors PX, QY and RZ in terms of **p, q** and **r**.
(c) Find the position vector of the point G, $\frac{2}{3}$ of the way
along $\overrightarrow{PX}$, and show that it is the same as the position
vector of a point $\frac{2}{3}$ along $\overrightarrow{RZ}$.

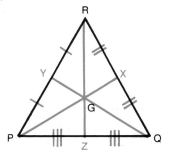

28·4 Scalar product

We have seen that it is possible to add vectors and it is natural to ask
whether vectors can be multiplied. It is convenient to form a product
which is in fact *not a vector itself.*
This product is called the scalar product* and is written **a.b**
The scalar product is $|\mathbf{a}| |\mathbf{b}| \cos \theta$, where θ is the angle between the two
vectors.

*Sometimes called *dot* product.

Two different ways of showing the scalar product of vectors.

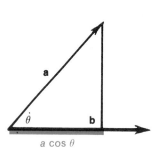 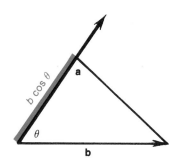

Example:
Calculate the scalar products of the pairs of vectors shown.

i 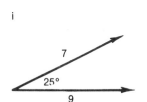 ii 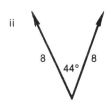 iii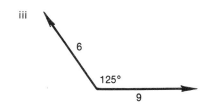

(i)   Scalar product is $7 \times 9 \times \cos 25° = 57·1$
(ii) Scalar product is $8 \times 8 \times \cos 44° = 46·04$
(iii) Scalar product is $6 \times 9 \times \cos 125° = -31$ The negative sign shows that the angle between the vectors is more than 90°.

Note: All these are pure numbers.

The following are important consequences of the definition.
*$\mathbf{p}.\mathbf{q} = 0 \Rightarrow \theta = 90°$, i.e. the vectors are perpendicular.
*$\mathbf{p}.\mathbf{q} = |\mathbf{p}||\mathbf{q}| \Rightarrow \theta = 0°$, i.e. the vectors are parallel.
*If $\mathbf{i}$ and $\mathbf{j}$ are unit vectors along the Ox and Oy axes,
 $\mathbf{i}.\mathbf{i} = 1, \mathbf{i}.\mathbf{j} = 0, \mathbf{j}.\mathbf{i} = 0$ and $\mathbf{j}.\mathbf{j} = 1$.

Exercise 28·4
The following questions explore scalar multiplication of vectors. In each case you should go to the definition for a proof of results.
1   Is it true that $\mathbf{p}.\mathbf{q} = \mathbf{q}.\mathbf{p}$?
2   What is wrong with the expression $(\mathbf{p}.\mathbf{q}).\mathbf{r}$?
3   Is there a vector $\mathbf{x}$ which satisfies the equation $\mathbf{v}.\mathbf{x} = \mathbf{v}$?
4   (a) Is it true that $\mathbf{p}.(\mathbf{q} + \mathbf{r}) = \mathbf{p}.\mathbf{q} + \mathbf{p}.\mathbf{r}$? Give examples and a proof if possible.
    (b) Show how the result $(\mathbf{p} + \mathbf{q}).(\mathbf{p} + \mathbf{q}) = p^2 + q^2 + \mathbf{p}.\mathbf{q} + \mathbf{q}.\mathbf{p}$ can be deduced from **4(a)**.
5   Is it true that $\mathbf{p}.\mathbf{q} = \mathbf{p}.\mathbf{r} \Rightarrow \mathbf{q} = \mathbf{r}$? Give examples or counter-examples to prove your point.

6 A vector **p** can be expressed as $p_1\mathbf{i} + p_2\mathbf{j}$ where **i** and **j** are perpendicular unit vectors. Use this to show that
  (a) $\mathbf{p} \cdot \mathbf{p} = p_1{}^2 + p_2{}^2$ (b) $\mathbf{p} \cdot \mathbf{q} = p_1q_1 + p_2q_2$

7 Since $\mathbf{a} \cdot \mathbf{b} = |\mathbf{a}||\mathbf{b}|\cos\theta$ and also $a_1b_1 + a_2b_2$, it should be possible to calculate the angle between two vectors from the lengths of the vectors and their components. Show that this is so and use the method to calculate angle $P\hat{O}Q$ in the diagram.

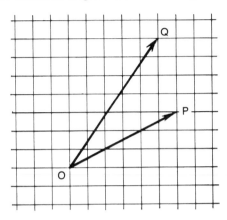

8 Study the following demonstration of Pythagoras's Theorem by scalar product:

  10 $\mathbf{c} = \mathbf{a} + \mathbf{b}$, $\mathbf{a} \perp \mathbf{b}$.
  20 $\mathbf{c} \cdot \mathbf{c} = (\mathbf{a} + \mathbf{b}) \cdot (\mathbf{a} + \mathbf{b})$
  30 $c^2 = \mathbf{a} \cdot \mathbf{a} + \mathbf{b} \cdot \mathbf{a} + \mathbf{a} \cdot \mathbf{b} + \mathbf{b} \cdot \mathbf{b}$
  35 $\mathbf{a} \cdot \mathbf{a} = a^2$, $\mathbf{b} \cdot \mathbf{b} = b^2$, $\mathbf{a} \cdot \mathbf{b} = 0$
  40 $c^2 = a^2 + b^2$ from 30, 35

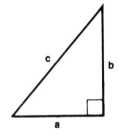

Do you think this is an acceptable proof of Pythagoras's Theorem?

9 Use scalar product of vectors to prove the **cosine rule** for an acute-angled triangle in the form
$c^2 = a^2 + b^2 - 2ab\cos\theta$

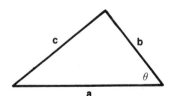

10 Extend the proof in question **9** to cover the case when $\theta > 90°$.

Unit 29 Sampling

29·1 Gathering information

One of the main problems in commerce, government and science is the
collection of reliable information. This is both difficult and expensive.
Even the most carefully collected information can be biassed. *
In this unit we explore ways of collecting information, ways of avoiding
bias and ways of using information to make good guesses.

Exercise 29·1

A Some of the difficulties in the collection of information are listed below:
- **Cost.** A lot of people are needed to collect data. Expensive scientific equipment is needed.
- **Time.** Data takes a long time to collect, or is only collected by a very slow process.
- **Change.** Some information is changing while it is being measured.
- **Sensitivity.** Some data is altered by the measuring process.

Which of the above difficulties would apply to the following situations?

1   Finding out how many people are unemployed.
2   Finding the cause of an illness in new-born babies.
3   Finding out about the atmospheres of planets.
4   Finding out the population of a country like India (population 700 million).
5   Testing metal fatigue in a giant aeroplane.
6   Obtaining data about burglaries for insurance purposes.
7   Deciding the popularity of a TV programme.
8   Finding out why people buy certain brands of food.
9   Finding out why some children fail to learn at school or why some young children are backward.
10 Finding out the best way to train an Olympic sportsman or sportswoman (are there training techniques which are better for women?).
11 Finding out how to control pests like locusts or mosquitoes.
12 Studying the effects of fertilizers on crops.
13 Testing public opinion on an issue like nuclear disarmament.
14 Estimating the population of animals such as whales, butterflies and eagles.

*Information which is distorted by the way it is collected.

B Make a summary of the methods you use to obtain information about the things that interest you.

29·2 Sampling

The usual method of overcoming the difficulty of collecting information is sampling. This involves selecting a small number of things and studying them. Guesses are then made about the whole population based on the sample statistics
The most useful sample is one which has been chosen at random (by pure chance).

Example 1:
A newspaper used the letters it received about a particular issue as a sample of opinion. Was this a random sample?

No, because:
(i) People who write letters to newspapers are not typical.
(ii) People who read that newspaper belong to a special group.
The sample was biassed.

Example 2:
A doctor used every tenth patient as a sample of all his patients. Was this a random sample?

Yes. Suppose he had 4000 patients on his books. He would make up his sample from patients numbered 10, 20, . . ., etc in his files.

Exercise 29·2
Decide which of the following sampling methods will give random or almost random samples.
Give reasons for your answers.
1 A newspaper journalist getting opinions on marriage phoned up 100 people picked with a pin from the London Telephone Directory.
2 In a study of the number of rooms per household, all the cornerhouses in a town were visited.
3 In a school reorganisation, it was proposed that a boys' school and a girls' school should be joined. All the parents of children at both schools were asked their views.
4 Electric irons were tested for safety. The first and last irons in each factory batch were tested.
5 Tinned food is tested for quality by food inspectors. Ten tins from each batch of 100 000 tins are opened and tested.
6 To pick a team of 4 players, 10 names on pieces of paper were put in a hat. 4 pieces of paper were picked out.
7 A school gives 10 free places on the school ski-trip. 900 children apply for the free places. Each of the children are given a number from 1 to 900. One child is asked to choose a three-figure number and this is entered into the calculator. $\boxed{\text{sin}}$ is then pressed and the last 3 figures on the display are used to pick a child. This process is repeated 10 times.
8 To estimate how many children smoke in a school of 2000 children, all the children in class 4b were interviewed.

29·3 Interpreting sample data

The statistics of a sample can be measured and these used as estimates of the statistics of the population. (Remember, it is not usually possible to obtain population statistics directly.)

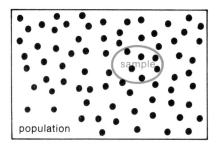

Three very important rules apply. These are:
- The larger the sample, the closer its mean will be to the population mean.
- Biassed samples cannot be trusted, however large they are.
- Sample means are more reliable than single values.

Population mean μ pronounced 'mew'
Population standard σ pronounced 'sigma'
deviation
Sample mean m
Sample standard s
deviation

Population statistics are given Greek letters, sample statistics are given ordinary letters

m and s are used to estimate μ and σ

Examples:
1 The average earnings per week of the girls in class 4, aged 15, were £10. Estimate the average earnings for all girls in the same age group.
The only estimate possible from this information is that $\mu = 10$. We do not know anything about the class that suggests it will be a random sample of all girls, so the estimate is very unreliable.

2 Local elections are to be held in a town with 20 000 voters. A sample of 40 people indicates 10 Conservative, 9 Liberal/SDP and 9 Labour voters. The rest said they would not vote. Estimate the election results.

	Cons	Lib/SDP	Lab	No vote	Total
Sample	10	9	9	12	40
Election	5000	4500	4500	6000	20 000

The estimate keeps the votes in the same proportion as the sample.

Exercise 29·3
1 A doctor tests 10 people for high blood pressure and finds that 3 people have above average blood pressure. How many patients with above average blood pressure could he expect from the 8000 people who go to his medical centre?

2 4 out of the ten cats brought to a vet were found to have fleas. Another vet saw 320 cats in a month. How many of those would you have expected to have fleas?

3 By conducting a survey on a sample of pupils in your school, make an estimate of the number of pupils
   (a) who smoke
   (b) whose family keep a pet
   (c) whose family has more than two living grandparents.

4 When five cards are dealt from a pack of cards you obtain one possible member from the set of all 5-card selections. Investigate a sample of ten 5-card selections.
   (a) In how many cases out of 10 are the cards all of different values?
   (b) In how many cases does the 5-card selection contain exactly one pair?
   (c) In how many cases does the 5-card selection contain two pairs (5 5 5 would count as three pairs)?

5 In an experiment to measure the speed of light the following results were obtained:

$1\cdot82 \times 10^5$ $1\cdot88 \times 10^5$

$1\cdot89 \times 10^5$ $1\cdot88 \times 10^5$

$1\cdot83 \times 10^5$ $1\cdot87 \times 10^5$

Find m for the sample of results. Estimate μ. What does μ represent in this case?

6 Follow the sequence below on your calculator.
   1∅ Choose any number between 1 and 90
   2∅ Put the number into your calculator
   3∅ Press ⬚sin⬚
   4∅ Add the last three digits on the display
   (a) Repeat ten times to obtain a sample. Calculate m for the sample.
   (b) Repeat 20 times to obtain a second sample. Calculate m.
   (c) What estimate would you make for μ? What *is* μ?

29·4   Gambling and probability

All gambling contains an element of chance and sometimes the risks can be calculated. Even if they cannot be exactly calculated, they can be estimated by simulation.

Example:

Suppose there are six horses in a race, A, B, C, D, E and F. If we know all the horses are equally likely to win we can simulate the race by allocating each horse a number from 1 to 6. A dice is then thrown to decide the winner. The shape of the dice gives an equal chance to each number (horse).

Suppose the horses are not equal but we know that
   (i) A is better than B   (ii) B is better than C
   (iii) D is better than E   (iv) E is better than F
   (iv) A and D are about equal

Two-digit random numbers can be used to simulate a race under the above conditions,

1∅   Allocate 01–24 to A   25–48 to D
                   49–64 to B   65–80 to E
                   81–88 to C   89–96 to F

2∅   Choose a two-digit random number (including 01, 02, etc). If it turns out to be 97, 98 or 99 choose again.

Exercise 29·4

A 1   (a)   Study the horse racing example carefully. Make sure you understand how the allocation of numbers gives better chances to the better horses.

         (b)   Make a spinner as shown and compare the results of 20 spins with the results obtained by using 20 random numbers for choosing the winner. Comment.

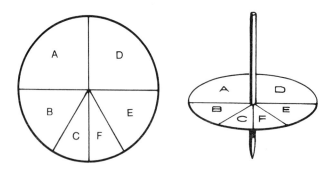

   2   In another race there are four good horses and four bad ones. Give a number allocation which would simulate this race (assume the good horses are twice as likely to win as the bad ones).

   3   Explain how 3-figure random numbers could be used to simulate a fruit machine
         (a)   with 10 different sets of fruit on each wheel, and
         (b)   with 5 different sets of fruit on each wheel.

Government warning: fruit machines are bad for your health . . .

4 A 'bingo' card contains 12 numbers as shown. Estimate the number of 2-figure random numbers that would have to be called before the card was completed. What difference would it make if the random numbers were chosen by crossing a number off a list 1 . . . 99 (so that each random number was only used once)?
Carry out an experiment to confirm your estimate.

4		30	40				81
	16			52	63	72	
9			49	58			90

5 Construct a method of simulating six football matches if
(a) one team wins in every match
(b) some results are draws.
6 The chance of winning the pools is very small indeed. The football pools only pay out 30% of the gambled money in prizes. Why do you think so many people gamble on the pools every week?
7 *Investigation*
Study the following table which shows how much money is returned as winnings in different forms of gambling. Write your comments.
(*Note:* Both government and betting organisers take a large share of the money!)
Source: Gambling in England, Scotland and Wales (1976), HMSO.

Gambling in England, Scotland & Wales (1976)

Type of Gambling	Money Staked (£ million)	Winnings (£ million)	Money Lost (£ million)	Percentage of Money Staked kept by Operators	Tax (£ million)	Winnings as Percentage of Money Staked
Casinos	4020	3919	101	2·5	5·2	97·5
Football Pools	233	70	163	70	93	30
Slot Machines	420	294	126	30	9	70
Bingo	299	284	15	5	15	95
Betting Shop	1868	1513	355	19	140	81
Race Courses	275	242	34	12	11	88
Total	7115	6322	794		274	

All these figures should be *doubled* for 1985/86 because of inflation.

Unit 30 Miscellaneous problems

The questions in the following exercises are examination level. Take
your time over each question. The aim is to draw together everything
you have learned so far. Follow the flow chart if you cannot solve any
problem straight away.

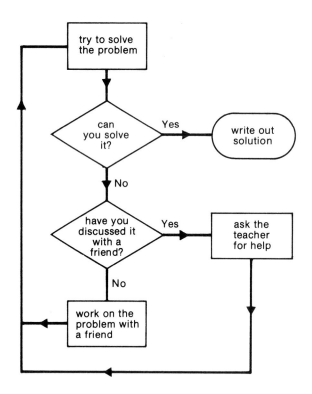

Exercise 30·1

1 (a) $25·6 - (3·2 - 1·11) =$

    (a) 23·51 (b) 27·69 (c) 21·29 (d) 30·11 or (e) 27·61? *(WM)*

  (b) Which of the following are true statements?

    (i) $1988 \div 1000 = 19·88$

    (ii) $1988 = 19·88 \times 10^3$

    (iii) In 1988 the digit 9 represents 9×10^2

    (iv) $0·01988 = 1·988 \times 10^{-1}$

    (v) 1988 correct to two significant figures is 2000 *(EA)*

2 I took £150 on holiday to Switzerland and changed it for Swiss Francs. The rate of exchange is
4·3 SF to the British pound. How many Swiss Francs could I buy for my British money?

3 Match up the answers to the questions below:

questions	answers
$(160)^2$	40
$\frac{3}{5}$ of 160	6·4
$\sqrt{1600}$	25 600
4% of 160	0·625
100 ÷ 160	96

4 Sketch the graph of $y = x(2 - x)$. Use the graph to answer the following questions:
(a) For what values of x is $2x > x^2$?
(b) What value of x gives the greatest value of y?

5 Find the areas of the two squares in the diagram. Explain why this demonstrates that $2 < \pi < 4$.

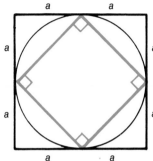

6 Work out the following matrix operations:

(i) $\begin{pmatrix} 3 & 6 \\ -4 & 2 \end{pmatrix} + \begin{pmatrix} 2 & -1 \\ -7 & 4 \end{pmatrix}$

(ii) $\begin{pmatrix} 2 & 3 \\ 5 & 9 \end{pmatrix}\begin{pmatrix} 6 & 12 \\ 5 & 0 \end{pmatrix}$

(iii) $8\begin{pmatrix} 3 & 4 \\ 2 & -6 \end{pmatrix}$

(iv) $\begin{pmatrix} 0 & 3 & 0 \\ 2 & 1 & 6 \end{pmatrix}\begin{pmatrix} 0 & 3 \\ 1 & 0 \\ 0 & 1 \end{pmatrix}$

Exercise 30·2

1 Solve the equations $\left.\begin{array}{r} 2x + y = 5 \\ 4x + 3y = 9 \end{array}\right\}$

Show that the above equations can be written in matrix form

$\begin{pmatrix} 2 & 1 \\ 4 & 3 \end{pmatrix}\begin{pmatrix} x \\ y \end{pmatrix} = \begin{pmatrix} 5 \\ 9 \end{pmatrix}$ *(WM)*

2 (a) Simplify $(4x + 3y) - (3x - 3y)$

(b) If $\frac{3x}{4} = 6$, what is x?

(c) If $x = 2$ and $y = -3$, work out the values of (i) $3x^2$ (ii) $4xy$.

3 If $x = -2$, which one of the following statements is correct?
(a) $4 - 2x = 0$ (b) $x + 2 = 2 - x$
(c) $\frac{1}{2}x + 4 = 3$ (d) $x^3 = 8$ (e) $\frac{1}{2}x + 4 = 5$ *(WM)*

4 A transformation T_1 maps the point (x, y) into $(2x, 2y)$;
A transformation T_2 maps (x, y) into $(x + y, y)$;
A transformation T_3 maps (x, y) into $(x - y, x + y)$.
O is the point $(0, 0)$, P is $(1, 0)$, Q is $(1, 1)$ and R is $(0, 1)$.
Thus OPQR is a square of side 1 unit.
Draw three separate diagrams to show the mapping of the square OPQR under the three transformations.

5 The sequences S, S_1 and S_2 are as follows:

S $= 7, 14, 33, 70, 131, \ldots$
$S_1 = 7, 19, 37, 61, \ldots$
$S_2 = 12, 18, 24, \ldots$

(a) Explain how S_1 is obtained from S and S_2 from S_1.
(b) Write down the next two terms of S_2, S_1 and S.

6 Consider the following information:

$1^3 = 1 = 1^2$
$2^3 + 1^3 = 9 = 3^2 = (1 + 2)^2$
$3^3 + 2^3 + 1^3 = 36 = 6^2 = (1 + 2 + 3)^2$

Calculate the value of $1^3 + 2^3 + 3^3 + 4^3$. What general rule can you see in the above?

Exercise 30·3

1 (a) $p = m(v - u)$
    (i) Find p if $m = 5$, $v = 100$ and $u = 20$.
    (ii) Find m if $p = 200$, $v = 70$ and $u = 20$.
    (iii) Given $p = m(v - u)$, rearrange the formula to express u in terms of p, m and v.

  (b) $V = \dfrac{\pi r^2 h}{2}$
    (i) Take $\pi = 3{\cdot}14$. Find V if $r = 3$ and $h = 20$.
    (ii) Find r if $V = 8\pi$ and $h = 2r$.
    (iii) Given $V = \dfrac{\pi r^2 h}{2}$, rearrange the formula to express r in terms of π, V and h.

2 (a) Solve the equation $3x - 1 = x + 3$
  (b) Factorise $3x^2 + 17x - 6$ and solve the equation $3x^2 + 17x - 6 = 0$.   (WM)

3 (a) If $(x - 2)(x + 3) = x^2 + ax - 6$, what is the value of a?
  (b) $y = (x - 2)(x - 5)$
    (i) Calculate the value of y when $x = 3$.
    (ii) Write down the values of x when $y = 0$.
    (iii) Give a value of x for which $y = 0$.

4 Singers, dancers and comics took part in an audition. There were 10 singers, 5 of whom danced. 9 comics were auditioned, 4 of whom sang and 3 danced. 3 of the people auditioned were comics who danced and sang. 3 of the eight dancers did not sing or tell jokes.
  (a) Draw a Venn diagram showing the above information.
  (b) How many people were auditioned altogether?   (SE)

5 (a) Make a sketch of the figures and draw in any lines of symmetry they possess. Mark with an X the centre of rotational symmetry.

 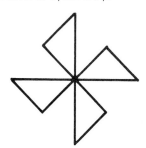 

  (b) For each of the cases below draw one figure which has the given symmetries (and no others). Give the name of the geometrical figure you have drawn and state some geometrical property the figure has due to its symmetry.

(i)   one line of symmetry
(ii) two lines of symmetry + 180° rotational symmetry
(iii) 180° rotational symmetry but *no* lines of symmetry.   (EM)

6 This question concerns the sequence of numbers:
5, 9, 13, 17, 21, 25, . . .
(a) How many of the given numbers are prime?
(b) What is the next number in the sequence?
(c) How many of the given numbers are squares?
(d) Express the numbers as a mapping from the sequence 1, 2, 3, 4, . . .

Exercise 30·4

1 The picture shows a telegraph pole with stretched wire. Calculate the length of the wire. *(ALS)*

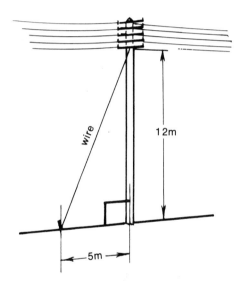

2 In the diagram ABCD is a square in which
AB = 8 cm. P is a point on DC produced such
that BP = 17 cm.
Calculate   (a) the length of CP   and
(b) the perimeter of the figure.   *(WM)*

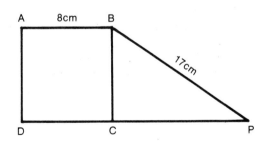

3 (a) The angle whose cosine is 0·688 is 46·5°
46°
43·5°
43°
(b) Show that sin 78° = 2 × sin 39° × cos 39°.

4 A wooden cube has each edge 3 cm in length and each face is painted red.
(a) If the 3 cm cube is cut into 1 cm cubes, how many small cubes will there be?
(b) How many small cubes will have 2 faces painted red?
(c) Describe all the other types of cube that will be obtained.

5 Mark two points X and Y, 5 cm apart.
P = {points 2 cm from X}   Q = {points 3 cm from Y};
R = {points < 2 cm from X}   S = {points > 3 cm from Y}.
(i)   Join with a line the points of set P.
(ii) Draw a line joining the elements of set Q.
(iii) How many points are there in P ∩ Q?
(iv) Shade R ∪ S with horizontal lines.
(v)   Shade R ∩ S with vertical lines.

6 (a) Given that $3^9 = 19\,683$, how would you calculate 3^{17} **without a calculator**?
(b) Use your calculator to find the ratio $3^{3^4} : 3^{4^3}$ in the form $n : 1$.

Exercise 30·5

1 The pyramid shown has a square base, side 6 cm. Its height is 4 cm. Calculate
(a) the area of one triangular face
(b) the surface area of the whole pyramid.

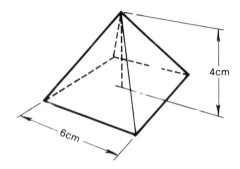

2 The volume of a cone is given by the formula $V = \frac{1}{3}\pi r^2 h$.
Calculate the height of a cone whose volume is 10 cm³ and whose base radius is 1·4 cm.

3 The diagram shows a solid cylinder 20 cm long. The diameter of the circular end is 14 cm.
Calculate the volume of the cylinder and its mass if it is made of brass (density 6 g/cm³).

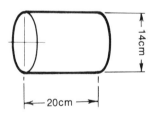

4 (a) Convert 217 (base 10) into a binary number.
(b) Multiply 11101_2 by itself and give the answer in base 2.
(c) Explain why binary numbers are important in computers and calculators.

5 Plan one of the following, showing how you would keep the accounts.
(a) A dance (include cost of group, disco, hire of hall, lighting, etc.).
(b) A trip to Edinburgh for your class.

6 A drug is manufactured in tablets. Each tablet should contain 45 milligrams (0·045 g) of the drug. A sample of 1300 of the tablets was analysed and the results are given in the table.

(a) Explain the meaning of the figures in the *f* column.
(b) Calculate the mean quantity of drug per tablet for this sample.

Milligrams of drug in tablet	f
40	2
41	31
42	38
43	152
44	464
45	391
46	110
47	87
48	23
49	1
50	1

Exercise 30·6

1 The equation of the straight line AB is $2x + 3y = 6$.

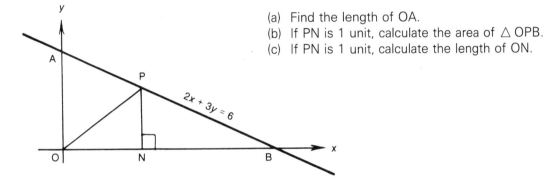

(a) Find the length of OA.
(b) If PN is 1 unit, calculate the area of $\triangle$ OPB.
(c) If PN is 1 unit, calculate the length of ON.

2 The points $(0, 4)$, $(2, 2)$, $(p, 0)$ and $(5, q)$ are all on the same straight line.
(a) Find the equation of this line.
(b) Write down the values of p and q.

3 A rhombus ABCD has each side 130 mm in length. If the diagonal AC is 200 mm long and X is the midpoint of AC, find
(i) the length of AX
(ii) the size of $A\hat{D}X$
(iii) the length of DX
(iv) the length of DB
(v) the area of ABCD.

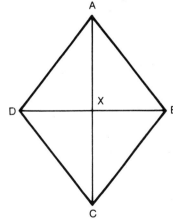

4 (a) The vector **a** is $\begin{pmatrix} 3 \\ -2 \end{pmatrix}$ and **b** is $\begin{pmatrix} 5 \\ 4 \end{pmatrix}$. What is the vector $\frac{1}{2}(\mathbf{a} + \mathbf{b})$?
   Show the vectors on a diagram.

(b) How many arrangements of the letters STAIRS begin *and* end with the letter S?   *(NW)*

5 (a) Given that $\begin{pmatrix} x \\ y \end{pmatrix} = \begin{pmatrix} 2 & 1 \\ 1 & 3 \end{pmatrix}\begin{pmatrix} 1 \\ 2 \end{pmatrix}$ find x and y.

(b) The first six terms of a sequence are 1, 1, 2, 3, 5, 8 ... Write down the next two terms.

(c) Find n so that $a^3 \times a^n = a^7$.

(d) Find m so that $(a^3)^2 = a^m$.

6 (i) Show by giving a numerical example that the implication $a < b \Rightarrow a^2 < b^2$ is *not* true.

(ii) **a**, **b** and **c** are the position vectors of A, B and C, three vertices of a parallelogram. Write down an equation connecting **a**, **b** and **c**.   *(NW)*

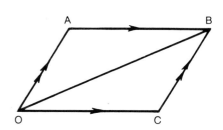

Exercise 30·7

1 Show how to construct an equilateral triangle PQR inside an acute-angled triangle ABC (whose sides are unequal) so that
   (i) RQ is parallel to BC
   (ii) The vertices P, Q and R lie on BC, CA and AB.   *(Lon)*

2 Draw a Venn Diagram which illustrates the following sets in relation to each other:
   $\mathscr{E}$ = set of all quadrilaterals   A = set of parallelograms
   B = set of squares   C = set of rhombi
   D = set of cyclic quadrilaterals   E = set of non-cyclic quadrilaterals   *(AEB)*

3 The point Q is the reflection of the point P(2, 4) in the line $y = x$, and the point R is the reflection of the point P in the line $y = 1$.
   Find (i) the coordinates of Q and R,
        (ii) the length of QR,
        (iii) the size of QR̂P to the nearest degree.   *(JMB)*

4 1326 is the product of four factors in *any* base greater than 6. Find the factors and hence the prime factors of 1326_7 expressed in base 10.   *(Lon)*

5 This question refers to the diagram which is not drawn to scale.
   A, B, C and D lie on a circle and AÊB = 90°.
   Calculate the lengths of AE, EB and EC.   *(AEB)*

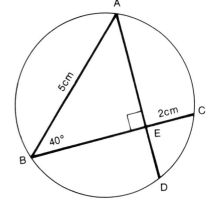

6 State which have no meaning and simplify the others:

(i) $(1 \quad 2) \begin{pmatrix} 3 & 4 \\ 5 & 6 \end{pmatrix}$

(ii) $\begin{pmatrix} 1 \\ 2 \end{pmatrix} \begin{pmatrix} 3 & 4 \\ 5 & 6 \end{pmatrix}$

(iii) $\begin{pmatrix} 3 & 4 \\ 5 & 6 \end{pmatrix} \begin{pmatrix} 1 \\ 2 \end{pmatrix}$

(iv) $\begin{pmatrix} 3 & 4 \\ 5 & 6 \end{pmatrix} (1 \quad 2)$

7 Find the mean value of 10, 13, 14, 15 and 18 and deduce the mean values of
(a) 710, 713, 714, 715, 718.
(b) $-6, -3, -2, -1, 2$.
(c) 50, 65, 70, 75, 90.

8 Choose the correct answer (or answers) from those offered. A bag contains red discs, blue discs and white discs. If the probability of choosing a red disc is x, a blue disc is y and a white disc is z, then
(a) $x + y < 1$
(b) $x + y + z > 1$
(c) $x + y + z = 1$
(d) $xy < z$

Exercise 30·8

1 In a bonus scheme, each worker is paid in proportion to the time they have been with the firm. The workers are listed below. How much will each get if the total bonus is £28 000?

George 18 years   Dick 16 years   Mavis 9 years
Anne   14 years   Joe   10 years   Jim   3 years

2 OA and OB are bounding radii of a sector of a circle. The length of OA is 13·5 cm and the size of AÔB is 120°. A circular cone is formed by joining OA and OB together.
Calculate
(i) the base radius of the cone,
(ii) the height of the cone,
(iii) show that the volume of the cone is $\dfrac{243\sqrt{2}\pi}{4}$

(The volume of a cone, base radius r and height h is $\frac{1}{3}\pi r^2 h$.) *(JMB)*

3 A closed rectangular tank of length 4 m and width 3 m contains water to a depth of 2·5 m. Calculate the volume of water in the tank. This water is pumped to a second tank through a pipe of cross sectional area 0·05 m² at a constant speed of 4 m/sec. Calculate the time taken to empty the first tank.
The dimensions of the second tank are proportional to those of the first tank. Given that the length of the second tank is 6 m, find its width. Find also the depth of water in the second tank.

4 Calculate x and y from the diagrams (which are not drawn to scale). In case (i), BD is a diameter. In case (ii) OP and OQ are tangents to the circle and OP is parallel to QR.

(i)

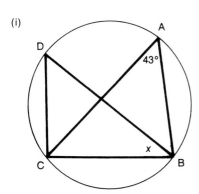

(ii)

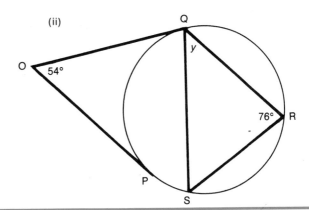

5 The two diagrams below represent a cube of unit side length and a net which could be folded to make a solid model of the unit cube.

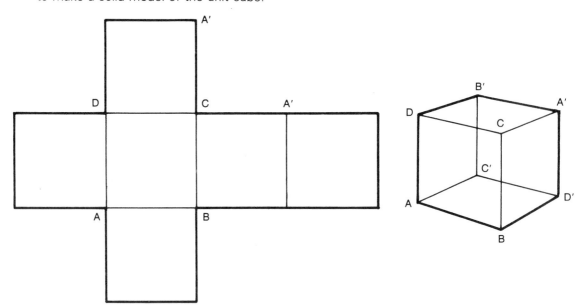

Copy the net and complete the labelling of all its vertices. Through a point Z on the edge of BC passes a path from A to A' across the two faces ABCD and BCA'D'. On your net, mark the shortest path AZA'. Also mark the shortest path AYA' if Y is a similar point on the edge DC for a path across the two faces ABCD and DCA'B'.

Calculate
(a) the lengths of the paths AZA' and AYA'
(b) the area of △ ZAY   (c) the angle ZÂY
If O is the midpoint of the diagonal AA' of the cube, show that ZOY is equilateral and that ZY is one side of a regular hexagon through whose vertices pass six equally short paths from A to A' each across two faces and one edge of the cube.   *(Lon)*

6 Given that O is a point inside triangle ABC and D, E and F are the midpoints of BC, CA and AB show that
(a) AD + BC + CF = AE   (b) OD + OE + OF = OA + OB + OC   *(JMB)*

7 (a) Find the percentage error in replacing 4 km per hour by 1 m per second. Hence or otherwise find the time needed to cover 200 metres at a speed of 40 km/h.   *(L)*
(b) The following table gives values of sin θ and tan θ for values of θ *measured in radians* (1 rad = 57·3°).

θ	0	0·100	0·200	0·300	0·400	0·500	0·600	0·700	0·800
sin θ	0	0·100	0·199	0·295	0·389	0·479	0·565	0·644	0·717
tan θ	0	0·100	0·203	0·309	0·423	0·546	0·684	0·843	1·030

Tabulate the percentage error in using $\theta \simeq \frac{1}{3}(2\sin\theta + \tan\theta)$ for the values given.

8 Given the functions $f: x \rightarrow \cos x°$ and $g: x \rightarrow \tan x°$, find x such that
(i) $x \xrightarrow{f} 0.8311$ (ii) $x \xrightarrow{g} 1.3068$
Draw graphs of both functions for $34 < x < 41$ and use your graphs to find an approximate solution to the equation $\cos x = \tan x$.
Sketch graphs of the functions for $0 < x < 90$.